ST(P) MATHEMATICS 4B

THE GRANGE GRAMMAR SCHOOL

Date Issued	Name	Form	
9th Mar 1993	Hannah Stoney	IVB	

ST(P) MATHEMATICS series

ST(P) 1A
ST(P) 1B
ST(P) 1A Teacher's Notes and Answers
ST(P) 1B Teacher's Notes and Answers

ST(P) 2A
ST(P) 2B
ST(P) 2A Teacher's Notes and Answers
ST(P) 2B Teacher's Notes and Answers

ST(P) 3A
ST(P) 3B
ST(P) 3A Teacher's Notes and Answers
ST(P) 3B Teacher's Notes and Answers

ST(P) 4A
ST(P) 4B
ST(P) 4A Teacher's Notes and Answers
ST(P) 4B Teacher's Notes and Answers

ST(P) 5A (with answers)
ST(P) 5B (with answers)

ST(P) 5C
ST(P) 5C Copy Masters
ST(P) 5C Teacher's Notes and Answers

ST(P) Resource Book

ST(P) Workbooks:
Drawing and Using Curved Graphs
Measuring Instruments
Symmetry and Transformation
Straight Line Graphs

ST(P) MATHEMATICS 4B

L. Bostock, B.Sc.

S. Chandler, B.Sc.

A. Shepherd, B.Sc.

E. Smith, M.Sc.

Second Edition

Stanley Thornes (Publishers) Ltd

First Published 1986 by
Stanley Thornes (Publishers) Ltd,
Old Station Drive,
Leckhampton,
CHELTENHAM GL53 0DN

Reprinted 1987 (twice)
Reprinted 1991
Second Edition 1992

A catalogue record for this book is available from the British Library.

ISBN 0 7487 1583 5

Typeset by Tech-Set, Gateshead, Tyne & Wear.
Printed and bound in Great Britain at The Bath Press, Avon.

CONTENTS

INTRODUCTION

This book is part of the ST(P) graded series in mathematics. It is intended for use in the fourth year (year 10) of secondary schools by pupils working towards Level 7/8 at GCSE in preparation for Key Stage 4 at the age of 16 plus.

Although there is some new work in this book much of the content uses basic processes introduced in earlier books but now applied to a wide variety of everyday situations.

ST(P) 5B completes the course for the written papers at the intermediate tier.

As before the exercises contain three types of questions.

The first type, identified by plain numbers, e.g. **2.**, help to see if you understand the work.

The second type, identified by a single underline, e.g. **2.**, are extra, but not harder, questions for extra practice or for later revision.

The third type, identified by a double underline, e.g. **2.**, are harder questions for those of you who enjoy more complicated work.

Many chapters end with mixed exercises and multiple choice questions. These will help you revise what you have done, either when you have finished the chapter or at a later date.

ACKNOWLEDGEMENTS

The authors and publishers would like to thank the following organisations for permission to include material.

British Rail: for the timetables on pages 7, 28, 31 and 428

BBC Magazines: for the extract from the *Radio Times* on page 29

Independent Television Publications: for the extract from the *TV Times* on page 29

Midland Electricity Board: for the sample bill on page 216

British Gas: for the sample bill on page 221

General Post Office for letter and parcel postage-rates on page 224

1 CHANGE OF UNITS

METRIC UNITS

Units of length: the basic unit of length is the metre (m). Other units in common use are the centimetre (cm), the millimetre (mm) and the kilometre (km), where

$$1\,km = 1000\,m$$
$$1\,m = 100\,cm$$
$$1\,cm = 10\,mm$$

1 cm

Units of area: these are derived from the units of length and in common use are the hectare, the square metre (m²), the square centimetre (cm²) and the square millimetre (mm²) where

$$1\,hectare = 10\,000\,m^2$$
$$1\,m^2 = 100 \times 100\,cm^2$$
$$1\,cm^2 = 10 \times 10\,mm^2$$

1 cm²

Units of volume: these are also derived from the units of length. Those in common use are the cubic metre (m³), the cubic centimetre (cm³) and the cubic millimetre (mm³), where

$$1\,m^3 = 100 \times 100 \times 100\,cm^3$$
$$1\,cm^3 = 10 \times 10 \times 10\,mm^3$$

1 cm³

Units of capacity: these are used to measure the volume of the contents of a container. The basic unit is the litre (l) and the other unit in common use is the millilitre (ml), where

$$1\,litre = 1000\,cm^3$$
$$= 1000\,ml$$

so

$$1\,ml = 1\,cm^3$$

1

Units of mass: the basic unit of mass is the gram (g). Other units in common use are the tonne (t), the kilogram (kg) and the milligram (mg) where

$$1\,t = 1000\,kg$$

$$1\,kg = 1000\,g$$

$$1\,g = 1000\,mg$$

The mass of an object is a measure of the quantity of matter it contains. In earlier books we used the word 'weight' to describe this but, although it is the word used in everyday language, it is not the correct scientific term.

Remember that to change from a large unit to a smaller unit we multiply. To change from a small unit to a larger unit we divide.

EXERCISE 1a

Express 2.5 m in centimetres.

$$2.5\,m = 2.5 \times 100\,cm$$

$$= 250\,cm$$

Express the given quantity in the unit in brackets.

1. 5.3 kg (g)
2. 8.6 cm^2 (mm^2)
3. 7.3 m (mm)
4. 1.5 litres (ml)
5. 3 cm^3 (mm^3)

6. 0.26 t (kg)
7. 0.8 hectare (m^2)
8. 0.025 km (cm)
9. $\frac{1}{2}$ litre (ml)
10. 0.0007 m^3 (cm^3)

Express 356 cm^2 in square metres.

$$356\,cm^2 = \frac{356}{100 \times 100}\,m^2$$

$$= 0.0356\,m^2$$

Express the given quantity in the unit in brackets.

11. 856 ml   (1)

16. 2930 cm³   (1)

12. 2500 g   (kg)

17. 187 kg   (t)

13. 8976 m²   (h)

18. 825 000 cm³   (m³)

14. 28 000 cm³   (m³)

19. 593 mm²   (cm²)

15. 2560 mm   (m)

20. 826 cm   (m)

21. 372 m   (km)

26. 1050 mm²   (cm²)

22. 0.56 cm²   (mm²)

27. 2.72 litres (ml)

23. 8.27 m³   (cm³)

28. 0.96 km   (m)

24. 39 000 ml   (1)

29. 3.25 t   (kg)

25. 25 kg   (t)

30. 299 800 cm³   (m³)

31. 0.628 kg   (g)

36. 400 cm³   (1)

32. 5000 m²   (hectare)

37. 82 000 kg   (t)

33. 80 mm³   (cm³)

38. 370 m   (km)

34. 9.62 m   (mm)

39. 0.0002 m³   (mm³)

35. 0.037 litres   (cm³)

40. 0.08 m²   (cm²)

41. Express 8 litres in   a) cm³   b) ml   c) m³.

42. Express 350 m in   a) cm   b) km   c) mm.

43. Express 35 000 cm² in   a) m²   b) mm².

44. Express 0.6 litres in   a) cm³   b) ml   c) m³.

45. Express 8500 cm in   a) mm   b) m   c) km.

46. Express 0.047 m² in   a) cm²   b) mm².

47. Express 5500 cm³ in   a) mm³   b) m³.

48. Express 3.5×10^5 cm³ in   a) mm³   b) m³   c) litres.

49. Express 1.6×10^6 cm² in   a) mm²   b) hectares   c) km².

50. Express 7.3×10^8 m² in   a) cm²   b) km²   c) hectares.

IMPERIAL UNITS

Units of length: the units in common use are the inch (in), the foot (ft), the yard (yd) and the mile.

$$1\,\text{ft} = 12\,\text{in}$$
$$1\,\text{yd} = 3\,\text{ft}$$
$$1\,\text{mile} = 1760\,\text{yds}$$

L—————————J
1 inch

Units of area: the common units of area are the acre, the square mile (sq mile) and the square yard (sq yd). The square inch and the square foot are not used much now.

Units of volume: cubic feet and cubic yards are sometimes used.
$$1\,\text{cu yd} = 27\,\text{cu ft}$$

Units of capacity: pints and gallons are still in use.
$$1\text{ gallon} = 8\text{ pints}$$

Units of weight: the ounce (oz), the pound (lb) and the ton are in common use. The hundredweight (cwt), and stone are sometimes used.
$$1\,\text{lb} = 16\,\text{oz}$$
$$1\text{ stone} = 14\,\text{lb}$$
$$1\text{ cwt} = 112\,\text{lb}$$
$$1\text{ ton} = 2240\,\text{lb}$$

EXERCISE 1b

Express $\frac{1}{2}\text{lb}$ in ounces.

$$\frac{1}{2}\text{lb} = \frac{1}{2} \times 16\,\text{oz}$$
$$= 8\,\text{oz}$$

Express the given quantity in the unit in brackets.

1. 2 ft   (in)

2. $\frac{1}{2}$ gallon   (pints)

3. $1\frac{1}{2}$ stone   (lbs)

4. 2 yd   (ft)

5. 3 cwt   (stones)

6. $\frac{3}{4}$ lb   (oz)

7. $2\frac{1}{2}$ ft   (in)

8. $1\frac{1}{2}$ lb   (oz)

Express 54 in in feet and inches.

$$54 \text{ in} = 54 \div 12 \text{ ft}$$
$$= 4 \text{ ft } 6 \text{ in}$$

$54 \div 12 = 4$, remainder 6

Express the given quantity in the units in brackets.

9. 36 in   (ft)

10. 32 oz   (lb)

11. 16 pints   (gallons)

12. 12 ft   (yd)

13. 18 in   (ft and in)

14. 20 oz   (lb and oz)

15. 12 pints   (gal and pints)

16. 56 lb   (stones)

17. Express 24 feet in   a) inches   b) yds.

18. What fraction of 1 lb is   a) 4 oz   b) 9 oz ?

19. How many inches is   a) 1 yd   b) $\frac{1}{2}$ yd   c) $\frac{1}{8}$ yd ?

20. How many ounces is   a) $\frac{1}{2}$ lb   b) $\frac{3}{4}$ lb   c) $\frac{1}{8}$ lb ?

21. What fraction of 1 gallon is   a) 4 pints   b) 6 pints ?

22. How many pints is   a) 2 gallons   b) $1\frac{3}{4}$ gallons ?

23. Express 224 lbs in   a) stones   b) cwt.

24. What fraction of 1 cu yd is   a) 18 cu ft   b) 21 cu ft ?

25. Express 3 sq ft in   a) sq in   b) sq yd.

TIME

Whether we use the metric system or the imperial system, the units in which time is measured are the same.

Units of time:

$$1 \text{ minute} = 60 \text{ seconds}$$
$$1 \text{ hour} = 60 \text{ minutes}$$
$$1 \text{ day} = 24 \text{ hours}$$

EXERCISE 1c

> Find the time that elapses between 9.15 a.m. and 11.10 a.m.
>
> Elapsed time $= 11 \text{ h } 10 \text{ min} - 9 \text{ h } 15 \text{ min}$
>
> $\qquad = 10 \text{ h } 70 \text{ min} - 9 \text{ h } 15 \text{ min}$
> $\qquad$ (changing 1 h to mins)
>
> $\qquad = 1 \text{ h } 55 \text{ min}$

1. Mr Smith arrived at the bus stop at 10.50 a.m. and the bus arrived at 11.05 a.m. How long did Mr Smith have to wait for the bus ?

2. An aeroplane takes off from Heathrow at 9.25 a.m. and arrives in Paris at 10.15 a.m. How long is the flight ?

3. Express 90 minutes in hours.

4. Express 36 hours in days.

5. How many seconds are there in a week ?

6. I left Calais by train at 8 a.m. and arrived in Milan the next day at 6 a.m. How many hours was the journey ?

7. Express 56 days in weeks.

8. How many minutes are there in a full day ?

9. How many hours are there in a year (365 days) ?

10. How many minutes are there in the month of June ?

11.

11.33 The Living World
12.00 News; You and Yours
12.27 All in the Mind
12.55 Weather
 1.00 The World at One

Use the extract from one day's Radio 4 programmes to answer the following questions.

a) How long does the programme 'The Living World' last ?

b) How long does the programme 'All in the Mind' last ?

c) A listener turned on for the start of 'The Living World' and turned off at the end of 'All in the Mind'. For how long did they have the radio on ?

12.

Waterloo	10.52
Wimbledon	11.03
Surbiton	11.09
Esher	11.13
Hersham	11.16
Walton-on-Thames	11.19
Weybridge	11.23

Use this extract from a railway timetable to answer the following questions.

a) How long does the train take to go from Waterloo to Hersham ?

b) How long does the train take to go from Surbiton to Weybridge ?

13.

GLASGOW	d							07 20
EDINBURGH	d							07 15
Carlisle	d	. 02 23		...	06 10	...	06 10	...	08 57
LIVERPOOL Lime Street	d ⁻.	...	06 25	07 10c	08 10	...	08 33 qq	...	10 30
MANCHESTER Piccadilly	d	. ...		06 35n	07 10	07 52ee	...	09 02	...	10 30
CREWE	d	. 06 20	07 25	08 01	09 15	...	10 03	...	11 31
Nantwich ●	★d	. 06 28	07 32	...	09 23	...		...	11 38
Wrenbury ●	★d ⁻.	...	07 38	...	09 30	...		...	11 44
Whitchurch (Salop) ●	★d	. 06 41	07 46	...	09 39	...		...	11 52
Prees ●	★d	. ...	07 52	...	09 46	...		...	11 58
Wem ●	★d	. 06 51	07 57	...	09 51	...		...	12 03
Yorton ●	★d ⁻.	...	08 02	...	09 57	...		...	12 08
SHREWSBURY	a	. 07 05	08 14	08 37	10 10	...	10 36	...	12 20

Use this extract from a railway timetable to answer the following questions.

a) How many trains stop at Wem ?

b) How long does the train take to go from Glasgow to Shrewsbury ?

c) How long does the 06 10 train from Carlisle take to go from Nantwich to Yorton ?

EQUIVALENTS BETWEEN METRIC AND IMPERIAL UNITS

We often need to change units between the metric and imperial systems and it is useful to know some approximate equivalents.

Length $\qquad$ $10\,\text{cm} \approx 4\,\text{inches}$

$1\,\text{metre} \approx 39\,\text{inches}$ (i.e. $1\,\text{m}$ is roughly $1\,\text{yd}$)

$8\,\text{km} \approx 5\,\text{miles}$

Area $\qquad$ $1\,\text{hectare} \approx 2\tfrac{1}{2}\,\text{acres}$

Weight $\qquad$ $100\,\text{g} \approx 3\tfrac{1}{2}\,\text{oz}$

$1\,\text{kg} \approx 2.2\,\text{lb}$

$1\,\text{tonne} \approx 1\,\text{ton}$ ($1\,\text{tonne}$ is slightly greater than $1\,\text{ton}$)

Capacity $\qquad$ $1\,\text{litre} \approx 1\tfrac{3}{4}\,\text{pints}$

$1\,\text{gallon} \approx 4\tfrac{1}{2}\,\text{litres}$

EXERCISE 1d

"My set of kitchen scales only weighs in lb and oz. When I weigh a letter it comes to $1\tfrac{1}{2}\,\text{oz}$. The postal rate is 24p for up to 60 g. Will my letter cost me more than 24 p?

(I need to know whether $1\tfrac{1}{2}\,\text{oz}$ is less than $60\,\text{g}$.)

$$3.5\,\text{oz} \approx 100\,\text{g}$$

$$\therefore \qquad 1\,\text{oz} \approx \frac{100}{3.5}\,\text{g}$$

$$\therefore \qquad 1\tfrac{1}{2}\,\text{oz} \approx \frac{100}{3.5} \times 1.5\,\text{g}$$

$$= 43\,\text{g}$$

$$43\,\text{g} < 60\,\text{g}$$

My letter can be posted for 24 p.

1. The distance between two towns in France is 140 km. How many miles is this?

2. The instructions in a model kit ask for a 40 cm length of string. How many inches is this?

3. My recipe for chocolate mousse calls for 4 oz of chocolate. The supermarket stocks 200 g bars of chocolate. Is one of these bars enough?

4. In a holiday brochure, a camp site in Germany is described as 12 hectares in area. Roughly how many acres is this?

5. When I put some petrol in my car, the pump reads 25 litres. How many gallons is this?

6. An old knitting pattern asks for 10 oz of wool. Wool is sold in 50 g balls. How many 50 g balls are needed?

7. I know that the petrol tank on my car holds 9 gallons. How many litres is this?

8. A recipe for marmalade specifies 13 lb of sugar. How many 1 kg bags of sugar will I need?

9. The diameter of the earth is roughly 8000 miles. How many kilometres is this?

10. Jane knows that she is 5 ft 6 in tall. When she comes to fill in a visa application form, her height is required in metres. What should she put down for her height?

RATES OF CHANGE

We often need to compare the rates at which objects travel or quantities are consumed.

Speed is the name for the rate at which an object covers distance, and it measures the distance covered per unit of time. So speed could be given as, for example, inches per second. The common units for speed are kilometres per hour (km/h), miles per hour (m.p.h.), and metres per second (m/s).

Petrol Consumption. The rate at which vehicles use petrol is usually measured in miles per gallon (m.p.g.). It can also be measured in kilometres per litre (km/l). For those vehicles that use vast quantities of fuel (rockets, for example) the units could be gallons per mile, or even gallons per second.

Coverage, of paint for example, is another 'rate' and might be measured in square metres per litre.

EXERCISE 1e

Use $8\,\text{km} \approx 5\,\text{miles}$ to express a speed of $100\,\text{km/h}$ in
a) km/min   b) m.p.h.

a) $100\,\text{km/h} = \dfrac{100}{60}\,\text{km/min}$

$= 1.7\,\text{km/min}$ (correct to 2 s.f.)

b) $8\,\text{km} \approx 5\,\text{miles}$

$\therefore$ $1\,\text{km} \approx \tfrac{5}{8}\,\text{miles}$

$\therefore$ $100\,\text{km/h} \approx \tfrac{5}{8} \times 100\,\text{m.p.h.}$

$= 62.5\,\text{m.p.h.}$

$100\,\text{km/h} \approx 63\,\text{m.p.h.}$

1. Change $30\,\text{km/h}$ to   a) km/min   b) m/h.

2. Change $100\,\text{m/s}$ to   a) km/s   b) m/min   c) km/min.

3. Using $8\,\text{km} \approx 5\,\text{miles}$, change $130\,\text{km/h}$ to m.p.h.

4. Change $10\,\text{m/s}$ to ft/sec using $1\,\text{m} \approx 3.1\,\text{ft}$.

5. Change $70\,\text{m.p.h.}$ to km/h using $8\,\text{km} \approx 5\,\text{miles}$.

Change $40\,\text{km/h}$ to m/s.

$40\,\text{km/h} = 40 \times 1000\,\text{m/h}$

$= \dfrac{40 \times 1000}{60}\,\text{m/min}$

$= \dfrac{40 \times 1000}{60 \times 60}\,\text{m/s}$

$= 11.1\,\text{m/s}$ (to 3 s.f.)

6. Change 130 km/h to m/s, giving your answer correct to 3 s.f.

7. Change 20 m/s to km/h.

8. Change 30 m.p.h. to ft/sec giving your answer correct to 3 s.f.

9. Change 100 gallons/minute to litres/second using 1 gallon $\approx$ 4.5 litres.

10. A car travels 560 miles on a full tank holding 20 gallons of petrol. Find, in m.p.g., the rate at which the car uses petrol.

11. The literature about a motor cycle states that the petrol consumption is 100 m.p.g. How far can a motorcyclist expect to travel on 5 gallons ?

12. On the back of a tin of paint it states that the coverage is 50 m² per litre. The tin holds 500 ml of paint. What area should it cover ?

13. A bag of granulated lawn fertilizer states that it should be applied at the rate of 1 oz per square yard. The bag contains $1\frac{1}{2}$ lb of fertilizer. What area of lawn will it cover ?

14. The label on a bottle of hair shampoo states that the contents are sufficient for 20 shampoos. The bottle holds 500 ml. At what rate, in ml per shampoo, should it be used ?

15. Biscuits are to be provided for refreshments at a meeting. It is anticipated that 100 people will attend the meeting and that they will consume biscuits at the rate of 3 per person.

a) How many biscuits need to be provided ?

b) The biscuits come in packets of 25. How many packets of biscuits need to be provided ?

16. A car has an average petrol consumption of 40 m.p.g. How many gallons of petrol should be needed for a journey of 450 miles ?

17. A water pump can pump water out of a basement at the rate of 2 pints per second. How many gallons of water can it pump out in 1 minute ?

18. A motor cyclist put 10 litres of petrol in his tank and travelled 200 miles on this amount of petrol.

Find, in miles per litre, the rate at which he used petrol.

19. Change 30 m.p.g. to km/litre using 5 miles $\approx$ 8 km and 1 gallon $\approx$ 4.5 litres.

20. A car manual gives the tyre pressures in kg/cm² and a pressure gauge measures in lb/sq in. Change a pressure of 2 kg/cm² to lb/sq in using 1 kg $\approx$ 2.2 lb and 1 in $\approx$ 2.5 cm.

CONVERSION GRAPHS

Graphs are particularly useful when several conversions have to be made from one system of units to another, e.g. changing feet into metres. Some examples of this type of graph are given in the following exercise.

EXERCISE 1f

This graph relates temperature in degrees Fahrenheit to temperature in degrees Celsius.

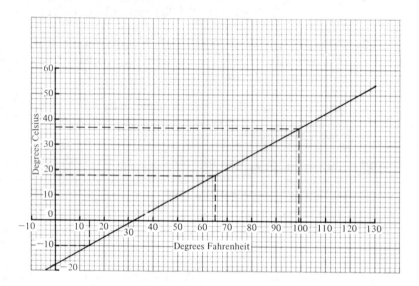

a) What temperature in degrees Fahrenheit corresponds to 37 °C ?

b) What is 65 °F expressed in degrees Celsius ?

c) What is −10 °F expressed in degrees Fahrenheit ?

a) 37 °C is 98.5 °F

b) 65 °F is 18 °C

c) −10 °F is 14 °C

1.

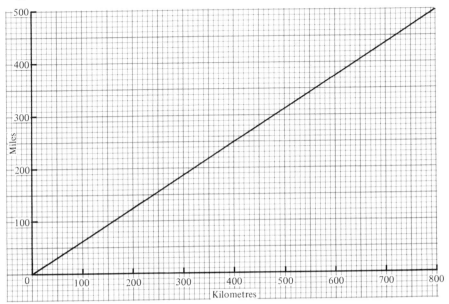

Use the graph to express

a) 200 miles in kilometres

b) 600 kilometres in miles

c) 430 kilometres in miles.

2.

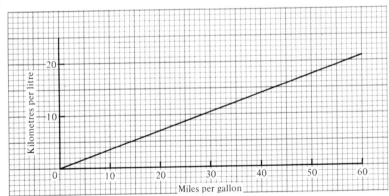

Use the given graph to express

a) 32 m.p.g. in kilometres per litre

b) 18 km/l in miles per gallon.

Mr Ryton's car does 42 m.p.g. on a long motorway drive but only 26 m.p.g. in town. Express each of these consumptions in kilometres per litre.

Questions 3 to 6 refer to the following graphs.

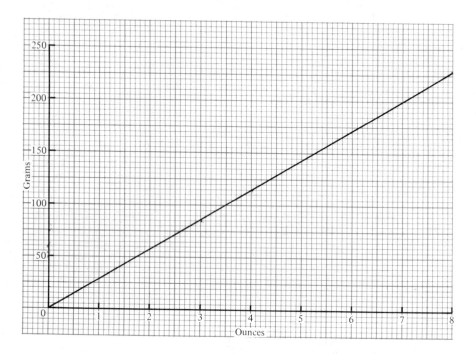

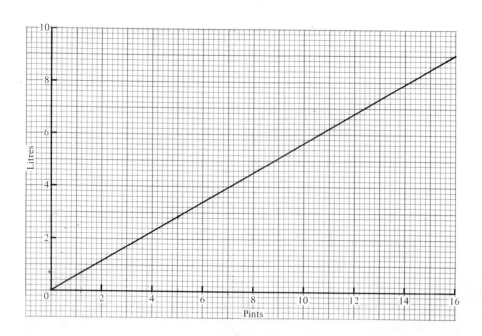

3. a) Express 200 g in ounces.

b) Express 5 oz in grams.

c) Which is heavier, a 4 oz packet of sweets or a 100 g bar of chocolate ?

4. a) Express 5 pints in litres.

b) Express 4 litres in pints.

c) A wine bottle holds 0.75 litres of wine. Express this in pints.

d) How many litres does a 2 gallon bucket hold ?   (1 gallon = 8 pints)

5. Mrs Selwood is using an old recipe book to make a cake but her scales are graduated in grams and kilograms. Convert the weights of the ingredients given in the recipe so that she can weigh the correct amounts on her scales.

SULTANA CAKE
8 oz flour
4 oz castor sugar
3 oz butter
2 oz sultanas
2 eggs

6. A fishpond holds 4000 litres of water.

a) Express 1 litre in pints.

b) Find, in pints, the volume of water in the pond.

7. A maximum-minimum thermometer in a greenhouse indicates that on February 20th the highest temperature was 58 °F and the lowest was 30 °F. Use the conversion graph given in the example at the beginning of this exercise to express each of these temperatures in degrees Celsius. What is the difference between the highest and lowest temperatures

a) in °F   b) in °C ?

8. Use the next graph, which relates inches to centimetres, to convert

a) 23 inches to centimetres   b) 15 centimetres to inches

c) 15 inches to centimetres.

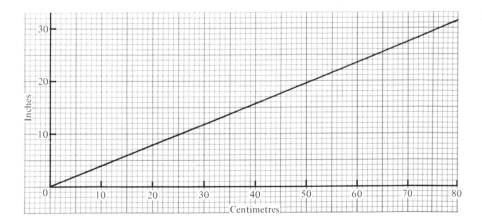

CURRENCY CONVERSION GRAPHS

When we need to compare prices in, say, deutschmarks with pounds sterling (£), a graph relating the two currencies gives quick and easy conversions. The *exchange rate* tells us how many units of the foreign currency are equivalent to one pound sterling. In the example below, the exchange rate used for the graph is £1 ≡ 2.90 DM.

EXERCISE 1g

This graph relates pounds sterling to deutschmarks.

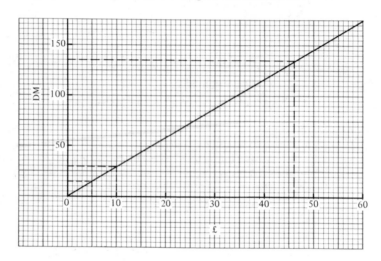

a) On holiday in Germany, Jean buys a camera for 135 DM. What does it cost her in pounds ?

b) What is the price, in pounds, of a map marked 15 DM ?

c) At the end of her holiday Jean has to repay £ 10 which she borrowed from her friend. How many deutschmarks does Jean need to repay this debt ?

From the graph,

a) Jean's camera costs her £ 46.

b) The map costs £ 5.

c) Jean needs 30 DM.

1. This graph gives the conversion between pounds sterling and US dollars when the exchange rate is £1 ≡ $1.75.

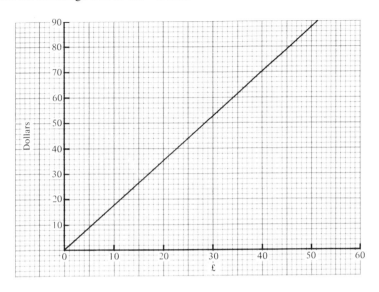

a) Find the value in dollars of   (i) £34   (ii) £27.

b) Find the value in pounds sterling of   (i) $76   (ii) $46.

2.

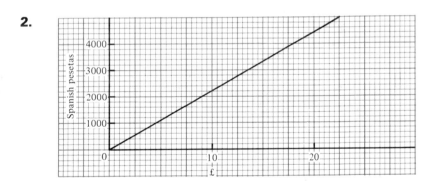

Use the graph given to answer the following questions.

a) The bill for a meal in a restaurant came to 3500 pta. What is this in pounds sterling ?

b) Bill changed a £5 note into pesetas. How many did he get ?

c) A pair of sandals is marked at 2800 pta. How much do the sandals cost in pounds sterling ?

d) Joan wanted to buy herself a watch while she was in Spain. She did not want to spend more than £15. Up to what sum in pesetas was she prepared to spend ?

3.

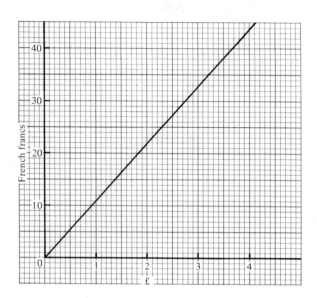

This graph was used by teachers accompanying a group of eleven-year-olds on a school trip to France. Use this graph to answer the following questions.

a) "Sir, can you change 50 p into francs for me ?" How many francs should the teacher give ?

b) "Miss, this pen is marked 22 f. How much is that ?"

c) Daniel lent Helen 30 f. Helen has to repay her debt in sterling. How much does she owe Daniel ?

d) David bought a packet of sweets costing 27 f. There were 25 sweets in the packet and David sold them to his classmates at 10 p each. Did he ask a fair price ?

Use the graph for question 3 to answer questions 4 and 5.

4. The duty free shop on the boat would accept francs or sterling, but always gave change in sterling. Katie bought a badge marked at 70 p and paid for it with a 10 f coin. How much change did she get ?

5. On the return trip the school party used a French ferry. The shop on the ferry would accept francs or sterling, but always gave change in francs. Primo paid for a meal costing 60 f with a £ 10 note. How much change did he get ?

DRAWING CONVERSION GRAPHS

To draw a currency conversion graph to enable us to convert values up to £ 14, say, to pesetas we start with the exchange rate. If this is £ 1 ≡ 180 pta then £ 2 ≡ 360 pta and £ 10 ≡ 1800 pta.

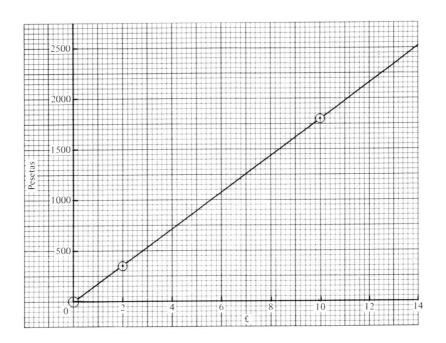

Using scales of 2 cm for £ 1 and 2 cm for 500 pta, we plot the points corresponding to £ 2 ≡ 360 pta and £ 10 ≡ 1800 pta. (We could use the point given by £ 1 ≡ 180 pta but this is difficult to plot accurately using the given scales.)

A straight line is then drawn through the two points.

This line should also go through the zero mark. You can use this as a check on the other two points.

From the graph,   1000 pta ≈ £ 5.60

£ 8 ≈ 1440 pta

2250 pta ≈ £ 12.50

£ 13 ≈ 2340 pta

EXERCISE 1h

1. a) Using £1 ≡ 9.5 French francs find the equivalent in French francs of
(i) £10   (ii) £100.

b) Using scales of 1 cm for £10 and 1 cm for 100 francs, draw and label a set of axes and plot the points given by your answers to (a).
Draw a straight line through the points.

c) Use your graph to find
(i) £55 in francs   (ii) 1000 f in pounds sterling.

2. a) If £1 ≡ 1.75 US$, find in dollars   (i) £2   (ii) £10.

b) Draw and label a set of axes using scales of 1 cm for £1 and 1 cm for $1. Plot the points given by your answers to (a) and draw a straight line through these points.

c) Use your graph to find   (i) £2.50 in $ (ii) $15 in £.

3. a) Using the exchange rate 1 Deutschmark ≡ 3.5 French francs find
(i) 10 DM in francs   (ii) 100 DM in francs.

b) Using scales of 1 cm for 10 DM and 1 cm for 20 francs draw a graph for conversions between DM and francs.

c) Use your graph to find   (i) 110 DM in francs   (ii) 280 f in DM.

4. a) Using   1 inch ≡ 2.5 centimetres,   find   (i) 10 inches   in   centimetres
(ii) 100 inches in centimetres.

b) Draw an axis for inches from 0 to 160 using a scale of 1 cm for 10 inches. Draw an axis for centimetres from 0 to 400 using a scale of 2 cm for 50 cm. Plot the points given by your answers to (a) and draw a straight line through them.

c) Use your graph to find   (i) 350 cm in inches   (ii) 40 inches in cm.

5. a) Using the exchange rate 100 pesetas ≡ 54 pence, find in pounds and pence the equivalent of   (i) 500 pta   (ii) 1000 pta.

b) Using scales of 2 cm for 100 pta and 2 cm for 50 p, draw and label a set of axes. Draw the graph for conversions between pesetas and sterling.

c) Use your graph to find   (i) £2.50 in pesetas   (ii) 900 pta in £.

MIXED EXERCISES

EXERCISE 1i

1. Express   a) 1.9 m in cm   b) 250 g in kg.

2. Express   a) 4 ft in inches   b) 64 oz in lb.

3. A train left Euston at 9.45 a.m. and arrived at Rugby at 10.38 a.m. How long did the journey take?

4. Using 5 miles ≈ 8 kilometres, express 60 miles in kilometres.

5. Change a speed of 40 m.p.h. to km/h using 5 miles ≈ 8 kilometres.

6. A cold water tank holds 500 litres of water. Use 1 gallon ≈ 4.5 litres to express the capacity of the tank in gallons.

EXERCISE 1j

1. Express   a) 500 ml in litres   b) 5 cm² in mm².

2. Express   a) 3 gallons in pints   b) 18 ft in yards.

3. A bus was timetabled to arrive at 3.45 p.m. but did not come until 4.12 p.m. How late was the bus ?

4. Express 2.5 kg in pounds using 1 kg ≈ 2.2 lb.

5. A dripping tap fills a 1 pint milk bottle in 5 minutes.

a) How many pints of water come out of the tap in 1 hour ?

b) How many gallons of water come out of the tap in 24 hours ?

6. A table cloth is 250 cm long. Is this long enough for a table which is 80 inches long ?   (Use 10 cm ≈ 4 in)

EXERCISE 1k

Each question is followed by several alternative answers. Write down the letter that corresponds to the correct answer.

1. 400 cm is the same as

A 4 km   **B** 4 m   **C** 40 mm   **D** 400 inches

2. The nearest equivalent to a 2.5 kg bag of potatoes is a bag weighing

A 2.5 lb   **B** 3 lb   **C** 10 lb   **D** 5 lb

3. The nearest equivalent weight to 4 oz is

A 100 g   **B** 1 kg   **C** 500 g   **D** 200 g

4. An area of 200 mm² can be expressed as

A 2 m²   **B** 20 cm²   **C** 1 cm²   **D** 2 cm²

5. A speed of 20 m.p.h. can be expressed as

A 32 km/h   **B** 200 cm/h   **C** 12 km/h   **D** 200 km/h

2 READING TABLES

Much of the everyday information we need is given either by means of a graph or in a table. The use of graphical data is dealt with in Chapter 21. In this chapter we will look at a variety of tabulated data.

CONVERSION TABLES AND CURRENCY CONVERSIONS

If we want to compare, say, British shoe sizes with European shoe sizes, a table is better than a graph because there is nothing between one size and the next. The following table gives corresponding sizes for ladies' shoes.

British size	2	3	4	5	6
Euro size	35	36	37	38	39

If we draw a graph from this table it would look as though we could compare size 36.8 with size 3.8 but of course there are no such sizes.

Conversion graphs are not always available when we need to compare prices in two currencies. In this case we can work directly with the exchange rate.

EXERCISE 2a

1. This table gives the approximate temperatures (both Celsius and Fahrenheit) that correspond to the numbers on the regulo of a gas cooker (this number is often called the Gas Mark).

Gas Mark	1	2	3	4	5	6	7	8	9
°C	140	150	165	180	190	200	220	230	240
°F	275	300	325	350	375	400	425	450	475

a) A cake has to be baked at 180 °C. What is the best number at which to set the regulo ?

b) If a turkey is cooked at Gas Mark 4, at what temperature is it being cooked   i) in °C   ii) in °F ?

c) Mrs Simpson's gas regulo is faulty and the temperature it gives is always 10 °C higher than it should be at each Gas Mark. If she wants to roast a joint at 200 °C, how should she set her regulo ?

2. Mr Salter goes to Switzerland on business for a year and while he is there he needs some new shirts and a pair of shoes. In England his shirt size is $16\frac{1}{2}$ and he takes size 9 shoes. Use the following tables to find what sizes he should ask for in Switzerland.

Shirts	British	15	$15\frac{1}{2}$	16	$16\frac{1}{2}$	17	$17\frac{1}{2}$
	European	39	40	41	42	43	44

Shoes	British	6	7	8	9	10	11
	European	40	41	42	43	44	45

Mr Salter sends two shirts back to England for his brother John to try. One shirt, size 40, is too small and the other, size 42, is too big. What is John's British shirt size ?

If £1 is equivalent to 1.5 dollars ($) in the USA, find the equivalent of

a) £120 in US dollars   b) $48 in pounds sterling.

a) £1 = $1.5   (We write this equation with dollars on the right because we are looking for a number of dollars)

∴ £120 = $1.5 × 120

= $180

b) $1.5 = £1   (This time we put £1 on the right because we are looking for a number of pounds)

∴ $1 = £$\frac{1}{1.5}$

∴ $48 = £$\frac{1}{1.5}$ × 48

= £32

---

3. If £1 is equivalent to 2.9 deutschmarks (DM), find the equivalent of

a) £47 in deutschmarks

b) 8.60 DM in pounds sterling.

4. If £1 is equivalent to 210 Greek drachmas, express

a) £2.50 in drachmas

b) 1073 drachmas in pounds sterling.

5. Given that 1.44 US dollars are equivalent to £1, find the equivalent of

a) £95 in US dollars

b) US $7.50 in pounds sterling.

6. If the exchange rate between Britain and Italy is £1 ≡ 2150 lira, find the equivalent of

a) 10 000 lira in pounds sterling

b) £14.25 in lira.

7. If 22.1 Austrian schillings are equivalent to £1, express

a) £18 in schillings

b) 95 schillings in pounds sterling.

The next table gives the equivalent of £1 in various currencies.

£	French franc (Ff)	US Dollar (US $)	Deutschmark (DM)
1	9.5	1.5	2.85

Use this table to find the value in pounds sterling of

8.	78 Ff	**11.**	4.50 Ff	**14.**	102 Ff
9.	32.60 DM	**12.**	US $4.75	**15.**	US $17.30
10.	US $143	**13.**	84 DM	**16.**	8 Ff

Use the table given above to find how many French francs are equivalent to 1 DM.

From the table   2.85 DM = 9.5 Ff

$$1 \, DM = \frac{9.5}{2.85} \, Ff$$

$$= 3.33 \, Ff$$

Use the table given on page 24 to find the value of

17. US $1 in Ff   **20.** 1 DM in Ff   **23.** £137 in DM

18. 1 DM in £   **21.** 1 Ff in DM   **24.** 18 Ff in DM

19. US $1 in £   **22.** £24 in Ff   **25.** 42 DM in US $

THE TWENTY-FOUR-HOUR CLOCK

We have two systems in this country for stating the time of day. One of them uses two periods of twelve hours in any one complete day. The first period starts at midnight and continues until 12 noon; times within this period are referred to as 'a.m.' For example, you may begin your school day at 9.00 a.m. For the second period of twelve hours from noon to midnight, p.m. is used, e.g. you might go to bed at 10.00 p.m.

The other system starts at midnight as before, but carries on through 24 hours to the next midnight. Hence, one hour after 12 noon is 13.00 hours and is written as 13.00 or 13 00 (or sometimes 1300). We say "thirteen hundred hours" or just "thirteen hundred". Note that 0800 is read as "oh eight hundred hours".

Most digital clocks and watches use the 24-hour system, whereas most, but not all, clocks and watches with hands use the repeated twelve-hour period.

EXERCISE 2b

What time on a 24-hour clock corresponds to

a) 7 a.m.   b) 5 p.m.   c) 11 p.m.   d) midnight ?

a)	7 a.m. ≡ 07.00	(7 hours after midnight)
b)	5 p.m. ≡ 17.00	(12 + 5 hours after midnight)
c)	11 p.m. ≡ 23.00	(12 + 11 hours after midnight)
d)	midnight ≡ 00.00	(zero hours after midnight)

In questions 1 to 9 give the equivalent time on a 24-hour clock.

1. 3.20 a.m.   **4.** 10.40 p.m.   **7.** 9.13 p.m.

2. 11.52 a.m.   **5.** Noon   **8.** 9.13 a.m.

3. 1 p.m.   **6.** 1 a.m.   **9.** 11.59 p.m.

In questions 10 to 18, times are given from a 24-hour clock. Give the corresponding time on a 12-hour clock, using a.m. and p.m.

10. 14.30   **13.** 20.20   **16.** 02.06

11. 09.15   **14.** 00.01   **17.** 10.45

12. 11.20   **15.** 16.25   **18.** 23.18

Find the period between
a) 10.45 a.m. and 2.20 p.m. on the same day
b) 23.12 on Tuesday and 01.35 on Wednesday.

    a) From 10.45 a.m. to noon is 1 h 15 min

    From noon to 2.20 p.m. is 2 h 20 min

    From 10.45 a.m. to 2.30 p.m. is 3 h 35 min

    b) From 23.12 to midnight is 48 min

    From midnight to 01.35 is 1 h 35 min

    From 23.12 to 01.35 next day is 2 h 23 min

In each question from 19 to 22, find the period of time between

19. 3.20 a.m. and 11.15 p.m. on the same day

20. 05.35 and 14.04 on the same day

21. 10.14 p.m. and 2.30 a.m. next day

22. 21.16 and 03.03 next day

23. A flight from Brussels Airport to Milan takes 2 hours 15 minutes. Find the time of arrival if the plane leaves at   a) 9.30   b) 13.15   c) 23.00. Give your answers referring to the 24-hour clock and also state whether the plane arrives in the morning or in the afternoon.

24. A train leaves King's Cross for Edinburgh, a journey which takes 4 hours 10 minutes. At what time does the train arrive

a) if it leaves on time at 10.58 and arrives on time ?

b) if it leaves on time at 14.40 and is 25 minutes late ?

If the train arrives on time at 11.10, at what time did it leave King's Cross ?

TIMETABLES

The 24-hour clock is used in practically all timetables. Because most people travel by bus, coach or train at some time in their lives, it is important to be able to read timetables correctly. The next exercise gives practice in this skill.

EXERCISE 2c

Here is part of a timetable for buses on the Redchester–Lenton route.

Redchester	11.05	11.20
Park Street	11.14	11.29
Mill Lane	11.24	11.39
Beacon Hill	11.31	
Manton	11.42	
Packingham	11.55	
Lenton	12.07	12.22

a) At what time is the first bus at
   (i) Beacon Hill   (ii) Packingham ?

b) How long does it take for the bus to go from Park Street to Manton ?

c) If I miss the first bus from Redchester by 1 minute, how long do I have to wait for the second bus ?

d) Assuming that the buses travel at the same speed over all sections of the route
   (i) state which two bus stops are closest together
   (ii) fill in the missing times for the second bus.

a) (i) 11.31   (ii) 11.55

b) 28 minutes   (from 11.14 to 11.42)

c) 14 minutes   (from 11.06 to 11.20)

d) (i) Mill Lane and Beacon Hill   (7 minutes apart)

   (ii) Beacon Hill   11.46

        Manton   11.57

        Packingham   12.10

Questions 1 to 3 refer to the following information.

The country bus service between Westwick and Plimpton runs only twice a day in each direction. Here is the timetable for Westwick to Plimpton.

Westwick		9.45	14.20
Red Farm Hill		10.04	14.39
Astleton	arr	10.56	15.31
	dep	11.15	15.45
Morgans Hollow		11.29	15.59
Plimpton		12.07	16.37

1. a) How long does each bus take to go from Westwick to Plimpton ?

b) How long does each bus stop at Astleton ?

2. Which two adjacent stopping places do you think are

a) farthest apart by road   b) closest together by road ?

3. Mrs Jones takes the first bus from Red Farm Hill to Astleton and stays there to visit a friend. She then catches the second bus to Plimpton. If both buses run exactly to time,

a) how long is Mrs Jones in Astleton ?

b) what is the interval of time between Mrs Jones' departure from Red Farm Hill and her arrival at Plimpton ?

4. Here is part of a train timetable on the Taunton–Plymouth route.

			125	**125**			**125**	**125**		
Taunton	d	17 57	18 33	18 43	18 49	19 04	19 27	—	—
Tiverton Parkway	d	—	—	18 57	—	19 18	—	—	—
Exeter St. David's	d	18 37	19 01	19 16	19 22	19 35	19 56	—	20 10
Exeter St. Thomas	d	—	—	—	—	—	—	—	20 13
Starcross	d	—	—	—	—	—	—	—	20 22
Dawlish Warren	d	—	—	—	—	—	—	—	20 27
Dawlish	d	—	19 14	—	—	—	—	—	20 31
Teignmouth	d	—	19 19	—	—	—	—	—	20 36
Newton Abbot	a	—	19 26	19 37	19 45	19 56	20 17	—	20 43
Newton Abbott	d	—	19 28	19 37	19 45	19 56	20 17	20 25	20 45
Torre	d	—	—	—	—	—	—	20 33	—
Torquay	d	—	19 42	—	—	—	—	20 36	—
Paignton	a	—	19 48	—	—	—	—	20 41	—
Totnes	d	—	—	19 51	—	—	—	—	20 58 a
Plymouth	a	19 43	—	20 21	20 29	20 36	20 57	—	—

a) How many 125 trains run between Taunton and Plymouth ?

b) Kiri leaves Taunton at 18 49 to visit a friend who lives in Dawlish. What time will she get to Dawlish ?

c) Ian misses the 19 28 at Newton Abbot by 10 minutes. How long must he wait for the next train that will take him to Paignton ?

Use the following sections from the programmes for a Saturday evening on BBC1 and ITV, to answer questions 5 to 10.

BBC1
5.05 News, Weather News, Sport.
5.20 Stay Tooned.
5.45 Jim'll Fix It.
6.20 That's Showbusiness.
7.05 The Little and Large Show.
7.40 Every Second Counts.
8.15 The Collectors.
9.05 News and Sport, Weather News.
9.20 Film: The Brink's Job.
11.10 The Horror Movie: Patrick.
12.50-12.55 Weather.

ITV
5.00 News from ITN.
5.05 Family Fortunes.
5.35 The A-Team.
6.30 Bobby Davro on the Box.
7.00 Barrymore.
8.00 Murder, Mystery, Suspense.
9.45 News from ITN and Sport.
10.00 Aspel and Company.
10.45 LWT News Headlines, followed by The Making of Mad Max.
11.40 A Song for Ireland.
12.35 Night Thoughts with Margaret Hebblethwaite.

5. a) How long is the 'Jim'll Fix It' programme ?

   b) How long does 'The A-Team' last ?

6. a) Find the total time given to News programmes, including Weather and Sport, on BBC1 in this extract.

   b) What is the length of the longest programme on either channel in this extract ?

7. Dave likes to watch 'That's Showbusiness' and 'Barrymore'. How much of 'Barrymore' does he miss if he watches the whole of 'That's Showbusiness' ?

8. a) If Peter switches on at 8.30, which two programmes can he choose from ?

   b) Sara watches 'The Little and Large Show' and 'The A-Team'. For how long can she switch off the television between these programmes ?

9. Katie doesn't want to watch the Murder, Mystery and Suspense Play on ITV. What complete programmes can she watch on BBC1 during the time taken by the Play on ITV ?

10. Are the programme times given for a 12-hour or 24-hour clock ? Give the reason for your answer and say what could be inserted to make the times clearer.

Coaches run between Newtown and Westport either via Winterton and Sleeth or via Lulham. The daily timetable for journeys in each direction is given below.

Newtown		8.45	10.27	13.15	Westport		9.12	11.50	16.28
Winterton	arr	11.03		15.33	Lulham	arr	11.27		
	dep	11.18		15.48		dep	11.37		
Sleeth	arr	12.30		17.00	Sleeth	arr		13.03	17.41
	dep	12.40		17.10		dep		13.30	18.08
Lulham	arr		12.18		Winterton	arr		14.42	19.20
	dep		12.40			dep		14.52	19.30
Westport		13.53	14.55	18.23	Newtown		13.28	17.10	21.48

a) State the time of each coach from Newtown that goes via Sleeth.

b) State the time of each coach from Westport that goes via Lulham.

c) Which coach does the journey from Newtown to Westport most quickly ?

d) Is it possible to go from Newtown to Lulham and return on the same day ?

e) If I take the first coach from Newtown to Winterton and return on the last coach of the day, how long do I spend in Winterton ?

f) For how long does ,
   (i) the third coach from Newtown stop at Winterton
   (ii) the second coach from Westport stop at Sleeth ?

a) The 8.45 and the 13.15

b) The 9.12

c) The 10.27

d) No. The only coach from Newtown to Lulham arrives at Lulham at 12.18. The only coach from Lulham to Newtown has already left at 11.37.

e) I arrive at 11.03 and leave at 19.30 so I spend 8 hours 27 minutes in Winterton.

f) (i) 15 minutes   (from 15.33 to 15.48)

   (ii) 27 minutes   (from 13.03 to 13.30)

Part of the British Rail timetable for London to Hertford North and Welwyn Garden City is given below. Use it to answer questions 11 to 15.

London King's Cross ..... ⊖ 25 d									1714		
Moorgate ⊖d	1611			1621	1631	1641	1655	1659		1708	
Old Street ⊖d	1613			1623	1633	1643	1657	1700		1710	
Essex Road d	1616			1626	1636	1646	1700	1704		1713	
Highbury & Islington ⊖d	1617			1627	1637	1647	1701	1705		1714	
Dayton Park d	1619			1629	1639	1649	1703	1707		1716	
Finsbury Park ⊖25 d	1622			1632	1642	1652	1706	1710	1719	1719	
Harringay d	1624			1634	1644	1654	1708	1712			
Hornsey d	1626			1636	1646	1656	1710	1714			
Alexandra Palace d	1628			1638	1648	1658	1712	1716		1723	
Bowes Park d			1641		1701		1719		1726		
Palmers Green d			1643		1703		1721		1728		
Winchmore Hill d			1645		1705		1723		1731		
Grange Park d			1647		1707		1725		1732		
Enfield Chase d			1649		1709		1727		1734		
Gordon Hill d			1651		1711		1729		1736		
Crews Hill d			1654		1714		1732				
Cuffley d			1657		1717		1735		1741		
Bayford d			1701		1721		1739				
Hertford North a			1706		1726		1744		1749		
New Southgate d	1631			1651			1715			1726	
Oakleigh Park d	1634			1654			1719			1729	
New Barnet d	1636			1656			1720				
Hadley Wood d	1639			1659			1723				
Potters Bar 25 d	1642			1702			1727			1734	
Bookman's Park d	1645			1705			1730			1737	
Hatfield 25 d	1650			1710			1734			1741	
Welwyn Garden City 25 a	1655			1715			1739			1746	

11. How many trains leave from a) King's Cross   b) Moorgate ?

12. a) How many trains go direct from Alexandra Palace to New Southgate ?

b) How many trains terminate at Hertford North ?

c) Which train makes fewest stops ?

13. How long does it take to go from

a) Finsbury Park to Harringay

b) New Southgate to Welwyn Garden City

c) King's Cross to New Barnet

d) Palmers Green to Gordon Hill ?

14. a) If I miss the 16.31 from Moorgate, what is the earliest time that I can arrive at Hatfield ?

b) Mr Shah meant to take the 16.55 from Moorgate to Oakleigh Park but, by mistake, he boarded the 16.59. Is there any way in which he can still travel to Oakleigh Park ? If so, how much later will he arrive than if he had caught the 16.55 ?

15. a) Peter misses the 16.52 at Finsbury Park by six minutes. How long must he wait for the next train to Bayford ? What time will he arrive ?

b) Ms Maurie arrives at Alexandra Palace at 16.30. She wishes to travel to Cuffley for a dental appointment, but must travel on to Bayford to arrive there before 17.45. What is the maximum time she can spend at Cuffley ?

HOLIDAY BROCHURES

The price of a holiday depends upon a number of factors such as the length of the holiday, the time of year it is taken, the chosen resort, the Tour Operator, the type of accommodation and so on. It is always worth checking carefully, and comparing different packages, so that the best holiday at the best price can be chosen.

EXERCISE 2d

Mr & Mrs Simmons are planning a holiday in Spain at some time from June to September. The costs of a Best-Tours package are given in the following table.

Basic Holiday Price per person in £'s.

No. of nights	7	10	14
June	210	250	290
July	240	280	320
August	260	310	350
September	220	260	300

a) What will Mr and Mrs Simmons have to pay Best-Tours if

  (i) they go for 7 nights in August

  (ii) they take a 14 nights holiday in June

  (iii) they go for 10 nights in September ?

b) If the most they can afford is £570 what is the longest holiday they can take ?

    a)   (i) £260 each, i.e. £520
  (ii) £290 each, i.e. £580
  (iii) £260 each, i.e. £520

    b) They can afford up to half of £570 each, i.e. £285 each.

   The longest holiday they can take is 10 nights (but not in August).

Questions 1 to 3 refer to the holiday details given in the following table.

TRAVEL BY COACH
Basic Holiday Prices per person in £'s

Hotel				
No. of nights	7	14	21	28
1 Nov–17 Nov	92	123	167	192
18 Nov–27 Nov	84	115	153	174
28 Nov–4 Dec	83	107	127	215
5 Dec–11 Dec	75	109	189	267
12 Dec–17 Dec	69	163	232	228
18 Dec–25 Dec	139	192	244	274
26 Dec–31 Dec	105	144	189	215
1 Jan–7 Jan	79	121	144	165
8 Jan–23 Jan	72	128	153	182
24 Jan–6 Feb	85	128	155	186
7 Feb–27 Feb	97	129	159	195
28 Feb–6 Mar	102	134	172	208

(Departures on or between)

*STOP PRESS

Three weeks for the price of two for departures from
4 Jan–31 Jan.

1. Katie and Carol book a 7-night holiday.

   a) If they leave on December 1st, how much do they pay ?

   b) If they postpone their departure until January 11th, what is the cost ?

   c) Do they qualify for an extra week free if they leave on January 11th ?

2. a) Mr and Mrs Robinson want a three week holiday at the lowest possible cost. During which period(s) should they depart ?

   b) There is one price in the table which can be deleted as a result of the Stop Press announcement. Which one is it ?

3. a) How much extra does a fourth week cost per person if the holiday begins on
   (i) Christmas Day   (ii) November 20th ?

   b) What is the average weekly cost of a holiday for
      (i) two weeks starting on March 1st
      (ii) three weeks starting on November 23rd
      (iii) three weeks starting on January 20th ?

4. Winter holidays are offered by Snow-n-Sun Tours and their terms are given in the following table.

Departure date	10 Dec.	17 Dec.	31 Dec.	7 & 14 Jan.	21 & 28 Jan.	4, 11, 18 Feb.	25 Feb. to 25 March
7 nights	194	230	264	235	244	230	210
14 nights	352	418	490	426	450	418	386

Prices given are in £'s per person.
Children aged under 2 travel free.
Children aged from 2 to 12: 50% reduction.

a) Mr and Mrs Thompson and their children James aged 14, Emma aged 8 and Thomas, eighteen months old, book a 7-night holiday beginning on January 28th. What is the total bill Mr Thompson gets from Snow-n-Sun Tours ?

b) If they could take their holiday one week later, how much would they save ?

c) Jenny Smith is 13 on January 7th. How much do her parents have to pay for Jenny for a 14-night holiday if it starts on   (i) 31 December (ii) 14 January ?

5. Mr and Mrs McKenzie are planning a Fly/Drive holiday in the United States of America. They are given the following terms for car hire.

		Small cars			Medium cars			Large cars		
		2 door	4 door		2 door	4 door		2 door	4 door	
		Group A2	Group A4		Group B	Group C		Group D	Group E	
	Per	**Week** Day	**Week** Day		**Week** Day	**Week** Day		**Week** Day	**Week** Day	
Florida	£	50 14	55 15		65 18	80 22		100 27	115 31	
California	£	65 18	70 19		80 22	100 27		120 32	135 35	
Nationwide	£	85 23	90 25		100 27	110 29		125 34	140 36	

Rentals of less than one week: The minimum charge is one week's rental.
Extra days in excess of a full week: For 1, 2 or 3 extra days the Per Day prices apply. For 4, 5 or 6 extra days the Per Week prices apply.

a) If they restrict their travelling to California, how much will they have to pay to hire
   (i) a Group B car for 10 days ?
   (ii) a Group C car for 12 days ?

b) If they hire a car in California and cannot afford to pay more than £70, what is the longest period for which they can hire a car and what car group should they book ?

c) Which costs more, hiring a Group D car from Nationwide travel for two weeks or hiring a Group C car for three weeks in Florida ? What is the difference in cost ?

Sometimes there are extra charges, called supplements, for special features such as a private bathroom, a room with a sea-view, extra meals, etc.

Miss Scott is going on a week's holiday to Bournemouth in May and is considering two hotels, Sunspot and Shoreside. She wants full board, a single room and a balcony. At which hotel will she pay less?

Sunspot

All rooms have private bathroom and balcony

Charge per person per week
(half board)

May	£ 84
June	£ 90
July/Aug.	£ 100
September	£ 90

Supplements per person per day:
Single room   £ 2
Full board   £ 1.25

Shoreside

Terms are for full board per person per week. All rooms have private bathroom.

May	£ 98
June	£ 106
July to September	£ 125

No extra charge for single room except, in July and August £ 1 per night.
Supplements per day:
Balcony   50 p
Sea view   50 p

At Sunspot (half board means bed, breakfast and evening meal)

Basic charge		= £ 84
Single room supplement	= 7 × £ 2	= £ 14
Full board supplement	= 7 × £ 1.25	= £ 8.75
Total charge		= £ 106.75

At Shoreside

Basic charge		= £ 98
Balcony supplement	= 7 × 50 p	= £3.50
Total charge		= £ 101.50

(Miss Scott gets her single room without extra charge in May)

Miss Scott will pay less at Shoreside.

The Fly-right Travel Group offer package holidays in Turkey at the prices and conditions shown below. Use the information to answer questions 6 to 8.

Departure dates and prices

By Air — Mondays

Holiday Number	017X	025X	08Y
Number of nights	7	14	21*
April	£245	£315	£291
May	£255	£325	£301
June		£359	
July		£369	
August		£375	
September		£345	
October	£219	£280	£280

*Third week is based on bed and breakfast accommodation, the supplement for half board is £35 per person.

Prices are per person based on half board accommodation and the shared occupancy of a twin-bedded room with private bath/shower and wc.

Children's Reductions
30% for children under 12 years of age providing that they share a room with two adults. Children under 2 travel free of charge providing that they do not occupy a seat on the aircraft.

Single Rooms A limited number of single rooms are available at no supplement. These will be allocated on a first-come, first served basis. Except June to August when a supplement of £2.50 per person per night will be charged.

6. Miss Fisher books a 14-night holiday and requires a single room. How much does she pay if she goes   a) in May   b) in July ?

7. John and Christine Carter and their daughter Sally aged 4 take a week's holiday in April. If Sally sleeps in her parents' room, what is the charge for the holiday ? What is the number of their holiday ?

8. Mr Walsh books a 21-night holiday in May but requires half board for all three weeks. He also requires a single room. How much does he pay ?

a) (Using the table)

   (i) 65 °F   (ii) 58 °F

b) (Using the chart)

   (i) $7\frac{1}{2}$ hours   (ii) Just over 6 hours.

c) Number of hours of sunshine in Malta is 5

   Number of hours of sunshine in England is $1\frac{1}{2}$

   Mark can expect $3\frac{1}{2}$ more hours of sunshine per day
   (on average)

   Temperature in Malta is 60 °F
   Temperature in London is 45 °F
   Malta should be warmer by 15 °F (on average)

Use the temperature chart given below to answer questions 1 to 3.

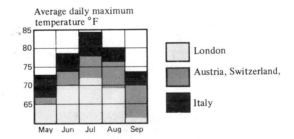

1. a) Which is the warmest country ?

   b) Which is the warmest month in each country ?

   c) Which is the coolest month in   (i) Austria   (ii) London ?

2. What is the approximate difference in temperature between

   a) London and Italy in August

   b) London and Austria in September ?

3. By how much does the average temperature rise or fall

   a) between May and June in Italy

   b) between July and September in Switzerland ?

Questions 4 and 5 refer to the sunshine guides given below.

Month						
APR	MAY	JUN	JULY	AUG	SEP	OCT
Average daily temperature (°F)						
67	73	82	87	88	82	74
Average hours of sunshine						
7	9	10	12	11	9	7

Corfu

Month						
APR	MAY	JUN	JUL	AUG	SEP	OCT
Average daily temperature (°F)						
70	75	81	87	90	87	80
Average hours of sunshine						
9	11	11	12	11	9	7

Morocco

4. Kathy and Claire want a hot sunny holiday. To which place and in which month should they go   a) for highest temperature   b) for most sun ?

5. Which is the hottest and which is the coolest month   a) in Corfu   b) in Morocco ?

6. Tenerife provides very good winter holidays for those who like sun and warmth. Here is the climate guide.

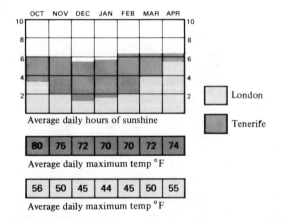

Average daily hours of sunshine

80	75	72	70	70	72	74

Average daily maximum temp °F

56	50	45	44	45	50	55

Average daily maximum temp °F

a) How much more sunshine than in London can I expect in Tenerife in
   (i) October   (ii) December   (iii) April ?

b) How much warmer than in London can I expect it to be in Tenerife in
   (i) November   (ii) January ?

If I spend the whole month of December in Tenerife,

c) how many hours of sunshine can I expect during the 31 days in Tenerife ?

d) how many hours of sunshine have there probably been in London during the same period ?

7. Referring to the chart given in Question 6, if I take a month's holiday in Tenerife from mid February to mid March

a) how much higher is the temperature likely to be when I arrive, than it was when I left London ?

b) how much lower is the temperature likely to be when I return to London than it was when I left Tenerife ?

TIME ZONES

When it is midnight in Britain it is not necessarily midnight in another country. If we consider India, for example, we find that the sun rises there about six hours before it rises in Britain. If Indian clocks were synchronised with British time, their hours of daylight would be from about 11 p.m. to 3 p.m. the next day, i.e. the sun has already risen when the clock says midnight! To avoid this paradox Indian clocks are set some six hours ahead of ours. Then, when it is midnight in England, but the sun is rising in India, it is 6.00 a.m. by their clocks.

This is why we often have to alter our watches when we go abroad. Our watches go *forward when we go East* and *back when we go West.*

For instance, when going westward from London to New York we put our watches back by 5 hours.

Now that international travel is so commonplace it would obviously be very confusing if every town had an individual time base, so there are areas, or zones, within which all towns use the same times. The sketch map below shows, approximately, the time zones in the USA, the times shown correspond to 12.00 noon in Britain.

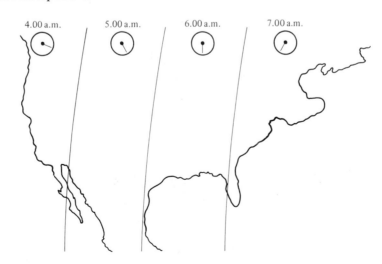

EXERCISE 2f

The following table gives the times, for a number of towns, which correspond to noon in London.

Athens	2 p.m.
Chicago	6 a.m.
Geneva	1 p.m.
Los Angeles	4 a.m.
Tehran	3.30 p.m.

a) When travelling from Chicago to Los Angeles, by how much, and which way, would you alter your watch ?

b) In going from London to Athens, are watches put forward or back and by how much ?

c) Mr Hoffman goes from Geneva to Tehran and forgets to alter his watch. If he gets up next morning at 7 a.m. by his watch, will most other people in Tehran be still in bed or already at work ?

a) When it is 6 a.m. in Chicago it is only 4 a.m. in Los Angeles. My watch goes back by 2 hours.

b) When it is noon in London it is 2 p.m. in Athens. Watches are put forward by 2 hours.

c) 1 p.m. Geneva time corresponds to 3.30 p.m. in Tehran
∴ 7 a.m. Geneva time corresponds to 9.30 a.m. in Tehran
∴ When Mr Hoffman gets up most people will already be at work.

Questions 1 to 4 refer to the table given in the example above.

1. When it is noon in Athens, what time is it in
a) Geneva   b) Los Angeles ?

2. When it is noon in Tehran, what time is it in   a) Chicago   b) Athens ?

3. What time is it in London when it is noon in   a) Geneva   b) Chicago ?

4. What time is it in Chicago when it is noon in
   a) Los Angeles   b) Athens ?

5. Mr Sanwaki has been living in England for a year on business and is
   now returning to Tokyo. He leaves London Heathrow, on a flight of
   duration $17\frac{1}{2}$ hours, at 9.40.

   a) If he does not alter his digital (24-hour) watch during the journey, at
      what time by his watch will he arrive in Tokyo ?

   b) When he arrives in Tokyo the time there is 12.10. By how much, and
      which way, should he alter his watch ?

   c) When it is noon in Tokyo, what time is it in London ?

6. When it is midnight in New York it is 5 a.m. in London.

   a) What time is it in New York when London time is
      (i) 5 p.m.   (ii) 2 a.m.   (iii) midnight ?

   b) Sally Peters lives in London and works in an office from 9 a.m. to 5 p.m.
      Her American friend Marcia lives in New York and also works in an
      office; her working hours are 8 a.m. to 2 p.m. Sally wants to phone
      Marcia while they are both in their offices. Between what times, London
      time, can Sally ring Marcia ?

3 FRACTIONS

EQUIVALENT FRACTIONS AND MIXED NUMBERS

Remember that we can find fractions equivalent to a given fraction by multiplying the top (the numerator) and the bottom (the denominator) by the same number,

e.g.
$$\frac{5}{6} = \frac{5 \times 2}{6 \times 2} = \frac{10}{12}$$

We can simplify fractions by dividing the numerator and the denominator by the same number,

e.g.
$$\frac{12}{15} = \frac{12 \div 3}{15 \div 3} = \frac{4}{5}$$

Mixed numbers, such as $1\frac{2}{3}$ mean $1 + \frac{2}{3}$. We can write this as $\frac{3}{3} + \frac{2}{3}$ i.e. $\frac{5}{3}$ This is called an improper fraction. Other examples are $\frac{23}{6}$ and $\frac{15}{9}$

Note that
$$\frac{23}{6} = \frac{18 + 5}{6} = \frac{18}{6} + \frac{5}{6} = 3 + \frac{5}{6} = 3\frac{5}{6}$$

EXERCISE 3a

1. Fill in the missing numbers to make equivalent fractions.

a) $\frac{3}{4} = \frac{}{16}$ c) $\frac{4}{7} = \frac{16}{}$ e) $\frac{3}{8} = \frac{12}{}$ g) $\frac{2}{7} = \frac{}{49}$

b) $\frac{4}{5} = \frac{}{10}$ d) $\frac{5}{9} = \frac{}{45}$ f) $\frac{8}{9} = \frac{}{36}$ h) $\frac{3}{13} = \frac{12}{}$

2. Simplify as far as possible.

a) $\frac{8}{10}$ b) $\frac{5}{45}$ c) $\frac{14}{21}$ d) $\frac{27}{81}$

3. Change the following improper fractions into mixed numbers.

a) $\frac{12}{7}$ b) $\frac{15}{9}$ c) $\frac{27}{4}$ d) $\frac{35}{9}$

4. Change the following mixed numbers to improper fractions.

a) $1\frac{2}{3}$ b) $3\frac{1}{4}$ c) $4\frac{2}{7}$ d) $5\frac{3}{5}$

COMPARING FRACTIONS

We can decide which of two fractions is the larger by changing both fractions into equivalent fractions with the same denominators. The new denominator must be a number that can be divided exactly by both the original denominators. So to compare $\frac{3}{5}$ and $\frac{4}{7}$ we can choose 35 for our new denominator because 35 can be divided exactly by both 5 and 7.

Now
$$\frac{3}{5} = \frac{3 \times 7}{5 \times 7} = \frac{21}{35}$$

and
$$\frac{4}{7} = \frac{4 \times 5}{7 \times 5} = \frac{20}{35}$$

Now we can see that $\frac{3}{5} > \frac{4}{7}$

EXERCISE 3b

Which is the bigger fraction ?

1. $\frac{1}{2}$ or $\frac{1}{3}$ **3.** $\frac{2}{3}$ or $\frac{4}{5}$ **5.** $\frac{2}{7}$ or $\frac{3}{8}$

2. $\frac{3}{4}$ or $\frac{5}{6}$ **4.** $\frac{2}{9}$ or $\frac{1}{7}$ **6.** $\frac{2}{3}$ or $\frac{3}{4}$

Arrange the fractions $\frac{3}{4}$, $\frac{7}{10}$, $\frac{1}{2}$, $\frac{4}{5}$ in ascending order of size.

(20 divides exactly by 4, 10, 2 and 5)

$$\frac{3}{4} = \frac{15}{20}, \quad \frac{7}{10} = \frac{14}{20}, \quad \frac{1}{2} = \frac{10}{20} \quad \text{and} \quad \frac{4}{5} = \frac{16}{20}$$

So the ascending order is $\frac{1}{2}$, $\frac{7}{10}$, $\frac{3}{4}$, $\frac{4}{5}$

Arrange the fractions in ascending order of size.

7. $\frac{2}{3}$, $\frac{1}{2}$, $\frac{3}{5}$, $\frac{7}{30}$ **8.** $\frac{13}{20}$, $\frac{3}{4}$, $\frac{4}{10}$, $\frac{5}{8}$

Arrange the fractions in descending order of size.

9. $\frac{5}{8}$, $\frac{9}{16}$, $\frac{17}{32}$, $\frac{3}{4}$ **10.** $\frac{5}{8}$, $\frac{5}{6}$, $\frac{7}{12}$, $\frac{2}{3}$

ADDING FRACTIONS

We can add fractions with the same denominators,

e.g. $$\frac{2}{7} + \frac{3}{7} = \frac{5}{7}$$

To add fractions with different denominators we must first change the fractions into equivalent fractions with the same denominator. For instance, if we want to add $\frac{3}{4}$ and $\frac{2}{5}$ we choose 20 for our new denominator because 20 can be divided by both 4 and 5.

Now $$\frac{3}{4} = \frac{3 \times 5}{4 \times 5} = \frac{15}{20} \quad \text{and} \quad \frac{2}{5} = \frac{2 \times 4}{5 \times 4} = \frac{8}{20}$$

so $$\frac{3}{4} + \frac{2}{5} = \frac{15}{20} + \frac{8}{20} = \frac{23}{20} = 1\frac{3}{20}$$

EXERCISE 3c

Find $\frac{4}{7} + \frac{1}{8}$

(7 and 8 both divide into 56)

$$\frac{4}{7} + \frac{1}{8} = \frac{32}{56} + \frac{7}{56} = \frac{39}{56}$$

Find

1. $\frac{2}{3} + \frac{1}{5}$

2. $\frac{1}{5} + \frac{1}{6}$

3. $\frac{3}{10} + \frac{2}{3}$

4. $\frac{3}{7} + \frac{1}{6}$

5. $\frac{2}{3} + \frac{2}{7}$

6. $\frac{1}{6} + \frac{2}{7}$

7. $\frac{5}{6} + \frac{1}{7}$

8. $\frac{3}{11} + \frac{5}{9}$

9. $\frac{2}{9} + \frac{3}{10}$

The new denominator, which is called the *common denominator,* is not always as big as you might first think. For example, if we want to add $\frac{3}{4}$ and $\frac{1}{12}$, the common denominator is 12 because it divides by both 4 and 12.

Find $\frac{3}{4} + \frac{1}{12}$

$$\frac{3}{4} + \frac{1}{12} = \frac{9}{12} + \frac{1}{12}$$

$$= \frac{\cancel{10}^{5}}{\cancel{12}_{6}} \quad \text{(This is called cancelling)}$$

$$= \frac{5}{6}$$

Find

10. $\frac{2}{5} + \frac{3}{10}$ **13.** $\frac{1}{4} + \frac{1}{8}$ **16.** $\frac{4}{11} + \frac{5}{22}$

11. $\frac{3}{7} + \frac{8}{21}$ **14.** $\frac{2}{3} + \frac{2}{9}$ **17.** $\frac{2}{5} + \frac{7}{15}$

12. $\frac{3}{10} + \frac{3}{100}$ **15.** $\frac{4}{9} + \frac{5}{18}$ **18.** $\frac{7}{12} + \frac{1}{6}$

More than two fractions can be added in a similar way. The common denominator must be divisible by *all* of the original denominators.

Find $\frac{1}{5} + \frac{1}{4} + \frac{1}{2}$

(5, 4 and 2 all divide into 20)

$$\frac{1}{5} + \frac{1}{4} + \frac{1}{2} = \frac{4}{20} + \frac{5}{20} + \frac{10}{20}$$

$$= \frac{19}{20}$$

Find

19. $\frac{1}{8}+\frac{1}{4}+\frac{1}{3}$ **22.** $\frac{1}{7}+\frac{1}{2}+\frac{3}{14}$ **25.** $\frac{2}{15}+\frac{1}{10}+\frac{2}{5}$

20. $\frac{3}{10}+\frac{2}{5}+\frac{1}{4}$ **23.** $\frac{1}{3}+\frac{1}{6}+\frac{1}{2}$ **26.** $\frac{7}{20}+\frac{3}{10}+\frac{1}{5}$

21. $\frac{1}{3}+\frac{5}{12}+\frac{1}{6}$ **24.** $\frac{1}{3}+\frac{2}{9}+\frac{1}{6}$ **27.** $\frac{1}{4}+\frac{1}{3}+\frac{1}{12}$

SUBTRACTING FRACTIONS

Exactly the same method is used for subtracting fractions as for adding them. To work out the value of $\frac{7}{9}-\frac{2}{9}$ we notice that the denominators are the same so

$$\frac{7}{9}-\frac{2}{9}=\frac{7-2}{9}$$
$$=\frac{5}{9}$$

EXERCISE 3d

Find $\frac{3}{4}-\frac{1}{5}$

(The denominators are not the same so we use equivalent fractions with denominator 20.)

$$\frac{3}{4}-\frac{1}{5}=\frac{15}{20}-\frac{4}{20}$$
$$=\frac{11}{20}$$

Find

1. $\frac{6}{17}-\frac{1}{17}$ **6.** $\frac{13}{18}-\frac{7}{18}$ **11.** $\frac{15}{16}-\frac{3}{4}$

2. $\frac{7}{10}-\frac{2}{10}$ **7.** $\frac{8}{11}-\frac{2}{5}$ **12.** $\frac{7}{15}-\frac{1}{5}$

3. $\frac{9}{10}-\frac{1}{2}$ **8.** $\frac{8}{13}-\frac{1}{2}$ **13.** $\frac{7}{12}-\frac{1}{3}$

4. $\frac{19}{20}-\frac{7}{20}$ **9.** $\frac{11}{12}-\frac{5}{6}$ **14.** $\frac{13}{18}-\frac{5}{9}$

5. $\frac{11}{15}-\frac{4}{15}$ **10.** $\frac{19}{100}-\frac{1}{10}$ **15.** $\frac{13}{15}-\frac{3}{5}$

Fractions can be added and subtracted in one problem

Find $\frac{1}{8} - \frac{3}{4} + \frac{11}{16}$

$$\frac{1}{8} - \frac{3}{4} + \frac{11}{16} = \frac{2}{16} - \frac{12}{16} + \frac{11}{16}$$

$$= \frac{13 - 12}{16}$$

$$= \frac{1}{16}$$

Find

16. $\frac{3}{4} + \frac{1}{2} - \frac{7}{8}$ **19.** $\frac{4}{5} - \frac{7}{10} + \frac{1}{2}$ **22.** $\frac{2}{9} - \frac{1}{3} + \frac{1}{6}$

17. $\frac{3}{8} + \frac{7}{16} - \frac{3}{4}$ **20.** $\frac{7}{10} - \frac{41}{100} + \frac{1}{20}$ **23.** $\frac{2}{5} - \frac{1}{2} + \frac{3}{10}$

18. $\frac{3}{5} + \frac{3}{25} - \frac{27}{50}$ **21.** $\frac{7}{12} - \frac{1}{6} + \frac{1}{3}$ **24.** $\frac{1}{6} - \frac{5}{18} + \frac{1}{3}$

PROBLEMS

EXERCISE 3e

In a class of school children, $\frac{1}{3}$ of the children come to school by bus, $\frac{1}{4}$ come to school on bicycles and the rest walk to school. What fraction of the children ride to school ? What fraction do not use a bus ?

The fraction who ride to school on a bicycle or a bus is

$$\frac{1}{3} + \frac{1}{4} = \frac{4}{12} + \frac{3}{12} = \frac{7}{12}$$

Therefore $\frac{7}{12}$ of the children ride to school.

The complete class of children is a whole unit, i.e. 1. The fraction of children who do not use a bus is found by taking the bus users from the complete class,

i.e. $\frac{1}{1} - \frac{1}{3} = \frac{3 - 1}{3} = \frac{2}{3}$

1. Angela spends $\frac{1}{5}$ of her pocket money on sweets and $\frac{2}{3}$ on tapes. What fraction has she spent ? What fraction has she left ?

2. A group of friends went to a hamburger bar. $\frac{2}{5}$ of them bought a hamburger, $\frac{1}{3}$ of them just bought chips. The rest bought cola. What fraction of the group bought food ? What fraction bought a drink ?

3. At a pop festival, $\frac{2}{3}$ of the groups were all male, $\frac{1}{4}$ of the groups had one girl and the rest had more than one girl. What fraction of the groups
   a) were not all male   b) had more than one girl ?

4. At a Youth Club, $\frac{1}{2}$ of the meetings are for playing table tennis, $\frac{1}{8}$ of the meetings are discussions and the rest are music sessions. What fraction of the meetings are
   (a) music sessions   b) not for discussions ?

5. At a school, $\frac{1}{8}$ of the time is spent in mathematics classes, $\frac{3}{20}$ of the time in English classes and $\frac{1}{20}$ on games. What fraction of the time is spent on
   a) English and maths together
   b) all lessons except games
   c) maths and games ?

6.

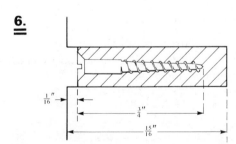

A hole is drilled in a wall to a depth of $\frac{15}{16}$″ to receive a screw of length $\frac{3}{4}$″. After the screw has been driven fully home, the face of its head is $\frac{1}{16}$″ below the surface of the wall. How far is the tip of the screw from the bottom of the hole ?

ADDING MIXED NUMBERS

If we want to find the value of $3\frac{1}{3} + 2\frac{1}{4}$ we add the whole numbers and then the fractions,

i.e.
$$3\frac{1}{3} + 2\frac{3}{4} = 3 + 2 + \frac{1}{3} + \frac{1}{4}$$
$$= 5 + \frac{4+3}{12}$$
$$= 5 + \frac{7}{12}$$
$$= 5\frac{7}{12}$$

Sometimes there is an extra step in the calculation. For example

$$3\frac{1}{2} + 2\frac{3}{4} + 1\frac{3}{8} = 3 + 2 + 1 + \frac{1}{2} + \frac{3}{4} + \frac{3}{8}$$
$$= 6 + \frac{4+6+3}{8}$$
$$= 6 + \frac{13}{8}$$

But $\frac{13}{8}$ is an improper fraction, so we change it into a mixed number

i.e.
$$3\frac{1}{2} + 2\frac{3}{4} + 1\frac{3}{8} = 6 + \frac{8+5}{8}$$
$$= 6 + 1 + \frac{5}{8}$$
$$= 7\frac{5}{8}$$

EXERCISE 3f

Find

1. $1\frac{1}{2} + 2\frac{1}{3}$

2. $4\frac{1}{5} + 1\frac{3}{8}$

3. $5\frac{1}{9} + 4\frac{1}{3}$

4. $2\frac{1}{7} + 1\frac{1}{14}$

5. $8\frac{1}{7} + 5\frac{2}{3}$

6. $7\frac{3}{8} + 3\frac{7}{16}$

7. $3\frac{5}{7} + 7\frac{1}{2}$

8. $8\frac{7}{8} + 3\frac{3}{16}$

9. $9\frac{2}{3} + 8\frac{5}{6}$

10. $6\frac{3}{10} + 4\frac{4}{5}$

11. $1\frac{1}{4} + 3\frac{2}{3} + 6\frac{7}{12}$

12. $5\frac{1}{7} + 4\frac{1}{2} + 7\frac{11}{14}$

13. $3\frac{3}{4} + 5\frac{1}{8} + 8\frac{5}{16}$

14. $3\frac{7}{10} + 9\frac{21}{100} + 1\frac{3}{5}$

15. $1\frac{5}{7} + 11\frac{1}{2} + 9\frac{1}{14}$

SUBTRACTING MIXED NUMBERS

If we want to find the value of $5\frac{3}{4} - 2\frac{2}{5}$ we can use the same method as for adding

$$5\frac{3}{4} - 2\frac{2}{5} = 5 - 2 + \frac{3}{4} - \frac{2}{5}$$

$$= 3 + \frac{15 - 8}{20}$$

$$= 3 + \frac{7}{20}$$

$$= 3\frac{7}{20}$$

But when we find the value of $6\frac{1}{4} - 2\frac{4}{5}$ we get

$$6\frac{1}{4} - 2\frac{4}{5} = 6 - 2 + \frac{1}{4} - \frac{4}{5}$$

$$= 4 + \frac{1}{4} - \frac{4}{5}$$

This time it is not so easy to deal with the fraction because $\frac{4}{5}$ is bigger than $\frac{1}{4}$. In this case we take one of the whole units and change it into a fraction, giving

$$3 + 1 + \frac{1}{4} - \frac{4}{5} = 3 + \frac{20 + 5 - 16}{20}$$

$$= 3 + \frac{9}{20}$$

$$= 3\frac{9}{20}$$

EXERCISE 3g

Find

1. $2\frac{3}{4} - 1\frac{1}{8}$

2. $3\frac{2}{3} - 1\frac{4}{5}$

3. $1\frac{5}{6} - \frac{2}{3}$

4. $3\frac{1}{4} - 2\frac{1}{2}$

5. $7\frac{3}{4} - 2\frac{1}{3}$

6. $3\frac{5}{6} - 2\frac{1}{3}$

7. $2\frac{6}{7} - 1\frac{1}{2}$

8. $4\frac{1}{2} - 2\frac{1}{5}$

9. $4\frac{4}{5} - 3\frac{1}{10}$

10. $6\frac{5}{7} - 3\frac{2}{5}$

11. $3\frac{1}{3} - 1\frac{1}{5}$

12. $5\frac{3}{4} - 2\frac{1}{2}$

13. $5\frac{7}{9} - 3\frac{5}{7}$ **16.** $8\frac{8}{11} - 2\frac{2}{3}$ **19.** $5\frac{3}{5} - 2\frac{9}{10}$

14. $6\frac{3}{4} - 3\frac{6}{7}$ **17.** $2\frac{1}{2} - 1\frac{3}{4}$ **20.** $6\frac{3}{10} - 3\frac{4}{5}$

15. $7\frac{6}{7} - 4\frac{3}{5}$ **18.** $5\frac{4}{7} - 3\frac{4}{5}$ **21.** $2\frac{5}{12} - 1\frac{3}{4}$

MULTIPLYING FRACTIONS

When fractions are multiplied the result is given by multiplying together the numbers in the numerator and also multiplying together the numbers in the denominator. For example

$$\frac{1}{2} \times \frac{1}{3} = \frac{1 \times 1}{2 \times 3}$$

$$= \frac{1}{6}$$

If we look at a cake diagram we can see that $\frac{1}{2}$ of $\frac{1}{3}$ of the cake is $\frac{1}{6}$ of the cake.

So $\frac{1}{2}$ of $\frac{1}{3} = \frac{1}{6}$

and $\frac{1}{2} \times \frac{1}{3} = \frac{1}{6}$

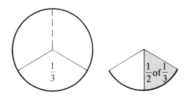

We see that 'of' means 'multiplied by'.

EXERCISE 3h

Draw cake diagrams to show that

1. $\frac{1}{2} \times \frac{1}{4} = \frac{1}{8}$ **3.** $\frac{1}{2} \times \frac{3}{4} = \frac{3}{8}$ **5.** $\frac{1}{3} \times \frac{2}{5} = \frac{2}{15}$

2. $\frac{1}{3} \times \frac{1}{2} = \frac{1}{6}$ **4.** $\frac{2}{3} \times \frac{1}{3} = \frac{2}{9}$ **6.** $\frac{1}{4} \times \frac{1}{3} = \frac{1}{12}$

SIMPLIFYING

Sometimes we can simplify a product by cancelling the common factors. For example

$$\frac{2}{3} \times \frac{3}{4} = \frac{\cancel{2}^1}{\cancel{3}_1} \times \frac{\cancel{3}^1}{\cancel{4}_2} = \frac{1 \times 1}{1 \times 2}$$

$$= \frac{1}{2}$$

The diagram confirms that

$$\frac{2}{3} \text{ of } \frac{3}{4} = \frac{1}{2}$$

EXERCISE 3i

Find $\frac{4}{25} \times \frac{15}{16}$

$$\frac{\cancel{4}^1}{\cancel{25}_5} \times \frac{\cancel{15}^3}{\cancel{16}_4} = \frac{1 \times 3}{5 \times 4}$$

$$= \frac{3}{20}$$

Find

1. $\frac{3}{4} \times \frac{1}{2}$

2. $\frac{2}{3} \times \frac{5}{7}$

3. $\frac{2}{5} \times \frac{1}{3}$

4. $\frac{1}{2} \times \frac{7}{8}$

5. $\frac{3}{4} \times \frac{4}{7}$

6. $\frac{4}{9} \times \frac{1}{7}$

7. $\frac{3}{7} \times \frac{2}{5}$

8. $\frac{2}{5} \times \frac{3}{5}$

9. $\frac{5}{6} \times \frac{1}{4}$

10. $\frac{7}{8} \times \frac{4}{21}$

11. $\frac{3}{4} \times \frac{16}{21}$

12. $\frac{21}{22} \times \frac{11}{27}$

13. $\frac{8}{9} \times \frac{33}{44}$

14. $\frac{7}{9} \times \frac{3}{21}$

15. $\frac{3}{4} \times \frac{5}{7}$

16. $\frac{4}{5} \times \frac{15}{16}$

17. $\frac{10}{11} \times \frac{33}{35}$

18. $\frac{2}{3} \times \frac{33}{40}$

Find $\frac{3}{5} \times \frac{15}{16} \times \frac{4}{7}$

$$\frac{3}{5} \times \frac{15}{16} \times \frac{4}{7} = \frac{3 \times 3 \times 1}{1 \times 4 \times 7}$$

$$= \frac{9}{28}$$

Find

19. $\frac{3}{7} \times \frac{5}{9} \times \frac{14}{15}$ **21.** $\frac{3}{10} \times \frac{5}{9} \times \frac{6}{7}$ **23.** $\frac{7}{16} \times \frac{9}{11} \times \frac{8}{21}$

20. $\frac{11}{21} \times \frac{30}{31} \times \frac{7}{55}$ **22.** $\frac{5}{7} \times \frac{3}{8} \times \frac{21}{30}$ **24.** $\frac{5}{14} \times \frac{21}{25} \times \frac{5}{9}$

MULTIPLYING MIXED NUMBERS

Suppose that we want to find the value of $2\frac{1}{3} \times \frac{5}{21} \times 1\frac{1}{5}$

We cannot multiply mixed numbers together unless we change them into improper fractions first. So we change $2\frac{1}{3}$ into $\frac{7}{3}$ and we change $1\frac{1}{5}$ into $\frac{6}{5}$. Then we can use the same method as before.

EXERCISE 3j

Find $2\frac{1}{3} \times \frac{5}{21} \times 1\frac{1}{5}$

$$2\frac{1}{3} \times \frac{5}{21} \times 1\frac{1}{5} = \frac{7}{3} \times \frac{5}{21} \times \frac{6}{5}$$

$$= \frac{2}{3}$$

Find

1. $1\frac{1}{2} \times \frac{2}{5}$ **3.** $3\frac{1}{4} \times \frac{3}{13}$

2. $2\frac{1}{2} \times \frac{4}{5}$ **4.** $4\frac{2}{3} \times 2\frac{2}{5}$

5. $2\frac{1}{5} \times \frac{5}{22}$

8. $\frac{10}{11} \times 2\frac{1}{5}$

6. $1\frac{1}{4} \times \frac{2}{5}$

9. $3\frac{1}{2} \times 4\frac{2}{3}$

7. $2\frac{1}{3} \times \frac{3}{8}$

10. $4\frac{1}{4} \times \frac{4}{21}$

11. $5\frac{1}{4} \times 2\frac{2}{3}$

13. $2\frac{1}{10} \times 7\frac{6}{7}$

12. $3\frac{5}{7} \times 1\frac{1}{13}$

14. $6\frac{1}{4} \times 1\frac{3}{5}$

15. $6\frac{2}{5} \times 1\frac{7}{8} \times \frac{7}{12}$

17. $3\frac{2}{3} \times 1\frac{1}{5} \times 1\frac{3}{22}$

16. $2\frac{4}{7} \times 4\frac{2}{3} \times 1\frac{1}{4}$

18. $7\frac{1}{2} \times 1\frac{1}{3} \times \frac{9}{10}$

A whole number can be written as a fraction with a denominator of 1. For instance $6 = \frac{6}{1}$.

Doing this makes it easier to multiply a whole number by a fraction or a mixed number.

Find $6 \times 7\frac{1}{3}$

$$6 \times 7\frac{1}{3} = \frac{\overset{2}{\cancel{6}}}{1} \times \frac{22}{\underset{1}{\cancel{3}}}$$

$$= 44$$

Find

19. $5 \times 4\frac{3}{5}$

23. $18 \times 6\frac{1}{9}$

27. $5\frac{5}{7} \times 21$

20. $2\frac{1}{7} \times 14$

24. $4 \times 3\frac{3}{8}$

28. $3 \times 6\frac{1}{9}$

21. $3\frac{1}{8} \times 4$

25. $3\frac{3}{5} \times 10$

29. $1\frac{3}{4} \times 8$

22. $4\frac{1}{6} \times 9$

26. $2\frac{5}{6} \times 3$

30. $28 \times 1\frac{4}{7}$

FRACTIONS OF QUANTITIES ▬▬▬▬▬▬▬▬▬▬▬▬▬▬▬▬▬▬

EXERCISE 3k

Find three fifths of 95 metres.

$$\frac{3}{\cancel{5}_1} \times \frac{\cancel{95}^{19}}{1} = 57$$

$\frac{3}{5}$ of 95 metres is 57 metres.

Find three quarters of £1.

$$£1 = 100 \text{ pence}$$

$$\frac{3}{\cancel{4}_1} \times \frac{\cancel{100}^{25}}{1} = 75$$

$\frac{3}{4}$ of £1 is 75 pence.

Find

1. $\frac{1}{3}$ of 18

2. $\frac{1}{5}$ of 30

3. $\frac{1}{7}$ of 21

4. $\frac{2}{3}$ of 24

5. $\frac{5}{7}$ of 14

6. $\frac{1}{4}$ of 24

7. $\frac{1}{6}$ of 30

8. $\frac{1}{8}$ of 64

9. $\frac{5}{6}$ of 36

10. $\frac{3}{8}$ of 40

11. $\frac{3}{5}$ of 20 metres

12. $\frac{5}{9}$ of 45 dollars

13. $\frac{9}{10}$ of 50 litres

14. $\frac{3}{8}$ of 88 miles

15. $\frac{7}{16}$ of 48 gallons

16. $\frac{4}{9}$ of 18 metres

17. $\frac{5}{8}$ of 16 dollars

19. $\frac{3}{7}$ of 35 miles

18. $\frac{4}{9}$ of 63 litres

20. $\frac{8}{11}$ of 121 gallons

21. $\frac{1}{4}$ of £2

26. $\frac{3}{8}$ of 1 day (24 hours)

22. $\frac{2}{9}$ of 36 pence

27. $\frac{1}{7}$ of 1 week

23. $\frac{3}{10}$ of £1

28. $\frac{1}{3}$ of £9

24. $\frac{2}{7}$ of 42 pence

29. $\frac{3}{5}$ of £1

25. $\frac{4}{5}$ of 1 year (365 days)

30. $\frac{7}{8}$ of 1 day (24 hours)

DIVIDING BY FRACTIONS

When we divide 6 by 3 we are finding how many threes there are in 6 and we say $6 \div 3 = 2$.

In the same way, when we divide 10 by $\frac{1}{2}$ we are finding how many halves there are in 10; we know that there are 20, so we say $10 \div \frac{1}{2} = 20$.

But we also know that $10 \times 2 = 20$ so

$$\frac{10}{1} \div \frac{1}{2} = 20 \quad \text{and} \quad \frac{10}{1} \times \frac{2}{1} = 20$$

This example shows that $\frac{10}{1} \div \frac{1}{2} = \frac{10}{1} \times \frac{2}{1}$.

To divide by a fraction we turn that fraction upside down and multiply.

EXERCISE 3I

How many thirds are there in 5 ?

$$5 \div \frac{1}{3} = 5 \times \frac{3}{1}$$
$$= \frac{5}{1} \times \frac{3}{1}$$
$$= 15$$

There are 15 thirds in 5.

Find the value of $36 \div \frac{3}{4}$

$$\frac{36}{1} \div \frac{3}{4} = \frac{36}{1} \times \frac{4}{3}$$

$$= \frac{48}{1}$$

$$= 48$$

Divide $\frac{7}{16}$ by $\frac{5}{8}$

$$\frac{7}{16} \div \frac{5}{8} = \frac{7}{{}_{2}\cancel{16}} \times \frac{\cancel{8}^{1}}{5}$$

$$= \frac{7}{10}$$

1. How many $\frac{1}{2}$s are there in 6 ?

2. How many $\frac{1}{4}$s are there in 7 ?

3. How many times does $\frac{1}{7}$ go into 3 ?

4. How many $\frac{3}{5}$s are there in 12 ?

5. How many times does $\frac{2}{3}$ go into 8 ?

Find

6. $12 \div \frac{4}{5}$ **9.** $72 \div \frac{8}{11}$ **12.** $7 \div \frac{7}{8}$

7. $12 \div \frac{6}{7}$ **10.** $28 \div \frac{14}{15}$ **13.** $28 \div \frac{4}{9}$

8. $40 \div \frac{8}{9}$ **11.** $15 \div \frac{5}{6}$ **14.** $\frac{21}{32} \div \frac{7}{8}$

15. $\frac{21}{22} \div \frac{7}{11}$ **17.** $\frac{8}{21} \div \frac{4}{7}$ **19.** $\frac{15}{26} \div \frac{5}{13}$

16. $\frac{28}{27} \div \frac{4}{9}$ **18.** $\frac{3}{56} \div \frac{9}{14}$ **20.** $\frac{22}{45} \div \frac{11}{15}$

DIVIDING BY WHOLE NUMBERS AND MIXED NUMBERS

If we want to divide 3 by 5 we can say

$$3 \div 5 = \frac{3}{1} \div \frac{5}{1}$$

$$= \frac{3}{1} \times \frac{1}{5}$$

$$= \frac{3}{5}$$

So $3 \div 5$ is the same as $\frac{3}{5}$

Division with mixed numbers can be done as long as all the mixed numbers are first changed into improper fractions. For example if we want to divide $3\frac{1}{8}$ by $8\frac{3}{4}$ we first change $3\frac{1}{8}$ into $\frac{25}{8}$ and $8\frac{3}{4}$ into $\frac{35}{4}$. Then we can use the same method as before.

EXERCISE 3m

Write 7 divided by 11 as a fraction.

$$7 \div 11 = \frac{7}{11}$$

Find the value of $3\frac{1}{8} \div 8\frac{3}{4}$

$$3\frac{1}{8} \div 8\frac{3}{4} = \frac{25}{8} \div \frac{35}{4}$$

$$= \frac{\overset{5}{\cancel{25}}}{\underset{2}{\cancel{8}}} \times \frac{\overset{1}{\cancel{4}}}{\underset{7}{\cancel{35}}}$$

$$= \frac{5}{14}$$

Find

1. $5\frac{4}{9} \div 7$

2. $3\frac{1}{8} \div 3\frac{3}{4}$

3. $7\frac{1}{5} \div 1\frac{7}{20}$

4. Divide $8\frac{1}{4}$ by $1\frac{3}{8}$

5. Divide $6\frac{2}{3}$ by $2\frac{4}{9}$

6. $4\frac{2}{7} \div 15$

7. $5\frac{5}{8} \div 6\frac{1}{4}$

8. $6\frac{4}{9} \div 1\frac{1}{3}$

9. Divide $5\frac{1}{4}$ by $2\frac{11}{12}$

10. Divide $7\frac{1}{7}$ by $1\frac{11}{14}$

11. $10\frac{2}{3} \div 1\frac{7}{9}$

12. $8\frac{4}{5} \div 3\frac{3}{10}$

13. $9\frac{3}{4} \div 1\frac{5}{8}$

14. $12\frac{1}{2} \div 8\frac{3}{4}$

15. Divide $11\frac{1}{4}$ by $\frac{15}{16}$

16. Divide $9\frac{1}{7}$ by $1\frac{11}{21}$

17. $31\frac{1}{2} \div 5\frac{5}{8}$

18. Divide $10\frac{5}{6}$ by $3\frac{1}{4}$

19. Divide $8\frac{2}{3}$ by $5\frac{7}{9}$

20. $22\frac{2}{3} \div 1\frac{8}{9}$

EXERCISE 3n

In this exercise you will find, +, −, × and ÷. Read the question carefully and then decide which method to use. Find

1. $1\frac{1}{2} + 3\frac{1}{4}$

2. $2\frac{3}{8} - 1\frac{1}{4}$

3. $1\frac{1}{5} \times \frac{5}{8}$

4. $3\frac{1}{2} \div \frac{7}{8}$

5. $\frac{4}{7} + 1\frac{1}{2}$

6. $4\frac{1}{4} \times \frac{2}{9}$

7. $3\frac{2}{3} \div \frac{1}{6}$

8. $2\frac{1}{5} - 1\frac{1}{3}$

9. $5\frac{1}{2} \times \frac{6}{11}$

10. $1\frac{3}{8} + 2\frac{1}{2}$

11. $5\frac{1}{2} + \frac{3}{4}$

12. $4\frac{1}{3} \times \frac{6}{13}$

13. $3\frac{4}{5} - 2\frac{1}{10}$

14. $3\frac{1}{7} \div 1\frac{3}{8}$

15. $4\frac{1}{5} \times \frac{4}{7}$

16. $2\frac{5}{6} \div 3\frac{1}{3}$

17. $1\frac{4}{7} + 2\frac{1}{2}$

18. $2\frac{3}{4} - 1\frac{7}{8}$

19. $2\frac{3}{8} + 1\frac{7}{16}$

20. $5\frac{1}{4} \div 1\frac{1}{6}$

21. $1\frac{1}{4} + \frac{2}{3} - \frac{5}{6}$

22. $2\frac{1}{2} - \frac{2}{3} - 1\frac{1}{4}$

23. $3\frac{1}{2} + 1\frac{1}{4} + \frac{5}{8}$

24. $2\frac{1}{3} + 1\frac{1}{2} - \frac{3}{4}$

25. $4\frac{1}{8} - 5\frac{3}{4} + 2\frac{1}{2}$

26. $4\frac{1}{2} - 5\frac{1}{4} + 2\frac{1}{8}$

27. $3\frac{4}{5} + \frac{3}{10} - 1\frac{1}{20}$

28. $5\frac{1}{2} - 1\frac{3}{4} - 2\frac{1}{4}$

29. $3\frac{1}{7} + 2\frac{1}{2} - \frac{3}{14}$

30. $5\frac{1}{2} - \frac{3}{4} - 4\frac{1}{4}$

RECIPROCALS

When we turn a fraction upside down we are finding its *reciprocal*.

For example, the reciprocal of 3, i.e. $\frac{3}{1}$, is $\frac{1}{3}$

the reciprocal of $1\frac{1}{4}$, i.e. $\frac{5}{4}$, is $\frac{4}{5}$

EXERCISE 3p

Write down the reciprocals of the following numbers.

1. 5   **4.** $\frac{7}{8}$ <u>**7.**</u> 2   <u>**10.**</u> $\frac{1}{7}$

2. 8   **5.** $1\frac{3}{4}$ <u>**8.**</u> 6   <u>**11.**</u> $1\frac{2}{5}$

3. $\frac{2}{9}$ **6.** $2\frac{1}{5}$ <u>**9.**</u> $\frac{8}{9}$ <u>**12.**</u> $3\frac{1}{2}$

13. a) Write down the reciprocal of $\frac{2}{5}$

     b) Calculate $1 \div \frac{2}{5}$

     What do you notice about your answers to (a) and (b)?

14. a) Write down the reciprocal of $\frac{5}{6}$

     b) Calculate $1 \div \frac{5}{6}$

     What do you notice about your answers to (a) and (b)?

15. a) Write down the reciprocal of $1\frac{2}{3}$

     b) Calculate $1 \div 1\frac{2}{3}$

     What do you notice about your answers to (a) and (b)?

Questions 13 to 15 illustrate a general rule:

> the reciprocal of any number a, is $\dfrac{1}{a}$

and

> $1 \div a$ can be written as $\dfrac{1}{a}$

Any division can be written as a fraction.

Consider $3 \div 2$ $3 \div 2 = \frac{3}{1} \div \frac{2}{1} = \frac{3}{1} \times \frac{1}{2} = \frac{3}{2}$

i.e.

> $a \div b$ can be written as $\dfrac{a}{b}$

PROBLEMS

EXERCISE 3q

> If Jane can iron a shirt in $4\frac{3}{4}$ minutes, how long will it take her to iron 10 shirts ?
>
> $$\text{Time to iron } 1 \text{ shirt } = 4\frac{3}{4} \text{ minutes}$$
>
> $$\text{Time to iron } 10 \text{ shirts} = 4\frac{3}{4} \times 10 \text{ minutes}$$
>
> $$= \frac{19}{4_2} \times \frac{\overset{5}{\cancel{10}}}{1} \text{ minutes}$$
>
> $$= \frac{95}{2} \text{ minutes}$$
>
> $$= 47\frac{1}{2} \text{ minutes}$$

> A piece of string of length $22\frac{1}{2}''$ is to be cut into small pieces each $\frac{3}{4}''$ long. How many pieces can be obtained ?
> ($''$ is the abbreviation for inch(es))
>
> Number of small pieces
>
> $\quad$ = length of string ÷ length of one short piece
>
> $$= 22\frac{1}{2} \div \frac{3}{4}$$
>
> $$= \frac{\overset{15}{\cancel{45}}}{\cancel{2}_1} \times \frac{\cancel{4}^2}{\cancel{3}_1}$$
>
> $$= 30$$
>
> 30 pieces can be obtained.

1. A bag of flour weighs $2\frac{1}{2}$ lbs. What is the weight of 20 bags ?

2. A cook adds $3\frac{1}{2}$ cups of water to a stew. If the cup holds $\frac{1}{4}$ of a pint how many pints of water were added ?

3. If you read 30 pages of a book in $\frac{3}{4}$ of an hour, how many minutes does it take to read each page ?

4. The distance round one lap of a cycle track is $\frac{2}{3}$ of a mile. John is sponsored at £1 for each lap he completes, for charity. On the day, John retired exhausted after cycling $37\frac{1}{2}$ laps. How far did he cycle and how much did he raise for charity ?

5. Temperature can be measured as C° Celsius or as F° Fahrenheit. The formula for C in terms of F is given by $C = \frac{5}{9}(F - 32)$.
My oven thermometer reads 300° Fahrenheit. What is this temperature in degrees Celsius ?

6. The diameter of a water pipe is $\frac{3}{4}''$. Lagging, which is $\frac{1}{8}''$ thick, is wrapped in a single layer round the pipe. What is the total diameter of the pipe and lagging ?

7. The diagram shows a bolt fitted into a hole drilled in a wall. The diameter of the bolt is $\frac{7}{16}''$ and the diameter of the hole is $\frac{3}{4}''$. What is the thickness (marked x'' on the diagram) of the packing needed round the bolt ?

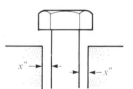

8. The printout from a wordprocessor set for 'single line' spacing, prints six lines of type per inch. If 'one and a half line' spacing is chosen, how many lines of type can be fitted onto a sheet of paper $11\frac{3}{4}''$ deep if $1''$ is allowed for margins top and bottom ?

MIXED EXERCISES

EXERCISE 3r

1. Calculate: a) $\frac{3}{4} + \frac{11}{12}$ b) $3\frac{1}{8} - 2\frac{1}{4} + 1\frac{1}{2}$

2. Find how many times $2\frac{1}{4}$ goes into $13\frac{1}{2}$

3. What is $\frac{7}{9}$ of $1\frac{1}{14}$?

4. Arrange the following fractions in ascending order of size: $\frac{7}{10}$, $\frac{3}{5}$, $\frac{2}{3}$

5. Find: a) the reciprocal of 4   b) $4\frac{1}{7} \times 4\frac{2}{3}$ c) $3\frac{3}{8} \div 2\frac{1}{4}$

6. What is $\frac{3}{4}$ of $\frac{8}{9}$ added to $1\frac{1}{2}$?

7. What is $\frac{2}{7}$ of 1 hour 3 minutes (in minutes)?

8. Fill in the missing numbers

a) $\frac{7}{9} = \frac{21}{}$ b) $\frac{10}{11} = \frac{}{44}$

9. Express as mixed numbers

a) $\frac{13}{5}$ b) $\frac{31}{8}$ c) $\frac{27}{5}$

10. State whether the following statements are true or false

a) $\frac{4}{11} > \frac{3}{10}$ b) $\frac{3}{7}$ of $5 = \frac{3}{7} \times \frac{5}{1}$ c) $2\frac{1}{7} = \frac{7}{15}$

11. A handyman takes $1\frac{1}{8}$ minutes to lay one brick. How long will it take him to lay 56 bricks?

12. A caterer allows one-sixth of a cake for a portion. How many cakes will be needed to give 65 portions?

EXERCISE 3s

1. Find

a) $4\frac{1}{2} \times 3\frac{1}{3}$ b) $3\frac{2}{5} \div \frac{3}{10}$ c) the reciprocal of $1\frac{3}{4}$

2. Find

a) $\frac{8}{9} + \frac{21}{27}$ b) $2\frac{1}{3} + \frac{4}{9} + 1\frac{5}{6}$

3. Put > or < between the following pairs of numbers.

a) $\frac{4}{7}$ $\frac{5}{8}$ b) $\frac{11}{9}$ $1\frac{3}{10}$

4. Arrange in ascending order: $\frac{7}{15}$, $\frac{1}{3}$, $\frac{2}{5}$

5. What is $1\frac{1}{2}$ subtracted from $\frac{2}{3}$ of $5\frac{1}{4}$?

6. What is $1\frac{2}{3}$ of 1 minute 15 seconds (in seconds)?

7. Fill in the missing numbers

a) $\frac{4}{5} = \frac{}{30}$ b) $\frac{2}{7} = \frac{6}{}$

8. Express as mixed numbers

a) $\frac{25}{8}$ b) $\frac{49}{9}$ c) $\frac{37}{6}$

9. Write the first quantity as a fraction of the second quantity.

a) 24 p; £1   b) 233 days; a leap year   c) 7 minutes; 1 hour

10. A rectangular print is $5\frac{1}{2}''$ wide and $7\frac{3}{4}''$ deep. It has to be mounted on card to give a margin $1\frac{1}{2}''$ wide on each side, $1\frac{3}{4}''$ at the top and $2\frac{1}{2}''$ wide at the bottom. What are the measurements of the card required ?

11. A man can paint a door in 1 hour 15 minutes. How many similar doors can he paint in $7\frac{1}{2}$ hours ?

EXERCISE 3t

1. Find

a) $1\frac{5}{6} + \frac{5}{18} + \frac{7}{12}$ b) $1\frac{2}{3} - 2\frac{1}{5} + \frac{8}{15}$

2. Find

a) $1\frac{5}{6} \div 7\frac{1}{3}$ b) $2\frac{1}{4} \times \frac{16}{45}$

3. What is $\frac{5}{6}$ of the number of days in June ?

4. Arrange in descending order: $\frac{17}{20}$, $\frac{3}{4}$, $\frac{7}{10}$

5. Which is smaller $\frac{8}{11}$ or $\frac{7}{9}$?

6. What is $\frac{4}{7}$ of $4\frac{2}{3}$ divided by $1\frac{1}{9}$?

7. Express as mixed numbers:

a) $\frac{22}{3}$ b) $\frac{46}{5}$ c) $\frac{106}{10}$

8. Write either > or < between the following pairs of fractions.

a) $\frac{7}{10}$ $\frac{5}{9}$ b) $\frac{2}{3}$ $\frac{5}{7}$ c) $\frac{8}{9}$ $\frac{7}{8}$

9. Which of the following statements are true ?

a) $3\frac{1}{2} \div 1 = 3\frac{1}{2} \times 1$ b) $\frac{1}{2} \times \left(\frac{1}{4} + \frac{1}{8} \right) =$ half of $\frac{3}{8}$

10. It takes $1\frac{3}{4}$ minutes to wrap a parcel and a half a minute to address it. How long does it take to wrap and address 8 similar parcels ?

11. The area, A sq inches, of a circle with radius r inches can be found by using the formula

$$A = \frac{22}{7}r^2$$

Find the area of a circle whose radius is $3\frac{1}{2}''$.

4 DECIMALS

PLACE VALUE

We know that fractions can be written as $\frac{1}{2}$, $\frac{2}{5}$, etc. We can also represent fractions by placing a point after the unit position and continuing to add figures to the right.

The first figure after the point is the number of tenths,

e.g. $$0.5 = \frac{5}{10}$$

The second figure after the point is the number of hundredths,

e.g. $$0.57 = \frac{5}{10} + \frac{7}{100}$$ and so on.

INTERCHANGING DECIMALS AND FRACTIONS

EXERCISE 4a

Express 0.12 as a fraction.

$$0.12 = \frac{1}{10} + \frac{2}{100}$$

$$= \frac{10}{100} + \frac{2}{100}$$

$$= \frac{\cancel{12}^{3}}{\cancel{100}_{25}}$$

$$= \frac{3}{25}$$

Express the following decimals as fractions.

1. 0.5   **3.** 0.08   **5.** 0.03   **7.** 0.125

2. 0.04   **4.** 0.15   **6.** 0.35   **8.** 0.75

| **9.** | 0.002 | **11.** | 1.25 | **13.** | 0.7 | **15.** | 0.25 |
| **10.** | 0.008 | **12.** | 3.75 | **14.** | 0.05 | **16.** | 0.005 |

Express $\frac{3}{4}$ as a decimal.

(Remember that $\frac{3}{4} = 3 \div 4$)

$$\frac{3}{4} = 0.75$$

$$\begin{array}{r} 0.7\,5 \\ 4\overline{)3.0^20} \end{array}$$

Express the following fractions as decimals.

17. $\frac{1}{2}$	**21.** $\frac{3}{8}$	**25.** $3\frac{1}{8}$	**29.** $\frac{3}{5}$
18. $\frac{1}{4}$	**22.** $\frac{3}{100}$	**26.** $1\frac{3}{4}$	**30.** $\frac{3}{25}$
19. $\frac{2}{5}$	**23.** $\frac{7}{50}$	**27.** $2\frac{1}{2}$	**31.** $\frac{27}{100}$
20. $\frac{7}{10}$	**24.** $\frac{5}{8}$	**28.** $1\frac{1}{4}$	**32.** $2\frac{3}{4}$

Copy and complete the following table.

	Fraction	Decimal
33.	$\frac{4}{5}$	
34.		0.25
35.	$\frac{3}{4}$	
36.		0.5
37.	$1\frac{9}{10}$	
38.		0.125

39. Write $\frac{7}{20}$, $\frac{21}{50}$ and $\frac{3}{25}$ as decimals. Hence arrange $\frac{7}{20}$, 0.38, $\frac{21}{50}$, 0.09, $\frac{3}{25}$ in ascending order of size.

40. Write down the value of the digit 5 in each of the following numbers.
a) 1.524   b) 52.01   c) 6.015

ADDITION AND SUBTRACTION OF DECIMALS

Decimals are added and subtracted in the same way as whole numbers. It is sensible to write them in a column so that the decimal points are in a vertical line. This makes sure that units are added to units, tenths are added to tenths and so on.

It is also sometimes necessary to use noughts after the decimal points so that both numbers have the same number of decimal places.

For example, $3 - 0.82$ can be written as

$$\begin{array}{r} 3.00 \\ -0.82 \\ \hline \end{array}$$

EXERCISE 4b

Find $1.5 - 0.92$

$$1.5 - 0.92 = 0.58$$

$$\begin{array}{r} 1.50 \\ -0.92 \\ \hline 0.58 \\ \hline \end{array}$$

Without using a calculator, find

1. $1.2 + 0.7$ **4.** $1.3 - 0.16$ **7.** $2.1 - 0.8$

2. $1.2 - 0.7$ **5.** $0.73 - 0.002$ **8.** $3.5 + 1.2$

3. $3.6 + 0.8$ **6.** $1.7 + 0.08$ **9.** $1.5 - 0.47$

10. $18.04 - 12$ **13.** $26.56 + 1.24$ **16.** $24.5 - 8$

11. $5 + 0.17$ **14.** $17 - 1.92$ **17.** $6 - 5.73$

12. $8 - 1.25$ **15.** $25 - 10.6$ **18.** $3 - 0.72$

MULTIPLICATION OF DECIMALS

One way to multiply decimals is first to convert them to fractions.

For example

$$\underset{\text{(2 d.p.)}}{0.02} \times \underset{\text{(1 d.p.)}}{1.5} = \frac{2}{100} \times \frac{15}{10}$$

$$= \frac{30}{1000}$$

$$= \underset{\text{(3 d.p.)}}{0.030}$$

From examples like this we get the following rule.

First ignore the decimal point and multiply the numbers together.

Then add together the number of decimal places in the original numbers. This gives the number of decimal places in the answer, including any noughts at the end.

EXERCISE 4c

Find a) 1.3×0.004 b) 2.5×0.08

a) $1.3 \times 0.004 = 0.0052$ 13
    (1 d.p.) (3 d.p.)   (4 d.p.) $\times\ \underline{\ 4}$
                                                              $\underline{52}$

b) $2.5 \times 0.08 = 0.200 = 0.2$ 25
    (1 d.p.) (2 d.p.)   (3 d.p.) $\times\ \underline{\ \ 8}$
                                                              $\underline{200}$

Find

1.	1.3×0.2	**6.**	1.9×0.02	**11.**	0.8×0.5
2.	0.5×0.5	**7.**	0.05×0.008	**12.**	0.1×0.1
3.	0.02×0.3	**8.**	1.002×0.07	**13.**	0.07×0.05
4.	1.04×0.5	**9.**	0.003×0.006	**14.**	1.5×0.02
5.	2.3×0.4	**10.**	1.09×0.02	**15.**	2.06×0.003

DIVISION BY DECIMALS

To divide a decimal by a whole number you do the same as you would with whole numbers, and add noughts after the point when needed.

For example, to find $3.7 \div 2$ we have

$$
\begin{array}{r}
1.\ 8\ 5 \\
2\overline{)3.^17^10}
\end{array}
$$

Division by a decimal can be converted to division by a whole number, using the fact that

> the top and bottom of a fraction can be multiplied by the same number without changing its value.

For example

$$2.3 \div 0.2 = \frac{2.3}{0.2}$$

$$= \frac{23}{2} \qquad \left(\frac{2.3 \times 10}{0.2 \times 10} \right)$$

$$= 11.5 \qquad \begin{array}{r} 1\ 1.\ 5 \\ 2\overline{)2\ 3.^10} \end{array}$$

EXERCISE 4d

Find

1.	$3.5 \div 7$	**6.**	$0.7 \div 0.2$	**11.**	$2.8 \div 1.4$
2.	$3.5 \div 0.7$	**7.**	$0.08 \div 0.4$	**12.**	$3.7 \div 0.02$
3.	$1.3 \div 2$	**8.**	$1.02 \div 0.2$	**13.**	$3.9 \div 0.3$
4.	$1.3 \div 0.02$	**9.**	$1.5 \div 0.05$	**14.**	$1.02 \div 0.05$
5.	$2.6 \div 0.4$	**10.**	$3.06 \div 0.4$	**15.**	$2.7 \div 0.9$

MIXED EXAMPLES

EXERCISE 4e

Without using a calculator, find

1.	$1.27 + 3.6$	**5.**	$3.7 + 0.12$
2.	$2.5 + 3.1$	**6.**	$2.5 + 0.05$
3.	$0.2 + 1.6$	**7.**	$1.82 + 0.8$
4.	$1.8 + 0.9$	**8.**	$3.02 + 1.4$
9.	$4.8 - 0.7$	**13.**	$3.6 - 0.12$
10.	$0.2 - 0.02$	**14.**	$0.7 - 0.7$
11.	$5 - 4.2$	**15.**	$5.05 - 3.6$
12.	$3.6 - 1.2$	**16.**	$5 - 3.6$

17. 1.2×0.2	**21.** 1.3×0.04
18. 0.5×0.05	**22.** 0.5×1.2
19. 1.1×1.1	**23.** 0.4×0.4
20. 0.2×0.2	**24.** 4×0.4

25. $4.2 \div 0.6$	**29.** $5 \div 0.1$
26. $2.8 \div 7$	**30.** $2.7 \div 0.09$
27. $0.36 \div 0.9$	**31.** $5.6 \div 0.08$
28. $0.012 \div 0.6$	**32.** $0.77 \div 11$

With mixed operations remember to do multiplication and division before addition and subtraction.

33. $1.7 + 0.2 \times 1.2$	**38.** $1.7 + 0.3 \times 0.8$
34. $2.8 \div 0.7 + 0.3$	**39.** $1.8 \div 0.9 \times 0.02$
35. $3.2 + 0.04 \div 0.2$	**40.** $4.6 - 3.2 \times 0.01$
36. $1.6 \div 0.8 \times 0.1$	**41.** $0.2 + 1.8 \div 0.3$
37. $0.3 - 0.4 \times 0.5$	**42.** $3.6 \div 0.9 - 2.1$

DECIMAL PLACES AND SIGNIFICANT FIGURES

Many calculations do not have exact answers, and even if they do it is not always necessary to give the exact value. Most problems specify the degree of accuracy required as, for example, correct to three significant figures or correct to 1 decimal place or correct to the nearest ten units.

Decimal places are easy to identify; the first decimal place is the first digit to the right of the point, and so on.

To give a number correct to one decimal place we look at the second decimal place; if it is 5 or more we add one to the first decimal place; if it is less than 5 we leave the first decimal place alone. Similar ideas are used to find a number correct to two or more decimal places.

For example	$1.7624 = 1.8$ correct to 1 d.p.
and	1.76 correct to 2 d.p.
Similarly	5.0178 is 5.0 correct to 1 d.p.
	5.02 correct to 2 d.p.
and	5.018 correct to 3 d.p.

Remember that when we give a number correct to a given number of significant figures, the first significant figure is the first non zero digit, e.g.

$$72.36 \text{ is } 70 \quad \text{correct to 1 s.f.}$$
$$0.059\,26 \text{ is } 0.06 \quad \text{correct to 1 s.f.}$$

Similarly
$$53.294 \text{ is } 53.3 \quad \text{correct to 3 s.f.}$$
$$1.0936 \text{ is } 1.09 \quad \text{correct to 3 s.f.}$$

and
$$0.093\,67 \text{ is } 0.094 \text{ correct to 2 s.f.}$$

EXERCISE 4f

Write down each of the following numbers correct to the number of decimal places indicated in brackets.

1. 0.275 (2)   **3.** 0.032 (2)   **5.** 3.6666 (3)

2. 5.078 (1)   **4.** 2.0347 (3)   **6.** 2.834072 (4)

Write down the third significant figure in

a) 82.63   b) 0.021 79, and give its value.

a) 82.63   The third s.f. is 6 and its value is $\dfrac{6}{10}$.

b) 0.021 79   The third s.f. is 7 and its value is $\dfrac{7}{10\,000}$.

For each of the following numbers write down the significant figure indicated in brackets and give its value.

7. 16.29 (2nd)   **10.** 0.1426 (3rd)   **13.** 0.596 (2nd)

8. 843.09 (4th)   **11.** 0.0761 (2nd)   **14.** 707 (3rd)

9. 18.03 (2nd)   **12.** 5291 (2nd)   **15.** 0.040 57 (3rd)

Give the following numbers correct to 2 s.f.

16. 8.254   **19.** 12.8   **22.** 0.824

17. 4.073   **20.** 172   **23.** 0.0873

18. 2.16   **21.** 43.7   **24.** 0.00307

Give the following numbers correct to 3 s.f.

25.	9.267	**28.**	86.59	**31.**	0.02544
26.	6.058	**29.**	759.42	**32.**	0.87766
27.	4.397	**30.**	3699	**33.**	0.00050992

Give the following numbers correct to 4 s.f.

34.	8.5028	**37.**	58.924	**40.**	0.502937
35.	2.0193	**38.**	851.82	**41.**	0.0722384
36.	6.9237	**39.**	50456	**42.**	0.00990394

Give the following numbers correct to the number of significant figures indicated in the brackets.

43.	73.14	(2)	**46.**	70945	(4)	**49.**	1.2799	(3)
44.	0.05737	(3)	**46.**	0.009372	(2)	**50.**	0.788010	(4)
45.	889.4	(3)	**48.**	3.14159	(4)	**51.**	0.002657	(3)

USING A CALCULATOR

Calculators are marvellous aids because they take the drudgery out of many calculations. We cannot always be certain, however, that the answer they give is correct because *we* make mistakes when using them, particularly when we enter numbers. Our mistakes often result in outrageously incorrect answers so we should always ask "Is the answer reasonable ?" One way to answer this question is to get a rough idea of the size of the answer that we expect. We can do this by correcting each number in the calculation to one significant figure and then working out the rough answer.

For example $257.38 \times 9.837 \approx 300 \times 10 = 3000$

On a calculator $257.38 \times 9.837 = 2531.8471$

This is the same sort of size as the rough estimate, so it is probably correct.

In this example we have written down all the figures shown in the display but this is not usually necessary. Answers are usually required correct to either three or four significant figures.

EXERCISE 4g

> Calculate 82.59×0.7326 giving the answer correct to 3 s.f.
>
> $(82.59 \times 0.7326 \approx 80 \times 0.7 = 56)$
>
> $82.59 \times 0.7326 = 60.50$ (writing down the first 4 s.f.)
>
> $= 60.5$ correct to 3 s.f.

First give a rough estimate for the following calculations, then use your calculator to give the answers correct to 3 s.f.

1. 27.8×5.243
2. $57.2 \div 2.9$
3. 8.742×0.2015
4. $604 \div 58.2$
5. 13.6×25.2

6. 8.99×4.06
7. $278 \div 27.3$
8. $26.9 \div 5.37$
9. 67.3×0.92
10. $55.5 \div 1.66$

11. 0.0278×6.34
12. 102.8×0.00792
13. $0.0392 \div 0.04273$
14. 587.3×9046
15. $(0.07332)^2$

16. $(0.09374 \div 2.83) \times 11$
17. $(0.00572 \times 8.65) \div 54$
18. $(372 \times 953) \div 103$
19. $(889 \div 9.07) \times 15.42$
20. $(5055 \times 2202) \div 759$

EXERCISE 4h

In this exercise you are given several alternative answers.
Write down the letter that corresponds to the correct answer.

1. The second significant figure of 825.3 represents

   A tens   **B** hundreds   **C** units   **D** tenths

2. Correct to two significant figures, the value of 0.796 is

   A 1.0   **B** 0.79   **C** 0.8   **D** 0.80

3. The value of $(0.04)^2$ is

   A 0.16   **B** 1.6   **C** 0.08   **D** 0.0016

4. A rough answer for 0.29×5.7 is

    A 2   **B** 5   **C** 0.3   **D** 6

5. The third significant figure of 80.53 represents

    A units   **B** tens   **C** hundredths   **D** tenths

6. Correct to three significant figures, the value of 0.020 765 is

    A 0.02   **B** 0.020 77   **C** 0.0208   **D** 0.021

7. A rough answer for $0.8736 \div 0.011\,25$ is

    A 80   **B** 8   **C** 0.8   **D** 0.08

8. Which of the following sets of fractions are in ascending order of size ?

    A $\frac{1}{2}, 0.57, \frac{5}{9}$ **B** $0.57, \frac{1}{2}, \frac{5}{9}$ **C** $\frac{1}{2}, \frac{5}{9}, 0.57$ **D** $0.57, \frac{5}{9}, \frac{1}{2}$

THE RANGE IN WHICH A CORRECTED NUMBER CAN LIE

Suppose that the height of a table is given as 75 cm to the nearest centimetre.

The smallest number that can be rounded up to 75 is 74.5, and the largest number that can be rounded down to 75 is just less than 75.5.

Therefore the table can be any height from 74.5 cm up to, but not including, 75.5 cm.

This gives a range of numbers that can be illustrated on a number line.

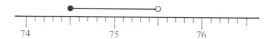

74.5 is called the *lower bound* of the range
75.5 is called the *upper bound* of the range

(● indicates that 74.5 is included while ○ indicates that 75.5 is not.)

If the height of the table is denoted by h cm then we can say that

$$74.5 \leqslant h < 75.5$$

EXERCISE 4i

For each of the following measurements give the lower and upper bounds.

    1. The length of a piece of string is 34 cm to the nearest centimetre.

    2. The length of a path is 14 metres correct to the nearest metre.

3. The distance between two houses is 5 kilometres correct to the nearest kilometre.

4. The height of a table is 30 cm correct to the nearest centimetre.

In questions 5 to 8 use inequalities to give the upper and lower bounds.

5. The length of a piece of wood, l cm, is 48 cm correct to the nearest centimetre.

6. The width of a table, w cm, is 83 cm correct to the nearest centimetre.

7. The height of a door, h cm, is 210 cm correct to the nearest 10 centimetres.

8. The thickness of a pen, t mm, is 12 mm correct to the nearest millimetre.

APPROPRIATE UNITS OF MEASUREMENT AND ACCURACY

It would be quite inappropriate to give the mass of a train in grams or the dimensions of this page in kilometres. For most things there are units of measurement that are generally considered to be the most suitable.

For example, we would be likely to give the mass of a train in tonnes, the dimensions of this page in centimetres (or possibly millimetres) and a quantity of petrol bought in gallons or litres.

There are also generally assumed degress of accuracy for measurements. For example, if we are told that a table is 74 cm wide, it is reasonable to assume that the width is given to the nearest centimetre. Similarly, if the road distance between two villages is given as 15 km, it can be assumed that the distance is between 14.5 km and 15.5 km.

EXERCISE 4j

In questions 1 to 8 each question is followed by several alternative answers. Write down the letter that corresponds to what you consider to be the most suitable unit for measuring the quantity referred to.

1. Angela's height

   A kilometres   **B** millimetres   **C** centimetres

2. Katherine's mass

   A grams   **B** kilograms   **C** tonnes

3. The capacity of my teapot

   A litres   **B** gallons   **C** millilitres

4.   The distance from London to Australia

     A   kilometres   **B**   thousands of miles   **C**   miles

5.   The area of a small farm

     A   hectares   **B**   square metres   **C**   square miles

6.   The mass of the passenger liner *Canberra*

     A   milligrams   **B**   thousands of kilograms   **C**   thousands of tons

7.   The length of cotton on a new reel

     A   centimetres   **B**   metres   **C**   kilometres

8.   The length of time Waheed's lawn mower will run on 1 litre of petrol

     A   hours   **B**   seconds   **C**   days

In questions 9 to 15 suggest a suitable unit and degree of accuracy for measuring the quantities referred to.

9.   The capacity of a tea cup.

10.   The distance my car will travel on 10 litres of petrol.

11.   The area of my lounge.

12.   The distance around the equator.

13.   The area of China.

14.   The mass of a saccharin tablet.

15.   The quantity of oil produced by an oilfield each day.

16.   a) Tim needed to measure the length of his garden fence because he wanted to replace it. Which unit of length would you use if you were doing the job, kilometres, metres or millimetres ?

     b) He measured it to the nearest 10 cm and gave the length as 16.2 m. What was the shortest possible length for the fence ?

17.   At an airport the announcer stated that there would be a delay of about 3 hours. If this were true to the nearest hour, what was the shortest possible delay ?

18.   The capacity of a jug is 1.26 litres, correct to 2 d.p.

     a) Is this value correct to the nearest cubic centimetre, ten cubic centimetres or hundred cubic centimetres ?

     b) Give, in the unit you have chosen as your answer to part (a), the smallest possible capacity of the jug.

19. Lorraine's mass is correctly given as 56.4 kg.

   a) Is this figure correct to the nearest kilogram or tenth of a kilogram ?

   b) What, in grams, is her smallest possible mass ?

20. a) What is the most suitable unit to use to measure the area of my dining table ?

   b) I measured its length as accurately as I could and found it to be 2.621 m. Was this correct to the nearest m, cm or mm ? Give this length correct to the nearest tenth of a metre.

MIXED EXERCISES

EXERCISE 4k

1. Give, correct to 2 s.f.

   a) 5.915   b) 3.269   c) 7.008

2. Give, correct to 2 d.p.

   a) 12.6392   b) 0.2741   c) 0.0493

3. Find, without using a calculator

   a) 5.3×0.4 b) $0.24 \div 0.6$

4. Give a rough estimate for the value of 97.6×0.0516.
   Use your calculator to give the answer correct to 3.s.f.

5. The distance between two trees is 86 m, correct to the nearest metre. Give the upper and lower bounds of this measurements.

6. What is the most suitable unit for measuring the length of time for which you hope to go away on holiday ? What unit do travel brochures use ?

EXERCISE 4l

1. Give 69.0218 correct to

   a) the nearest 10   b) the nearest 100   c) 3 s.f.

2. Find, without using a calculator

   a) 0.6×0.7 b) $1.8 \div 0.3$

3. Give a rough estimate for the value of $51.26 \div 9.736$.
   Use your calculator to give the answer correct to 2 d.p.

4. Dinah gives the thickness of a book as 4.5 cm, correct to the nearest tenth of a cm. If the actual thickness of the book is t cm use inequalities to give the range of possible values of t.

5. What is the most suitable unit and degree of accuracy for measuring
   a) the quantity of cornflakes in a packet
   b) the amount of water in a swimming pool ?

6. The length of a car is correctly given as 4.572 m. What is its length
   a) correct to the nearest metre
   b) correct to the nearest centimetre ?

5 TRAVEL GRAPHS

DISTANCE, TIME AND SPEED

Reminders:

$$\text{Distance} = \text{speed} \times \text{time}$$

$$\text{Time} = \frac{\text{distance}}{\text{speed}}$$

$$\text{Speed} = \frac{\text{distance travelled}}{\text{time taken}}$$

EXERCISE 5a

> An aeroplane travels at 600 m.p.h. How far will it travel in
> a) $3\frac{1}{2}$ hours   b) 24 minutes ?
>
> a) In 1 hour the aeroplane travels 600 miles
>
> $\therefore$ in $3\frac{1}{2}$ hours it travels $\quad 600 \times 3.5$ miles
> $= 2100$ miles
>
> b) In 60 minutes the aeroplane travels 600 miles
>
> $\therefore$ in 1 minute the aeroplane travels $\dfrac{600}{60}$ miles i.e. 10 miles
>
> and in 24 minutes it travels 10×24 miles i.e. 240 miles.

1. An express train travels at 125 m.p.h. How far will it travel in

   a) 2 hours   b) 12 min ?

2. A bus travels at 56 km/h. How far will it travel in

   a) $\frac{1}{2}$ hour   b) $1\frac{3}{4}$ hours   c) 15 min ?

3. An aeroplane travels at 600 m.p.h. How far will it travel in

   a) $4\frac{1}{2}$ hours   b) $\frac{3}{4}$ hour   c) 20 min ?

4. John can cycle at 20 km/h. How far will he travel in

a) 3 hours   b) $1\frac{3}{4}$ hours   c) 75 min ?

5. How long will it take Lorraine cycling at 18 km/h to go

a) 27 km   b) $13\frac{1}{2}$ km ?

6. A rally driver drives at 70 m.p.h. How far will he drive in
a) $\frac{1}{2}$ hour   b) 24 min ?

7. How long will it take a bullet travelling at 120 m/s to travel
a) 144 m   b) 312 m ?

Find the average speed for each of the following journeys.

8. 120 km in 3 hours

9. 100 m in $12\frac{1}{2}$ sec

10. 75 miles in 50 min

11. 180 km in 135 min

12. 288 miles in 4 hours

13. 374 m in 34 sec

14. 70 km in 35 min

15. 20 miles in 16 min

The following table shows the distances in miles between various American airports.

	Chicago					
Dallas	800	Dallas				
Las Vegas	1500	1050	Las Vegas			
Los Angeles	1750	1200	250	Los Angeles		
New York	750	1400	2200	2450	New York	
San Francisco	1800	1500	450	300	2550	San Francisco
Washington	600	1200	2100	2300	200	2400	Washington

Use this table to find the average speeds for the journeys between the various cities.

16. New York, leaving at 1300, to Las Vegas, arriving at 1700

17. Chicago, leaving at 0530, to San Francisco, arriving at 1130

18. New York, leaving at 0600, to Dallas, arriving at 1040

19. Washington, leaving at 0830, to Los Angeles, arriving at 1415

20. San Francisco, leaving at 1236, to New York, arriving at 1742

AVERAGE SPEED

Frequently we wish to find the average speed for a journey where different parts of the journey are travelled at different speeds. Some journeys also include a rest.

The most important thing to remember is

$$\text{Average speed of journey} = \frac{\text{total distance travelled}}{\text{total time taken}}$$

Suppose that a car makes a motorway journey of 110 miles. The first 30 mile section is completed at an average speed of 60 m.p.h. while, for the remainder, the average speed is 40 m.p.h., and we want to find the average speed for the whole journey.

We know the total distance travelled, but the total time must be calculated by finding the sum of the times taken for all parts of the journey.

$$\text{Time for first part of journey} = \frac{\text{distance travelled}}{\text{average speed}}$$

$$= \frac{30}{60} \text{ hours}$$

$$= \tfrac{1}{2} \text{ hour}$$

$$\text{Time for second part of journey} = \frac{80}{40} \text{ hours}$$

$$= 2 \text{ hours.}$$

∴ total distance of 110 miles is travelled in $2\tfrac{1}{2}$ hours

i.e. average speed for whole journey $= \dfrac{\text{total distance}}{\text{total time}}$

$$= \frac{110}{2.5} \text{ m.p.h.}$$

$$= 44 \text{ m.p.h.}$$

If the motorist had rested for 15 minutes at any time during the journey

$$\text{Average speed for whole journey} = \frac{110}{\left(2\frac{1}{2}+\frac{1}{4}\right)} \text{ m.p.h.} = \frac{110}{2\frac{3}{4}} \text{ m.p.h.}$$

$$= 110 \div \frac{11}{4} \text{ m.p.h.} = 40 \text{ m.p.h.}$$

EXERCISE 5b

Copy and complete the following table to find the average speed for the whole journey.

	Distance in miles	Speed in m.p.h.	Time in hours
First part of journey	100	25	
Second part of journey	80	40	
Whole journey			

	Distance in miles	Speed in m.p.h.	Time in hours
First part of journey	100	25	4
Second part of journey	80	40	2
Whole journey	180	30	6

Time to travel 100 miles at 25 m.p.h. $= \dfrac{100}{25}$ hours $= 4$ hours

Time to travel 80 miles at 40 m.p.h. $= \dfrac{80}{40}$ hours $= 2$ hours

$\therefore$ Average speed for whole journey $= \dfrac{\text{total distance}}{\text{total time}}$

$$= \frac{(100+80)}{(4+2)} \text{ m.p.h.}$$

$$= \frac{180}{6} \text{ m.p.h.}$$

$$= 30 \text{ m.p.h.}$$

In each of the following questions copy and complete the table that is given.

1.

	Distance in miles	Speed in in m.p.h.	Time in hours
First part of journey	60	15	
Second part of journey	36	18	
Whole journey			

2.

	Distance in kilometres	Speed in in km/h	Time in hours
First part of journey	100	50	
Second part of journey	120	40	
Whole journey			

3.

	Distance in miles	Speed in in m.p.h.	Time in hours
First part of journey	20	8	$2\frac{1}{2}$
Second part of journey			
Whole journey	38		4

4.

	Distance in kilometres	Speed in in km/h	Time in hours
First part of journey	300	60	
Resting period	—	—	1
Second part of journey	200	50	
Whole journey			

5.

	Distance in miles	Speed in in m.p.h.	Time in hours
First part of journey	80	60	
Resting period	—	—	$\frac{1}{6}$
Second part of journey	70	35	
Whole journey			

6.

	Distance in kilometres	Speed in in km/h	Time in hours
First part of journey		45	$\frac{2}{3}$
Second part of journey	130	65	
Third part of journey	40	30	
Whole journey			

7.

	Distance in miles	Speed in in m.p.h.	Time in hours
First part of journey	120	48	
Resting period	—	—	$\frac{1}{4}$
Second part of journey		72	$2\frac{1}{2}$
Resting period	—	—	$\frac{1}{2}$
Third part of journey	50	40	
Whole journey			

8. Paul walks for 1 mile at 4 m.p.h. and then runs for 5 miles at 10 m.p.h. Find his average speed for the whole journey.

9. Esther cycles for 20 miles at 10 m.p.h. but because her bicycle breaks down she has to push it for 1 mile at 2 m.p.h. to complete her journey. Find her average speed for the whole journey.

10. An express train from Edinburgh to London is scheduled to travel at an average speed of 144 km/h. When it passes through a small station south of Edinburgh it is 24 minutes late and still has 576 km to go. By how much must its speed be increased to arrive on time ?

11.

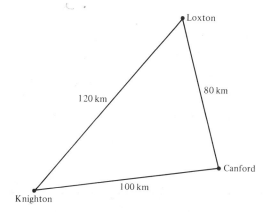

Roger Holmes wishes to travel from his home in Knighton to keep a business appointment in Loxton. He can either go by train or use his car. If he travels by train the journey is 120 kilometres and the train travels at an average speed of 100 km/h. In addition he needs 10 minutes to get to Knighton station and 20 minutes at Loxton before reaching his destination. If he travels by road he must drive via Canford. His car will average 80 km for the 100 kilometres from Knighton to Canford but only 60 km/h for the 80 kilometres from Canford to Loxton.

How long does the whole journey take if

a) he travels by train   b) he uses his car ?

12.

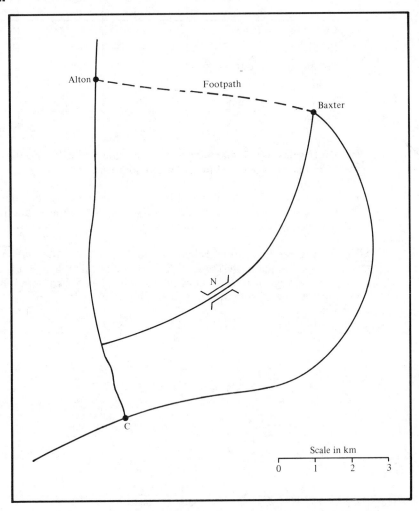

A pedestrian, a cyclist and a motorist are all at Alton and wish to travel to Baxter. The tracks and roads connecting these villages are shown on the map.

The pedestrian can use the footpath, the cyclist can use the most direct route by road but the motorist must travel via C because of a narrow bridge at N.

By walking a pair of dividers (set at 1 cm) along the map or by using a piece of thread, estimate the distance that each would cover in getting from Alton to Baxter.

They all leave Alton at 12 noon. If their respective average speeds are 6 km/h, 12 km/h and 36 km/h how long does each take ? In what order do they arrive ?

FINDING DISTANCE FROM A GRAPH

When we travelled from the airport to our holiday resort we travelled at a steady speed of 40 kilometres per hour (km/h), i.e. in each hour we covered a distance of 40 km.

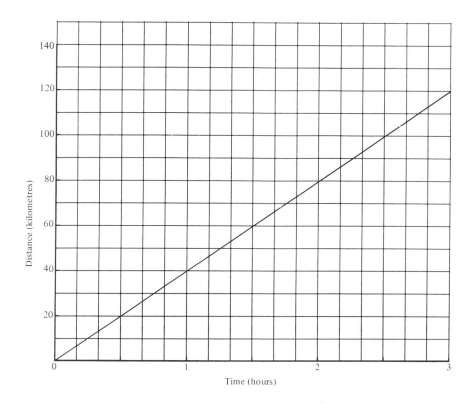

This graph shows our journey. It plots distance against time and shows that

in $\frac{1}{2}$ hour we travelled 20 km

in 1 hour we travelled 40 km

in 2 hours we travelled 80 km

in 3 hours we travelled 120 km

The journey was therefore a distance of 120 km and took 3 hours to complete.

EXERCISE 5c

The graphs that follow show four different journeys.
For each journey find   a) the distance travelled   b) the time taken
c) the distance travelled in 1 hour.

1.

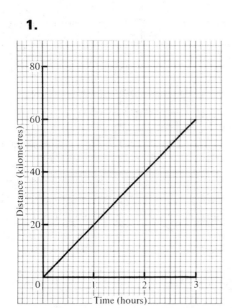

3.

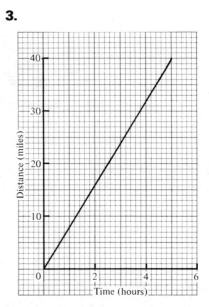

2.

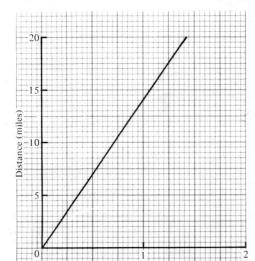

4.

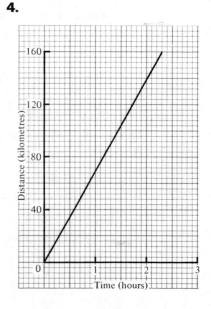

DRAWING TRAVEL GRAPHS

EXERCISE 5d

Jane travels 100 miles in a car at a steady speed and takes two hours. Draw a travel graph to show this journey. Use your graph to find out a) how far she travelled in the first half hour   b) how long it took her to travel 75 miles ?

(Plot the point representing 100 miles from the start after a time of two hours. Draw a straight line to this point from the origin which represents the starting point.)

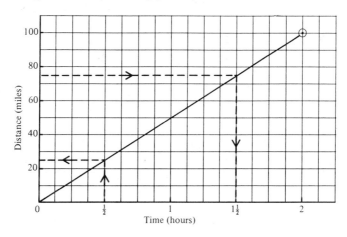

From the graph

a) Jane travels 25 miles in the first half hour

b) the first 75 miles take $1\frac{1}{2}$ hours.

Choose suitable scales and draw travel graphs to represent the following journeys.

1. 100 miles in a car in 4 hours

2. 24 km on foot in 4 hours

3. 1500 miles in a plane in 3 hours

4. 225 km in a coach in $2\frac{1}{2}$ hours

5. 160 km in a car at 40 km/h

6. 12 miles on foot at 4 m.p.h.

7. 1800 miles in a plane at 600 m.p.h.

8. 24 miles on a bicycle in 3 hours

9. 2 hours at 180 km/h   **11.** $2\frac{1}{2}$ hours at 120 km/h

10. 3 hours at 40 m.p.h.   **12.** 20 seconds at 5 m/s

13. John drives for 2 hours at 90 km/h. Show this on a travel graph and use it to find

  a) how long he takes to travel the first 45 km

  b) how far he travels in   (i) the first hour   (ii) the last $\frac{1}{2}$ hour ?

14. Judith cycles for $3\frac{1}{2}$ hours at 8 m.p.h. Show this on a travel graph and use it to find

  a) how far she travels in the first $2\frac{1}{2}$ hours

  b) how long she takes to travel 10 miles.

USING TRAVEL GRAPHS

The exercise that follows shows how to get useful information from slightly more complicated graphs.

EXERCISE 5e

1.

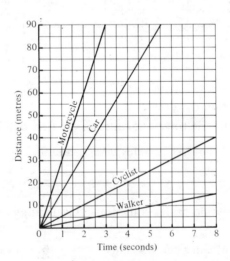

The graph shows four distance–time graphs.

  a) How far does the motorcycle travel in 3 seconds ? What is its speed ?

  b) How far does the car travel in 5 seconds ? What is its speed ?

  c) Find the speed of   (i) the cyclist   (ii) the walker.

2.

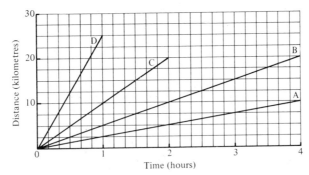

The graph shows the journeys of four travellers A, B, C and D. State whether the following statements are true or false.

a) B travels faster than A

b) C travels faster than both A and D

c) C travels four times as fast as A

d) B travels twice as far as C

e) D travels the furthest.

3.

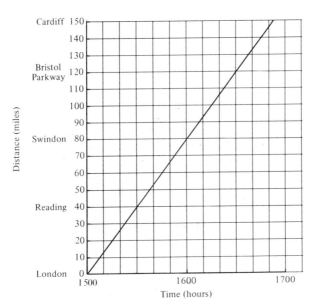

The graph shows a simplified version of the journey of an express train from London to Cardiff. Use the graph to answer the following questions.

a) How far is it from   (i) London to Swindon   (ii) Swindon to Cardiff ?

b) At what time did the train pass through
   (i) Reading   (ii) Bristol Parkway ?

c) How far did the train travel in one hour ?

d) Estimate the time taken for the journey.

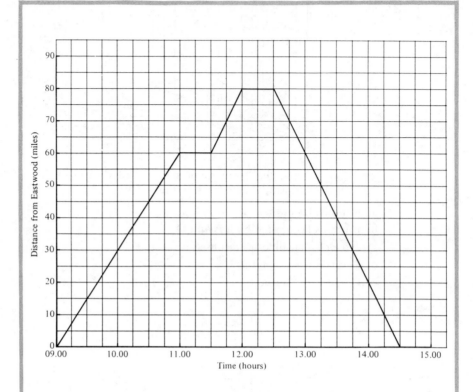

The graph represents the journey made by a car travelling from Eastwood to Westwood, and returning to Eastwood.

a) How far is it from Eastwood to Westwood ?

b) How long did the car take to travel
   (i) from Eastwood to Westwood
   (ii) Westwood to Eastwood ?

c) For how long did the car stop
   (i) on the outward journey
   (ii) at Westwood
   (iii) on the return journey ?

d) What was the average speed of the car
   (i) for the first 60 miles
   (ii) for the return journey
   (iii) for the entire trip ?

a) (The highest point on the graph represents the furthest distance from Eastwood.)

The distance from Eastwood to Westwood is 80 miles.

b) (i) The car leaves Eastwood at 9.00 a.m. and arrives in Westwood at 12 noon. The time for the outward journey is therefore 3 hours.

(ii) The car leaves Westwood at 12.30 and arrives in Eastwood at 14.30. The time for the return journey is 2 hours.

c) (The flat parts of the graph represent times when the distance is not changing, i.e. the car has stopped.)

(i) On the outward journey the car stopped for $\frac{1}{2}$ hour.

(ii) The car stopped at Westwood for $\frac{1}{2}$ hour.

(iii) There was no stop on the return journey.

d) (i) The car takes 2 hours to cover the first 60 miles. Therefore, for this section

$$\text{Average speed} = \frac{\text{distance}}{\text{time}}$$

$$= \frac{60}{2} \text{ m.p.h.}$$

$$= 30 \text{ m.p.h.}$$

(ii) (The downward sloping line shows that the distance from Eastwood is decreasing, i.e. the car is returning to Eastwood.) For the return journey

$$\text{Average speed} = \frac{80}{2} \text{ m.p.h.}$$

$$= 40 \text{ m.p.h.}$$

(iii) Total distance covered $= (80 + 80)$ miles

$$= 160 \text{ miles}$$

Total time taken $= 5\frac{1}{2}$ hours or 5.5 hours

$$\text{Average speed} = \frac{\text{total distance}}{\text{total time}}$$

$$= \frac{160}{5.5} \text{ m.p.h.}$$

$$= 29 \text{ m.p.h.}$$

(correct to the nearest whole number)

4.

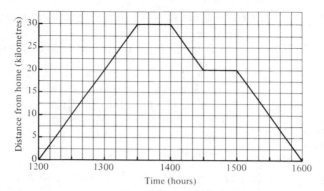

Lucy left home at 12 noon to visit her grandparents. After spending some time with them she returned home but called to see a school friend on the way. The travel graph shows her journey.

a) How far did Lucy travel to her grandparents' home and how long did she take ?

b) How long did she stay   (i) with her grandparents   (ii) with her school friend ?

c) Did Lucy always travel at the same speed ?

d) What was her average speed on the outward journey ?

e) Find   (i) the total distance travelled   (ii) the average speed for the whole journey including stops.

f) Do you think Lucy travelled on foot, on her bicycle or on a bus ? Give a reason for your answer.

5.

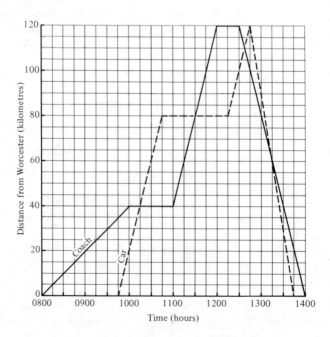

The graph represents the journeys made by a coach and a car starting at Worcester, travelling to Bath and returning to Worcester.

a) How much longer, including stops, did the coach take to travel from Worcester to Bath than the car did ?

b) At what times did the car overtake the coach ?

c) What was the fastest speed attained by each vehicle ?

d) What was the average speed of the car during the entire journey ?

e) For how long was the car nearer to Bath than the coach was ?

6.

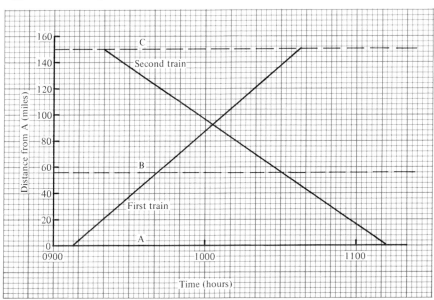

The graph shows the journeys of two trains between two stations A and C.

a) Use the graph to find
   (i) the time that the first train began and finished its journey
   (ii) the total time taken by the first train to complete its journey
   (iii) the distance from A to C
   (iv) the average speed of the first train
   (v) the time taken by the second train to complete the journey
   (vi) the average speed of the second train.

A train spotter spent the morning at B, arriving there at 9.40.

b) How far is B from   (i) A   (ii) C ?

c) How long did the train spotter have to wait before
   (i) the first train passed   (ii) the second train passed ?

7.

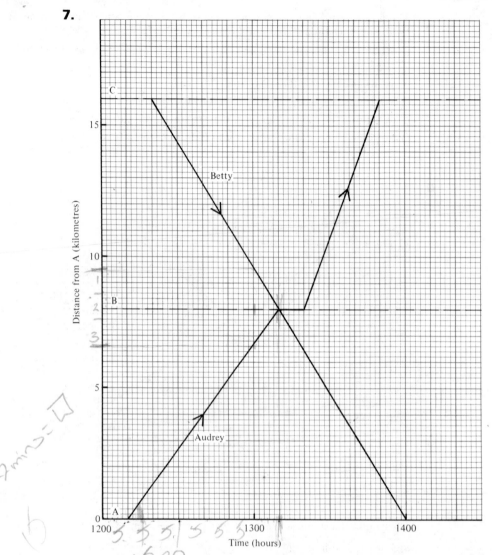

The graph shows the journeys of two hikers Audrey and Betty. Audrey walks from A to C while Betty covers the same route but in the reverse direction. Use your graph to answer the following questions.

a) How long did Audrey rest at B ?

b) How far did she still have to walk after resting ?

c) Did Audrey walk faster after the rest than she did before ? (You should not have to work out the two speeds to answer this question.)

d) Did Audrey spend more or less time actually walking than Betty ?

e) How far apart were they at 1300 ?

f) At what time was Betty exactly half-way ?

8. The graph represents the journeys of two motor cyclists Ron and Beth. Both start their journey at A, and travel, via B and C, along the same route to D. Use your graph to answer the following questions.

a) Find
   (i) the distances of B, C and D from A
   (ii) the time Beth takes before she takes a rest and the distance she has then travelled
   (iii) Beth's average speed for the first part of the journey
   (iv) Ron's average speed for the first part of his journey
   (v) the length of time Ron spent resting
   (vi) Ron's average speed for the whole journey
   (vii) Beth's average speed for the whole journey.

b) How many times did they pass ?

c) Was Ron moving when Beth passed him ?

d) Who was first to rest, and how long had that person been travelling when the rest period began ?

e) Estimate the time at which they were furthest apart.

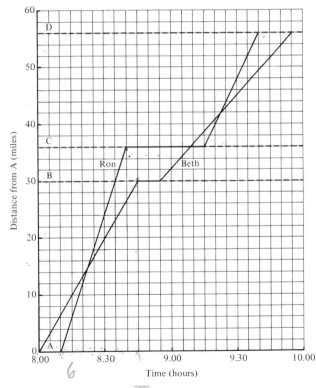

$5 \text{ mins} = \square$

6 CIRCLES, SOLIDS AND NETS

CIRCLE ARITHMETIC

The diagram shows a circle with centre O and radius r.

The diameter, d, is the distance right across the circle.

So $$d = 2r$$

The circumference, C, is the distance all the way round

and $$C = \pi d$$
or $$C = 2\pi r$$

where π is a number a little bigger than 3. On most calculators there is a button marked π but sometimes we prefer to use an approximation for π such as 3.14 (or even 3 for a rough estimate).

The area, A, of a circle of radius r is given by

$$A = \pi r^2$$

In all exercises in this chapter use the π button on your calculator unless you are given other instructions. Give non-exact answers correct to 3 s.f. unless otherwise instructed.

EXERCISE 6a

1. Find the diameter of a circle whose radius is

a) 3 cm   b) 1.2 cm   c) 0.3 m   d) 41 cm.

2. Find the radius of a circle whose diameter is

a) 9 cm   b) 2.6 m   c) 0.86 m   d) 62 cm.

3. Use the π button on your calculator to find the circumference of a circle whose radius is

a) 2.7 cm   b) 31 cm   c) 0.85 m   d) 10.6 cm.

4. Use $\pi \approx 3$ to estimate, without using a calculator, the circumference of a circle whose radius is

a) 2 cm   b) 1.3 m   c) 0.4 m   d) 5 cm.

5. Take $\pi \approx 3.14$ to find the circumference of a circle whose diameter is

a) 14 cm   b) 21.8 cm   c) 1.32 m   d) 0.76 m.

6. Find the area of each of the following circles.

a) The radius is 5.2 cm   (Use the π button)

b) The diameter is 6 cm   (Take $\pi \approx 3.14$)

c) The radius is 7 cm   (Take $\pi \approx 3\frac{1}{7}$ and do not use a calculator)

d) The radius is 3 cm   (Take $\pi \approx 3$ and do not use a calculator.)

7. A circle has a diameter of 17.4 cm. Find its circumference and its area.

8.

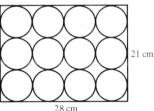

21 cm

28 cm

Twelve circular discs, each of diameter 7 cm, are stamped out of the rectangular sheet of plastic shown in the diagram. Find the area of the plastic sheet that is waste.

CYLINDER ARITHMETIC ━━━━━━━━━━━━━━━━━━━━━━━━━━━━━━━━━━━━━━

A solid cylinder has a circular base and a parallel circular top.

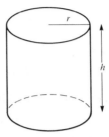

If the radius of the cylinder is r and its height is h, its volume, V, is given by

$$V = \pi r^2 h$$

Note that the radius and height must be measured in the same unit before using this formula.

Hollow cylinders are often used to hold food or drinks, e.g. tins of meat or cans of coke. Larger hollow cylinders are used as hot water tanks, oil drums, etc. In such cases we are likely to be interested in how much the cylinder holds. This is called the *capacity* of the cylinder and it is found in the same way as is the volume of a solid cylinder,

i.e. $$Capacity = \pi r^2 h$$

When the contents of a hollow cylinder are liquid, the capacity is often given in litres. (Remember that $1\,\text{litre} = 1000\,\text{cm}^3$)

Note that if a cylindrical container is not completely full, the volume of its contents can be found from $V = \pi r^2 h'$ where h' is the depth of the contents.

EXERCISE 6b

Find the volumes of the following cylinders. (Use the π button.)

1. $r = 3\,\text{cm}, h = 8\,\text{cm}$

3. $r = 7\,\text{cm}, h = 13\,\text{cm}$

2. $r = 0.2\,\text{m}, h = 0.7\,\text{m}$

4. $r = 18.3\,\text{cm}, h = 11.4\,\text{cm}$

5. The height is 27 cm and the diameter is 8 cm.

6. The height and radius are both 20 cm.

7. The radius is 46 cm and the height is 1.4 m.

8. The height is 37 cm and the radius is 13 mm.

9. A cylindrical water tank has a diameter of 50 cm and its height is 86 cm. What is the capacity of the tank? If the depth of water in the tank is 67 cm, what is the volume of the water?

10. An ornament consists of four solid wooden cylinders as shown in the diagram.

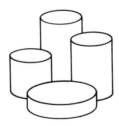

The radius of the shortest cylinder is 7 cm and its height is 3 cm. The other three cylinders are each of radius 4 cm and their heights are 7 cm, 10 cm and 12 cm. Find the total volume of wood in the ornament.

11. A pewter vase is cylindrical. Its inside diameter and height are 3 cm and 14 cm respectively. How much water will it hold?

12. In a cylindrical block of wood, radius 13 cm and height 20 cm, a cylindrical hole of radius 3 cm is drilled as shown. What is the volume of wood remaining?

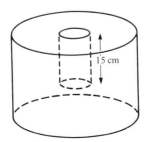

The volume of a cylinder is 240 cm³. Using $\pi \approx 3.14$, find
a) its height if its radius is 4 cm
b) its radius if its height is 12 cm.

a) $V = \pi r^2 h$

$240 = 3.14 \times 4^2 \times h$

$= 50.24 h$

$\dfrac{240}{50.24} = h$ (Dividing both sides by 50.24)

$4.777 = h$

The height is 4.78 cm.

b) $V = \pi r^2 h$

$240 = 3.14 \times r^2 \times 12$

$240 = 37.68 r^2$

$\dfrac{240}{37.68} = r^2$

$6.369 = r^2$

$2.524 = r$ (taking the square root of each side)

The radius is 2.52 cm.

13. A soft-drinks manufacturer requires cans with a capacity of 500 ml each. If the diameter of the can is 7 cm what must its height be ?

14. The capacity of an oildrum of height 46 cm is 37 litres. What is its radius ?

15. A metal paper-weight is in the form of a solid cylinder of height 5 cm and diameter 8 cm. What is its volume ?
The metal is melted down and cast into cylindrical tokens. If each token has a diameter of 2.5 cm and is 4 mm thick, how many tokens can be cast ?

SOLIDS

Most solids have faces, edges and vertices. Each flat surface is a face, e.g. a cube has six faces: top, bottom and four vertical sides.

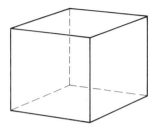

Whenever two faces join they have a common line called an edge, e.g. AB is an edge.

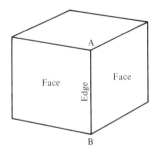

When several faces meet at a point we have a vertex (the plural of vertex is vertices), e.g. A is a vertex.

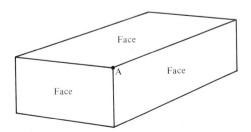

CUBES

A cube is a solid, all of whose faces are squares.

EXERCISE 6c

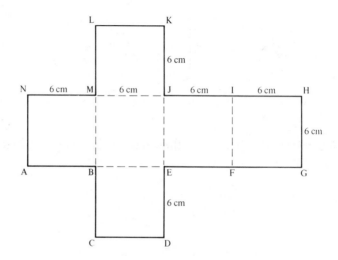

Draw the given net on thin card (all the angles are 90°) and cut it out. Score the dotted lines and fold the card to form a cube. Stick the edges together with Sellotape. Your drawing and cutting must be done accurately or the edges will not fit properly.

1. Which points meet with A ?

2. Which line meets with JK ?

3. How many faces has a cube ?

4. How many edges has a cube ?

5. How many vertices has a cube ?

6. What is the shape of each face ?

7. What is the area of each face ?

8. What is the total surface area of the cube ?

9. Draw a different net for the same cube.

THE VOLUME OF A CUBE

The volume, V, of a cube of edge a is given by

$$V = a^3$$

EXERCISE 6d

1. Find the volume of a cube whose edges are
a) 2 cm   b) 3 cm   c) 0.1 m.

2. How many cubes of edge 1.2 cm can be cast from liquid metal of volume 0.2 m³ ?

3. The area of one face of a cube is 16 cm². What is the volume of the cube ?

4. Find the volume of the solid in the diagram (all angles are 90°).

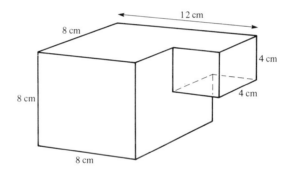

5. A concrete bollard consists of a cubical base of edge 0.4 m, surmounted by a cylinder of radius 0.2 m. If the total height of the bollard is 1 m, find the volume of concrete used in making it.

CUBOIDS

A cuboid is a rectangular block,

e.g.

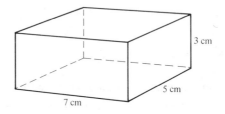

Here is a net for the given cuboid.

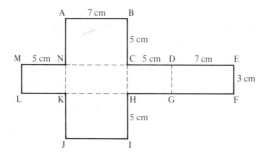

EXERCISE 6e

Draw the net given above on thin card, cut it out, score along the dotted lines, fold to form a cuboid and stick the edges together.

Repeat questions 1 to 9 from Exercise 6c for the cuboid given above.

THE VOLUME OF A CUBOID

The volume, V, of a cuboid whose edges are of lengths a, b and c, is given by

$$V = abc$$

Note that a, b and c must be measured in the same unit when using this formula.

EXERCISE 6f

Complete the following table for a cuboid.

	Length	Width	Height	Volume
1.	4 cm	3 cm	1.5 cm	
2.	9 cm	6 cm		108 cm³
3.		4.2 cm	3 cm	88.2 cm³
4.	0.2 m	0.15 m	36 cm	
5.	0.4 m		0.12 m	15 840 cm³

6. The volume of a cube of edge 4.1 cm is equal to the volume of a cuboid whose base is 3.2 cm by 2.5 cm. What is the height of the cuboid ?

7. A cylindrical hole is drilled right through a cuboid as shown in the diagram. Find the volume of the remaining material.

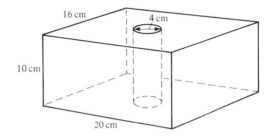

8. Arrange the following volumes in order of size; a cube of edge 4.6 cm, a cuboid whose dimensions are 5 cm by 3.2 cm by 4.9 cm and a cylinder of radius 3.9 cm and height 1.8 cm.

9. If an open box is made from this net what is the capacity of the box ?

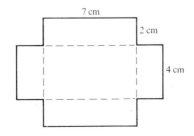

10. This is the net for an open box. When the box is made, what is its capacity ?

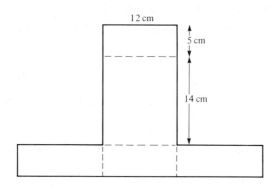

PRISMS

A prism is a solid which has the same cross-section from end to end,

e.g.

a triangular prism

a hexagonal prism

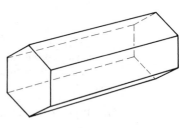

a trapezoidal prism

(Note that a cylinder is a circular prism and that a cuboid is a rectangular prism.)

Here is a net for a triangular prism.

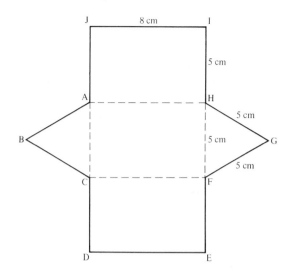

EXERCISE 6g

Questions 1 and 2 refer to the net given above.

1. Which points meet with B ?

2. Which points meet with E ?

3. How many edges has a triangular prism ?

4. How many vertices has a triangular prism ?

5. How many faces has a triangular prism ?

6. How many of the faces are rectangular ?

7. What is the shape of the other faces ?

8. Draw a net for this trapezoidal prism.

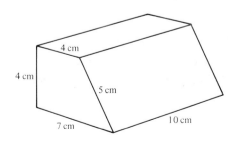

9. A triangular prism is made from this net.

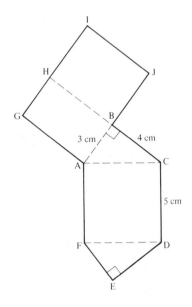

a) Which point (or points) join with   (i) G   (ii) C   (iii) I ?

b) Which line meets   (i) CD   (ii) FE   (iii) HI ?

c) Find the length of AC.

d) Find the total surface area of the prism.

10. The cross-section of a prism is a rectangle 7 cm by 2 cm and the length of the prism is 10 cm. Sketch this prism and draw a suitable net.

What is another name for this prism ?

What is its total surface area ?

11. A triangular prism is of length 12 cm and its cross-section is an isosceles triangle whose base is 6 cm and whose equal sides are of length 5 cm. Find

a) the perpendicular height of the cross-section

b) the area of each triangular face

c) the area of each rectangular face

d) the total surface area.

Draw a net for this prism.

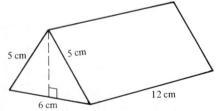

THE VOLUME OF A PRISM

The volume, V, of a prism is found from

$$V = \text{area of cross-section} \times \text{length}$$

All dimensions must be in the same unit when using this formula.

EXERCISE 6h

Find the volume of each of the prisms in questions 1 to 3.

1. A triangular prism, of length 10 cm, has a cross-sectional area of 9.4 cm².

2. a)

4 cm   7 cm   2 cm

b)

8 cm

The area of the cross-section is 11.1 cm².

3. A circular prism (cylinder) has radius 4 cm and length 20 cm.

The sketch illustrates Tim's workshop. Use the dimensions given on the sketch to find

a) the area of cross-section of the workshop

b) the volume of the workshop.

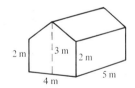

2 m   3 m   2 m   4 m   5 m

a)

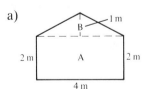

1 m   B   2 m   A   2 m   4 m

The cross-section can be divided into a rectangle A, and a triangle B.

Area of A $= 4 \times 2 \,\text{m}^2 = 8 \,\text{m}^2$

Area of B $= \frac{1}{2} \times 4 \times 1 \,\text{m}^2 = 2 \,\text{m}^2$

∴ area of cross-section is 10 m²

b) Volume of workshop $=$ area of cross-section $\times$ length

$= 10 \times 5 \,\text{m}^3$

$= 50 \,\text{m}^3$

4. A gold ingot is in the shape of a trapezoidal prism. The area of the cross-section is 150 cm² and the ingot is 25 cm long.

a) Find the volume of the ingot.

b) If the gold weighs 19.3 g per cm³, what is the weight of the ingot?

5. A foundry produces steel wire in lengths of 20 m. The diameter of the wire is $3\frac{1}{2}$ cm. Find

a) the cross-sectional area of the wire

b) the volume of steel in one length of wire

c) the weight of the wire if 1 cm³ of the steel weighs 7.7 g.

6. A ramp used by water-skiers to practise jumping is in the form of the triangular prism shown in the diagram.

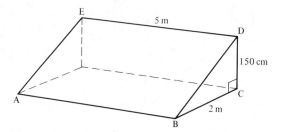

Using metres for all dimensions, find

a) the area of the cross-section (BCD)

b) the volume of the ramp

c) the area of the sloping face (ABDE).

7. A metal block is a cuboid, 7 cm × 4 cm × 3 cm. The metal is melted down and cast into circular discs of radius 15 mm and 4 mm thick. Find

a) the volume of the block in cubic centimetres

b) the volume of each disc in cubic millimetres

c) the maximum number of discs that can be made.

8. A copper pipe with internal and external diameters 8 mm and 14 mm respectively is 1 m long. It is melted down and recast into a cube. Find the length of the edge of this cube, giving your answer correct to the nearest millimetre.

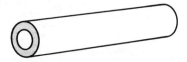

PYRAMIDS

Any solid with a flat base and which comes up to one point is a *pyramid*. The base can be of any shape and the name of the pyramid often includes the type of base.

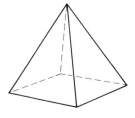

This is a *square pyramid* because its base is a square.

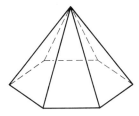

This is a *hexagonal pyramid*.

There are two pyramids with special names.

1. A pyramid with a triangular base is called a *tetrahedron*. All its faces are triangular.

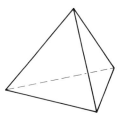

2. A pyramid with a circular base is called a *cone*.

EXERCISE 6i

1. A net of a square pyramid is shown in the diagram.

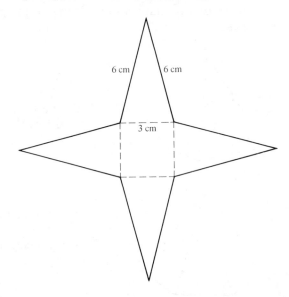

a) Draw this net accurately on thin card, using your compasses to construct the triangles which are all of the same size.

b) Cut out the net and fold it to form the pyramid.

2. How many faces has the square pyramid ?

3. How many vertices has the square pyramid ?

4. How many edges has the square pyramid ?

5. How many of its faces are triangular ?

6. Draw a suitable net for a tetrahedron whose faces are all equilateral triangles of side 5 cm.

7. a) Cut out a piece of thin card in the shape of a rectangle 9 cm by 7 cm.

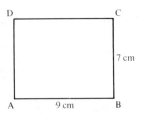

If the card is curved round until AD and BC can be stuck together, what object is formed ?

b) Cut out the shape given below from thin card and fold the circle so that it is perpendicular to the rectangle. Curve the rectangle until AD and BC can be stuck together. Then stick the point E of the circle to the join of A and B.

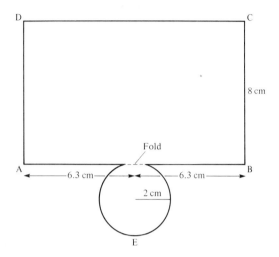

You have made a hollow cylinder with a base.

What net could be used to make a closed cylinder with a base and a top ?

8. On a piece of thin card, draw a circle of radius 6 cm and mark its centre O.

From O draw two radii OA and OB so that $A\widehat{O}B = 90°$. Cut out the quarter circle AOB and then curve the rest of the card until A meets B. Stick the two straight edges (OA and OB) together with Sellotape.

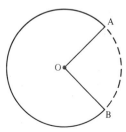

What is the name of the object you have made ?

MIXED EXERCISES ════════════════════════════════

EXERCISE 6j

    1. Draw a net for each of the following objects.

      a)    b)

      c)    d)

         (No top or bottom)   (With a top and bottom)

    2. Name the objects that can be made from each of the following nets.

      a)    b)

      c)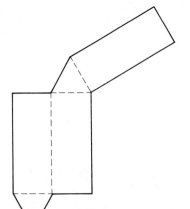

                               d)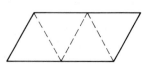

                               e)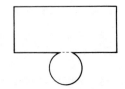

3. Which of the following four nets will form a tetrahedron ? (More than one net will.)

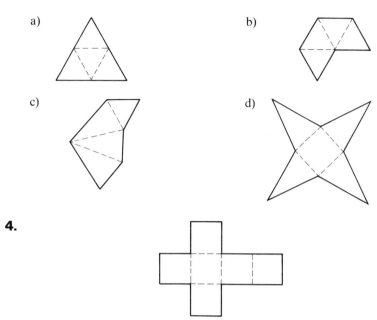

a)   b)

c)   d)

4.

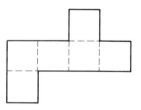

The net shown above can be made into a cube. There are other possible arrangements of the six squares which also given nets of a cube, such as

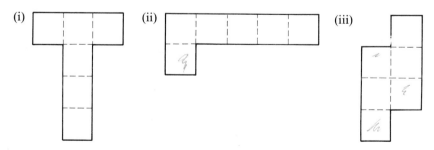

a) Which of the following shapes can be used as a net to make a cube ?

(i)   (ii)   (iii)

b) Draw other arrangements of six squares and find as many as possible that can be made into cubes.

5. Name this solid and sketch a net, marking the length of each edge.

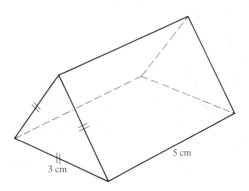

6.

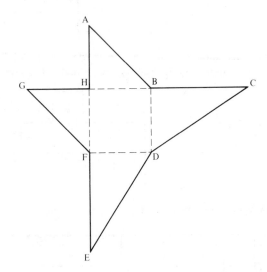

The diagram shows the net of a solid.

a) Which points will come together when the solid is made ?

b) What is the name of the solid ?

c) How many   (i) vertices   (ii) edges,   does it have ?

EXERCISE 6k

1. A circle has a radius of 14 cm. Find

   a) its circumference   b) its area

2. What is the volume of
   a) a cuboid which is 61 cm by 40 cm by 1.2 m
   b) a cylinder of radius 6.4 cm and length 11 cm
   c) a prism whose cross-sectional area is 45.3 cm² and whose length is 0.67 m ?

3. Name the object that can be made from each of the following nets.

   a) 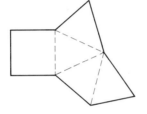   b)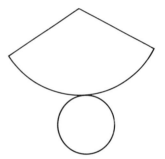

4. How many a) edges b) vertices c) faces, has a square pyramid ?

5.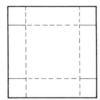

   A square piece of card of side 10 cm is cut along the plain lines and folded along the dotted lines. The cuts and folds are 2 cm from the edges of the card.
   If the card is folded and stuck together to form an open box, find

   a) the measurements of the box

   b) the capacity of the box

   c) the area where the card is double thickness.

6. a) This solid consists of one cuboid on top of another. How many small cubes are used to make it ?

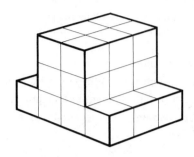

b) This solid consists of a cube with three holes cut right through it from one face to the other. How many small cubes are used to make it ?

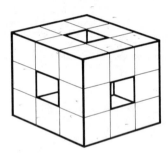

c) Why is it not possible to say how many cubes are used for this solid ?

What is the least number that could be used and what is the greatest number ?

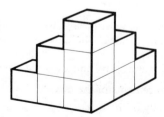

7. The shaded area in the diagram is a net of a solid. (The diagram is not drawn to scale.)

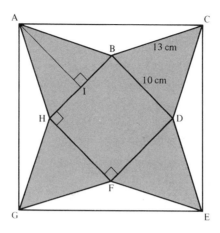

a) Name the solid.

b) Give the number of   (i) faces   (ii) edges   (iii) vertices, of the solid.

c) Use Pythagoras' theorem to find the length of AI. ($AH^2 = AI^2 + HI^2$)

d) Calculate the surface area of the solid (i.e. the area of the net).

EXERCISE 6I

1. The diameter of a circle is 11.2 cm. Find

a) its circumference   b) its area.

2. Find the volume of a cylinder with radius $10\frac{1}{2}$ cm and height 8 cm.

3. How many   a) vertices   b) edges   c) faces,   has a tetrahedron ?

4. The diagram shows a solid.

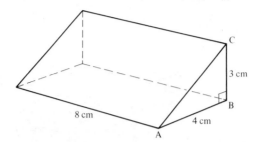

a) Name the solid.

b) Find the length of AC.

c) Find the volume of the solid.

d) Draw a suitable net.

e) Find the total surface area of the solid.

5. The net given below can be used to form the cylinder shown. (The diagrams are not to scale.)

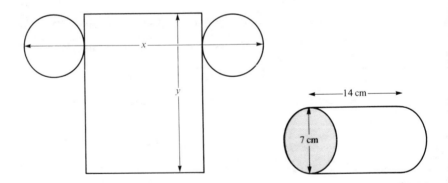

Calculate

a) the circumference of the shaded face

b) the area of the shaded face

c) the volume of the cylinder

d) the total surface area of the cylinder.

State the lengths marked x and y.

6.

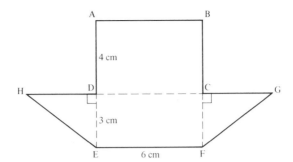

a) This drawing shows part of the net of a solid; one rectangular face EFIJ is missing. Sketch the net and add the missing face. Mark in the measurements of all the edges.

b) Points H and A come together. Name the third point which meets H and A.

c) Name three other points which come together.

d) Name the type of solid formed by this net.

e) Find the area of △ HDE.

f) Find the volume of the solid.

7. a) Which two of the following solids will fit together to form   (i) a cube   (ii) a cuboid ?   (There is more than one answer to (ii))

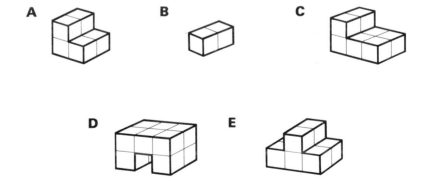

b) In each case state how many small cubes make up the cube or the cuboid.

c) Which three of the solids put together will form a cuboid ? (There is more than one answer to this question.)

EXERCISE 6m

In each question several alternative answers are given. Write down the letter that corresponds to the correct answer.

1. A triangular prism has

    A 9 edges   **B** 3 edges   **C** 6 edges   **D** 5 edges

2. A net of a square pyramid is

A
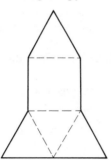

B
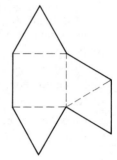

C
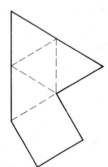

D
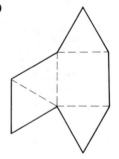

3. The number of faces of a hexagonal prism is

    A 6   **B** 12   **C** 8   **D** 9

4.

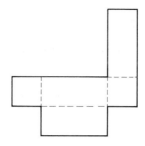

This net could be used to make

A a prism   **B** an open box

C a cuboid   **D** a cube

5. Taking $\pi \approx 3$, the circumference of a circle with diameter 6 cm is

   A 9 cm   **B** 27 cm   **C** 36 cm   **D** 18 cm

6. The height and radius of a cylinder are both 2 cm. In terms of π the volume of the cylinder is

   A $4\pi\,\text{cm}^2$ **B** $4\pi\,\text{cm}^3$ **C** $8\pi\,\text{cm}^3$ **D** $8\pi\,\text{cm}^2$

7. A circle has a radius of 9 cm. The expression 18π gives the value of its

   A Area   **B** Diameter

   C Circumference   **D** Net

7 SHAPE AND SPACE

COORDINATES IN THREE DIMENSIONS

Just as an ordered pair of coordinates is used to determine the position of a point in a plane, i.e. in two dimensions, so an ordered triple of coordinates is used to define the position of a point in space, i.e. in three dimensions (3-D for short). The coordinates give the distances, in order, from a fixed point O, along or parallel to three mutually perpendicular axes Ox, Oy and Oz. (Mutually perpendicular means that each axis is perpendicular to each of the other two.)

If we draw Ox and Oy as we did for two dimensions, then Oz comes 'out of the page'.

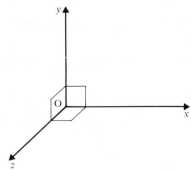

A point P is then located by giving its distances from O in the positive directions of these axes. These distances, given as an ordered triple, are called the *coordinates* of P.

For example, if P is the point $(4, 3, 2)$ then
the distance from O in the direction Ox is 4 units
the distance from O in the direction Oy is 3 units
the distance from O in the direction Oz is 2 units

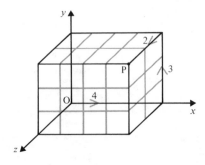

To find the position of P(4, 3, 2) we start at O, move 4 units along the x-axis, then 3 units up parallel to the y-axis, followed by 2 units parallel to the z-axis.

(You will find this much easier to follow if you build the model indicated on the opposite page using small cubes. You are strongly advised to do this!)

EXERCISE 7a

In this exercise the origin is at one vertex of the solid and the axes lie along three of its edges. Each axis is graduated in units.

Where you are asked to draw diagrams you will find it an advantage to use squared paper.

1. For each diagram write down the coordinates of A.

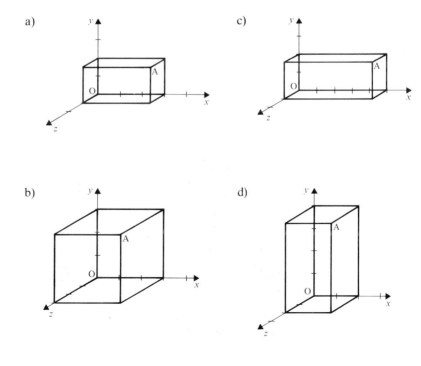

a)

c)

b)

d)

2. Draw diagrams, similar to those given in question 1 to show the position of A, when A has each of the following sets of coordinates

a) $(2, 2, 4)$ b) $(5, 3, 2)$ c) $(1, 3, 4)$ d) $(4, 4, 4)$.

3.

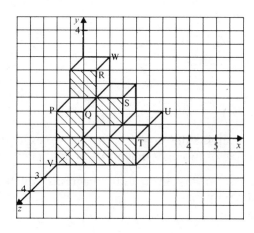

Each of the blocks in this diagram has an edge of one unit.
Write down the coordinates of the vertices P, Q, R, S, T, U, V and W.

4.

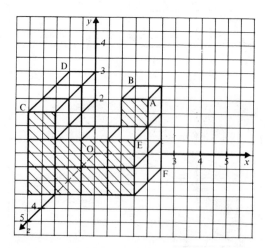

Each of the blocks in this diagram has an edge of one unit.
Write down the coordinates of the points marked A, B, C, D, E and F.

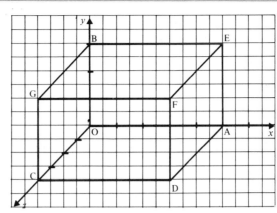

The diagram shows a cuboid where OA = 5 units, OB = 3 units and OC = 4 units. Find the coordinates of a) E   b) D   c) F.

a) To get to E, start at O and move 5 units in the direction Ox followed by 3 units in the direction Oy. We have not moved in the direction Oz.
   The coordinates of E are (5, 3, 0).

b) For D we move   5 units in the direction Ox
                        no units in the direction Oy
                        4 units in the direction Oz. .
   D is the point (5, 0, 4).

c) Similarly F is the point (5, 3, 4).

5. The diagram shows a cube of edge 3 units.

Find

a) the coordinates of all eight vertices

b) the coordinates of the midpoints of the edges
   (i) BC   (iii) DC
   (ii) BF   (iv) AD

c) the coordinates of the points of intersection of the diagonals of the square
   (i) ABFE   (iii) ABCD.
   (ii) BCGF

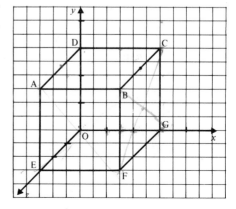

6. In this question the units are centimetres.

A, B and C are the points (6, 0, 0), (6, 4, 0) and (6, 4, 8) respectively.

a) Draw a diagram showing clearly the points A, B and C.

b) How far does a spider walk if it goes from A to C via B ?

7.

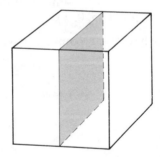

The diagram shows a cuboid labelled A to H. The coordinates of B are (3, 4, 0) and the coordinates of D are (−5, 4, 2).

a) Write down the coordinates of of the other vertices.

b) Write down the coordinates of the midpoint of
(i) AB   (ii) CD.

SECTIONS

Imagine cutting straight through the middle of a cube as shown in the diagram.

The cut face, which is shaded, is called a *section* of the cube. In this case the section is a square.

When we wish to make a straight cut through a solid, we say that the solid is *cut by a plane,* i.e. the section is flat.

EXERCISE 7b

1. A sphere of radius 2 cm is cut by a plane passing through the centre. Draw the section.

2. A cylinder is cut by a plane as shown in the diagram. Draw the section.

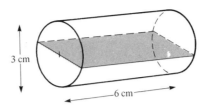

3 cm

6 cm

3.

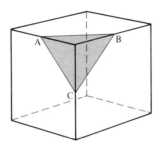

A, B and C are the midpoints of three edges of a cube. The corner of the cube is cut off by the plane through A, B and C.

a) What type of triangle is △ABC ?

b) What is the name of the piece cut off ?

4.

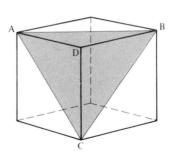

The cube is cut into two pieces by the plane through A, B and C.

a) Describe △ABC.

b) Describe the solid ABCD.

c) How many (i) vertices   (ii) edges   (iii) faces,   has the solid that remains when ABCD is removed ?

d) In how many different ways could a single plane cut through the original cube to give solids that are identical to the solid ABCD ?

5.

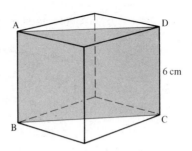

The cube is cut into two pieces by the plane through A, B, C and D.

a) Sketch ABCD, marking in any lengths and angles that you know. Is AB equal to AD ?

b) What type of quadrilateral is ABCD ?

6. Which of the cuts in questions 3 to 5 divides the cube exactly in half ?

7.

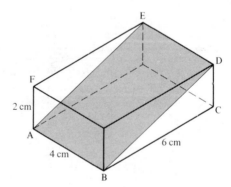

a) Sketch the quadrilateral ABDE. What type of quadrilateral is it ?

b) Arrange BD, BC, CD and BE in order of size, starting with the smallest.

c) Sketch the quadrilateral BFEC. Is it the same shape and size as ABDE ?

8.

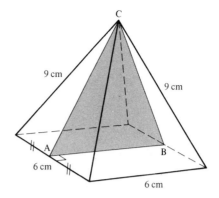

A symmetrical square pyramid is cut into two pieces by a plane through A, B and C.

a) Sketch △ABC. What type of triangle is it ?

b) Is AC of length 9 cm or is it shorter or longer than 9 cm ?

9.

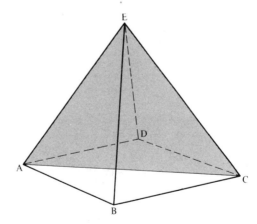

A symmetrical square pyramid is cut into two pieces by a plane through A, C and E.

a) Sketch △ACE. What type of triangle is it ?

b) Is AC longer or shorter than AB, or is it equal to AB ?

10.

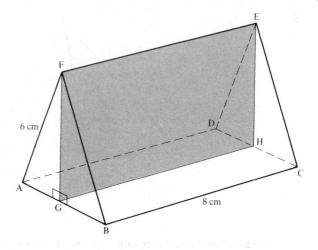

In the triangular prism above, the cross-section is an isosceles triangle. AF = FB and AB = 4 cm. The prism is cut into two pieces by a plane through E, F, G and H.

a) Sketch EFGH. What type of quadrilateral is it ?

b) Is FG shorter or longer than FB, or is it equal to FB ?

11.

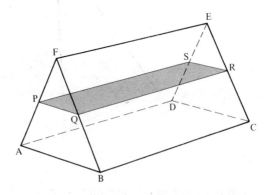

In the same prism as in question 10, P, Q, R and S are the midpoints of AF, FB, EC and ED. The prism is cut into two pieces by a plane through P, Q, R and S. Sketch PQRS. What type of quadrilateral is it ?

12.

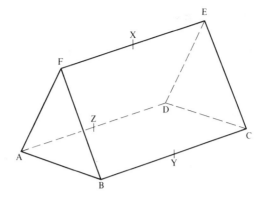

In the same prism as in question 10, X, Y and Z are the midpoints of FE, BC and AD. The prism is cut into two pieces by a plane through X, Y and Z.

a) Sketch the section and mark the lengths of the sides.

b) How does the section compare in shape with triangle ABF ?

13. Draw the shape of the section given by slicing down through the middle of each of the following solids.

a)   b)   c)

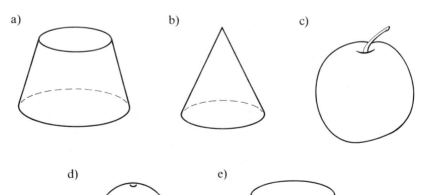

d)   e)

PLANES OF SYMMETRY

Imagine that a solid is cut into two pieces by a plane.

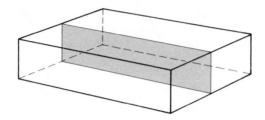

Now take one of the pieces and put the cut face against a mirror.

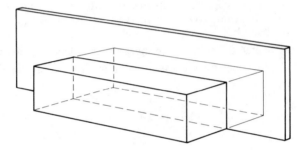

Does the piece, together with its reflection, look like the complete solid ?

If it does, as happens in this case, then the cut has been made in a *plane of symmetry.*

Not all planes which cut a solid in half are planes of symmetry. The cuboid below has *not* been cut in a plane of symmetry. If *one* half is placed against a mirror we do not see a cuboid.

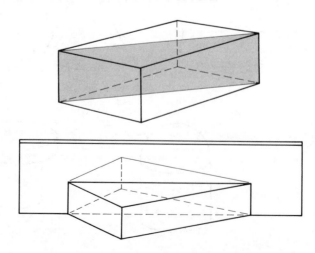

EXERCISE 7c

In each question state whether or not the shaded section is in a plane of symmetry of the object.

1.

5.

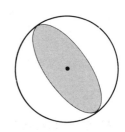

2.

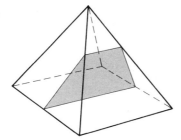

6.

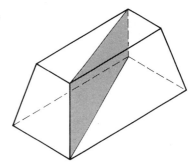

3.

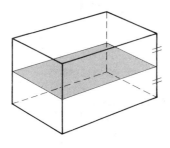

7.

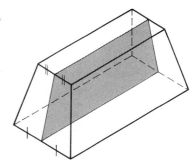

4.

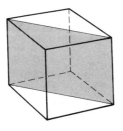

8.

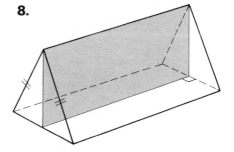

9. 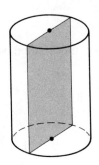   **10.**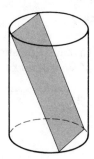

NUMBER OF PLANES OF SYMMETRY

Some objects have no planes of symmetry,

e.g.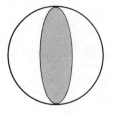

Some objects have one plane of symmetry,

e.g.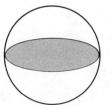

Some objects have more than one plane of symmetry,

e.g.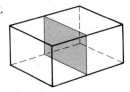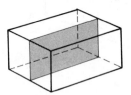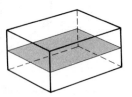

Some objects have an infinite number of planes of symmetry,

e.g. 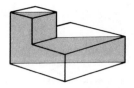 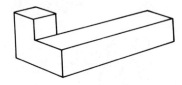   and so on.

EXERCISE 7d

In each question give the number of planes of symmetry of the object.

1.

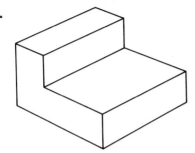

4.

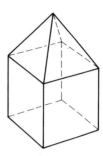

2.

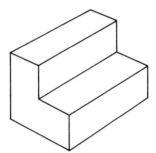

5.

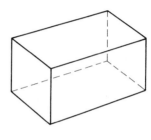

3.

6.

THREE DIMENSIONAL PROBLEMS

When dealing with solids like cuboids we often need to consider a section of the solid and use a convenient triangle within that section. Remember always to make a separate drawing of the triangle you are using.

EXERCISE 7e

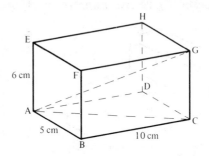

In the cuboid, EA = 6 cm, AB = 5 cm and BC = 10 cm. Find AG.

AG is in the section through AEGC

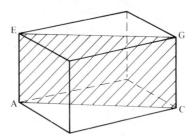

(To find AG, we use triangle AGC so we need to calculate AC^2 first. This can be found from $\triangle ABC$.)

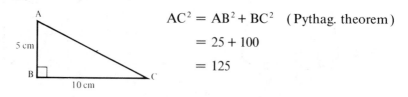

$$AC^2 = AB^2 + BC^2 \quad (\text{Pythag. theorem})$$
$$= 25 + 100$$
$$= 125$$

$$AG^2 = AC^2 + GC^2 \quad (\text{Pythag. theorem})$$
$$= 125 + 36$$
$$= 161$$
$$AG = \sqrt{161}$$
$$= 12.7 \text{ cm} \quad (\text{to 3 s.f.})$$

Questions 1 to 9 refer to the cuboid given below.

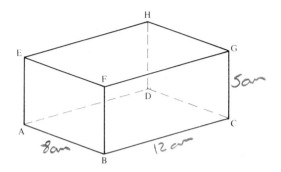

1. Name lengths equal in length to   a) AD   b) FC   c) FH

2. Which of these angles are right angles ?

a) $A\widehat{D}C$ b) $B\widehat{F}D$ c) $E\widehat{F}G$ d) $E\widehat{D}C$

3. Which of the following triangles are right angled triangles ?

a) $\triangle EAF$ b) $\triangle DCB$ c) $\triangle BFD$

4. Name three right-angled triangles in which one side is HD. In each case state which angle is the right angle.

5. In the cuboid above. AB = 8 cm, BC = 12 cm and CG = 5 cm.
Find   a) AC   b) EC

6. In the cuboid above, EF = 3 cm, EA = 2 cm and AD = 6 cm.
Find   a) EB   b) EG

7. In the cuboid above, HG = 6 cm, GC = 8 cm and BC = 12 cm.
Find   a) HC   b) HB

8. In the cuboid above, AD = 11 cm, AB = 10 cm and EA = 12 cm.
Find   a) AC   b) EC   c) BH

9. In the cuboid above, BC = 20 cm, CG = 8 cm and DC = 12 cm.
Find EC.

10.

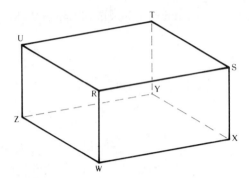

In the cuboid above, RS = 12 cm, SX = 7 cm and XY = 9 cm.
Find   a) WY   b) WT

11.   A, B and C are the points (3, 0, 0), (3, 4, 0) and (3, 4, 12) respectively.

a) Draw a diagram showing clearly the points A, B and C.

b) How far is it from O to C via A and B ?

c) How far is it directly from
   (i) O to B   (ii) O to C ?

12.   P, Q and R are the points (3, 0, 0), (3, 3, 0) and (3, 3, 3) respectively.

a) Draw a diagram showing clearly the points P, Q and R.

b) How far is it from O to R via P and Q ?

c) What is the direct distance from
   (i) O to Q   (ii) O to R ?

MIXED EXERCISES

EXERCISE 7f

1.   How many   a) edges   b) vertices   c) faces
does a square pyramid have ?

2.

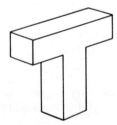

a) How many planes of symmetry has this solid ?

b) How many faces has this solid ?

3.

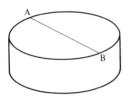

The cylinder above is cut in half vertically through AB. Sketch the shape of the cut face.

4.

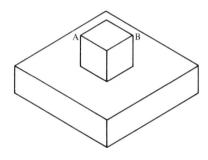

a) How many planes of symmetry has this solid ?

b) Sketch the section given by a vertical cut through A and B.

5. How many planes of symmetry does a cylinder have ?

6. In this question the origin is at one vertex of the cuboid and the axes lie along three of its edges. Each axis is graduated in units.

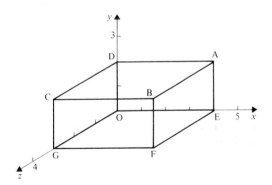

Write down the coordinates of   a) A   b) F   c) B

7. Use the diagram given for question 6 to answer this question.

a) Name lengths equal in length to   (i) OE   (ii) EF

b) Which of these angles are right angles ?

   (i) CD̂O   (ii) GÔD   (iii) CÂE   (iv) FB̂A

c) Find the length of   (i) OE   (ii) FE   (iii) OF   (iv) BF   (v) OB.

EXERCISE 7g

In each question several alternative answers are given. Write down the letter that corresponds to the correct answer.

1. The number of planes of symmetry of a cuboid is

   A 3   **B** 1   **C** 9   **D** 6

2.

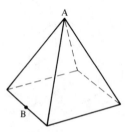

When the square pyramid is cut by a vertical plane through A and B, the section is

   A a trapezium   **B** a square   **C** a triangle   **D** a rectangle

3.

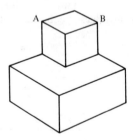

The object is cut by a vertical plane through A and B. The shape of the section thus made is

   A   **B**   **C**   **D**

  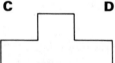

4. The number of planes of symmetry of a square pyramid is

   A 4   **B** 8   **C** 2   **D** 1

5.

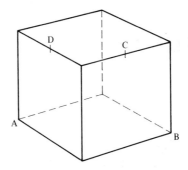

The solid shown above is a cube. C and D are the midpoints of two of its edges. Quadrilateral ABCD is a

A square   **B** rectangle   **C** trapezium   **D** parallelogram

6. In the cube shown in question 5, the length of an edge is 6 cm.
The length of DC is

A 3 cm   **B** 6 cm   **C** 4.24 cm   **D** 18 cm

7. D, E and F are respectively the points (2, 0, 0), (2, 6, 0) and (2, 6, 2).
The direct distance from O to F is

A 6 units   **B** 14 units   **C** 6.32 units   **D** 6.63 units

8 FORMULAE

A FORMULA

A formula is a set of instructions in algebraic form for calculating the value of a quantity.

Suppose, for example, that we wish to work out the perimeter of this rectangle.

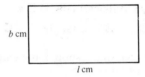

b cm

l cm

The instruction is 'Add two lengths and two widths'. Writing this in algebraic form we can say that the perimeter, *P* cm, is given by the formula

$$P = 2l + 2b$$

P is the *subject* of the formula.

Notice that there are no units in the formula.

SUBSTITUTING VALUES

The first exercise revises the use of a formula to work out values.

EXERCISE 8a

If $C = a + 2b$, calculate C when $a = 6$ and $b = 4.5$.

$$a = 6 \qquad b = 4.5$$
$$C = a + 2b$$
$$= 6 + 2 \times 4.5$$
$$= 6 + 9$$
$$= 15$$

1. If $p = q + r$, find p when $q = 7$ and $r = 15$

2. If $x = 3y + z$, find x when

  a) $y = 6$ and $z = 7$ b) $y = 9$ and $z = 21$

3. If $a = b - c$, find a when

  a) $b = 27$ and $c = 16$ b) $b = 9$ and $c = 23$

4. If $d = ef$, find d when

  a) $e = 31$ and $f = 7$ b) $e = 3.2$ and $f = 7.8$

5. If $t = \dfrac{u}{v}$, find t when

  a) $u = 36$ and $v = 9$ b) $u = 4.8$ and $v = 0.8$

6. If $m = \frac{1}{2}(p + n)$, find m when

  a) $p = 12$ and $n = 4$ b) $p = 2.5$ and $n = 3.7$

The volume of a pyramid is $V\,\text{cm}^3$, the area of the base is $A\,\text{cm}^2$ and its height is $h\,\text{cm}$.

V is given by the formula $V = \frac{1}{3}Ah$.

Find the volume when the area of the base is $8.4\,\text{cm}^2$ and the height is $6\,\text{cm}$.

$$A = 8.4 \qquad h = 6$$

$$V = \tfrac{1}{3}Ah$$

$$= \tfrac{1}{\cancel{3}} \times 8.4 \times \cancel{6}^{2}$$

$$= 16.8$$

$\therefore$ the volume is $16.8\,\text{cm}^3$

---

7. The cost, £C, of hiring a coach is given by the formula $C = 35 + 2d$ where d is the distance travelled in kilometres.
A coach is hired for a trip of $100\,\text{km}$.

  a) Give the value of d.

  b) Find the cost of hiring the coach.

8. The cost, C pence, of buying x daffodil bulbs and y snowdrop corms is given by the formula $C = 20x + 10y$.

7 daffodil bulbs and 3 snowdrop corms are bought.

a) Give the values of x and y.

b) Find the total cost of the bulbs and corms.

9. Mr and Mrs Brown are going on a picnic taking n children with them. The number of sandwiches they make is S, where S is given by the formula $S = 2 + 3n$.
Find the number of sandwiches to be made if they take with them

a) 2 children   b) 8 children.

10. A quarterly electricity bill for x units is C pence where C is given by the formula $C = 1000 + 7x$.
Find the bill if the number of units used is   a) 400   b) 750.

11. The sum, S, of three consecutive whole numbers (such as 8, 9 and 10) is given by $S = 3n + 3$ where n is the first of the three whole numbers. Find the sum of three consecutive whole numbers when the first is

a) 6   b) 77.

12. The simple interest, £I, when £P is invested for T years at R% per year is given by the formula $I = \dfrac{PTR}{100}$.
Find the interest when

a) £60 is invested for 5 years at 8%

b) £2400 is invested for $4\frac{1}{2}$ years at 10%.

In questions 13 to 15 several alternative answers are given. Write down the letter that corresponds to the correct answer.

13. If $g = \frac{1}{4}(h + k)$, $h = 8$ and $k = 12$, then the value of g is

A   80   **B**   11   **C**   14   **D**   5

14. If $t = p - 3q$, $p = 9$ and $q = 4$, then the value of t is

A   3   **B**   −3   **C**   −24   **D**   24

15. The area, A cm², of a triangle of base b cm and height h cm is given by the formula $A = \frac{1}{2}bh$. The area of a triangle of base 8 cm and height 6 cm is

A   48 cm²   **B**   24 cm   **C**   24 cm²   **D**   12 cm²

DIRECTED NUMBERS

Remember the rules for dealing with directed numbers

> subtracting a negative number has the
> same effect as adding a positive number

e.g.
$$+3 + (-4) = +3 - 4 = -1$$

but
$$5 - (-6) = 5 + 6 = 11$$

> when multiplying or dividing,
> like signs give a positive answer
> unlike signs give a negative answer

e.g.
$$(-3)^2 = (-3) \times (-3)$$
$$= 9$$

$$12 \div (-3) = 12 \times (-\tfrac{1}{3})$$
$$= -4$$

and
$$(-4) \div (+2) = -4 \times \tfrac{1}{2}$$
$$= -2$$

EXERCISE 8b

Find

1. $-3 + (-4)$

2. $2 - (-5)$

3. $-1 - (+2)$

4. $-4 - (-6)$

5. $3 - (-3)$

6. $(-3) \times (-6)$

7. $(+6) \div (-2)$

8. $(+9) \div (-3)$

9. $(-12) \div (-6)$

10. $(-4) \times 3$

11. $(-6)^2$

12. $-5 + 2 - 7 + 8$

13. $7 \times (-2)$

14. $(-14) \div (-7)$

15. $-4 + 3 - (-1)$

16. $3 - (-4) + 2$

17. $(-5) \times 7$

18. $3 - (-12) \div 3$

19. $(-3) \times (-1)^2$

20. $(-2)^2 + (-3)^2$

USING NEGATIVE NUMBERS

EXERCISE 8c

If $c = a - b$, find c if $a = -2$ and $b = -4$

$$a = -2 \qquad b = -4$$
$$c = a - b$$
$$= (-2) - (-4)$$
$$= -2 + 4$$
$$= 2$$

1. If $a = b + c$, find a if $b = -4$ and $c = -2$

2. If $a = 2b + c$, find a if $b = -3$ and $c = -4$

3. If $x = y - z$, find x if $y = -4$ and $z = -1$

4. If $s = t - u$, find s if $t = -2$ and $u = 4$

5. If $p = 2q + r$, find p if $q = 4$ and $r = -1$

6. If $a = b - 3c$, find a if $b = -6$ and $c = 2$

7. If $x = 3y - 2z$, find x if $y = -2$ and $z = 3$

If $a = bc + 6$, find a if $b = -2$ and $c = -3$

$$b = -2 \qquad c = -3$$
$$a = bc + 6$$
$$= (-2) \times (-3) + 6$$
$$= 6 + 6$$
$$= 12$$

8. If $x = yz$, find x if $y = 2$ and $z = -4$

9. If $p = qr + 2$, find p if $q = -3$ and $r = 5$

10. If $a = 3 + bc$, find a if $b = 7$ and $c = -2$

11. If $y = xz$, find y if $x = -7$ and $z = -8$

12. If $d = ef + g$, find d if $e = -3, f = 4$ and $g = -2$

MAKING A FORMULA

When you are asked to make a formula, it often helps to consider first an example with numbers in. Then the same process can be applied to letters.

In the next exercise the first part of each question gives a numerical example which will show how to make the formula.

EXERCISE 8d

When making tea, the number of spoonfuls of tea, N, is given by 'one for each person and one for the pot'.

a) How many spoonfuls are needed for 6 people ?

b) Make a formula for N if there are x people having tea.

a) Number of spoonfuls $= 6 + 1$

$$= 7$$

b) Number of spoonfuls $= x + 1$

So the formula is $\quad N = x + 1$.

---

1. Sally is 4 years older than John.

a) How old is Sally when John is 9 years old ?

b) Make a formula for Sally's age, y years, when John is x years old.

2. The cost of a bus fare between the bus station and the school is 40 p.

a) What is the total cost for 6 people making this journey ?

b) Make a formula for the total cost, Cp, for n people.

3. A car is travelling at a steady 50 m.p.h.

a) How far does it travel in 3 hours ?

b) Make a formula for the distance, d miles, travelled in t hours.

4. I think of a number, double it and add 3.

    a) If the number I think of is 6, what is the result ?

    b) If the number I think of is x, give a formula for the result R.

5. Paper is given out to a class. One sheet is given to each pupil and the remaining 5 sheets are put on the teacher's desk.

    a) Find the total number of sheets of paper if there are 20 pupils.

    b) Make a formula for N, the total number of sheets, if there are x pupils.

    c) On another occasion, two sheets are given to each pupil but there are no sheets left over. If there are x pupils, make a formula for M, the total number of sheets of paper.

6. A box of chocolates is handed round a group of friends and each person takes three chocolates. There is one left over and this is given to the dog.

    a) If there are 6 people, how many chocolates were there in the box ?

    b) Make a formula for N, the number of chocolates in the box, if there are p people.

7. a) Find the perimeter of a triangle with sides of length 4 cm, 5 cm and 6 cm.

    b) Give a formula for p, where p cm is the perimeter if the sides are of length a cm, b cm and c cm.

In questions 8 to 12, several alternative answers are given. Write down the letter that corresponds to the correct answer.

8. The next even number m after the even number n is given by the formula

    A $m = 2n$ **B** $m = n - 2$ **C** $m = n + 2$ **D** $2m = n$

9. In a triangle, one angle is $90°$ and another is $x°$. The size, $y°$, of the third angle is given by

    A $x = 90 - y$ **B** $y = 90 - x$ **C** $y = 90 + x$ **D** $y = 180 - x$

10. I think of a number, x, double it and subtract 5. The result is y. The formula for y is

    A $y = \dfrac{2x}{5}$ **B** $x = 2y - 5$ **C** $y = x + 2 - 5$ **D** $y = 2x - 5$

11. I think of a number, x, add 2 to it, and double the result.
If the result is y, the formula for y is

    A $y = x + 4$ **B** $y = 2x + 2$ **C** $y = 4x$ **D** $y = 2x + 4$

12. In a triangle the angles are $y°$, $2x°$ $3x°$.
The formula for y is

    A $y = 5x$ **B** $y = 180 + 5x$ **C** $y = 180 - 5x$ **D** $y = 5x - 180$

FINDING A QUANTITY OTHER THAN THE SUBJECT

Reminder Sometimes when a formula is given you are not asked to find the subject, but to find one of the other letters.

Put the given numbers into the formula in their correct positions. This gives an equation to be solved.

EXERCISE 8e

If $x = y - 2z$, find z when $x = 24$ and $y = 28$

$$x = 24 \qquad y = 28$$
$$x = y - 2z$$
$$24 = 28 - 2z$$

Add $2z$ to each side $\qquad 2z + 24 = 28$

Take 24 from each side $\qquad 2z = 4$

Divide both sides by 2 $\qquad z = 2$

---

1. If $a = b + c$, find b when $a = 23$ and $c = 11$

2. If $h = g - i$, find g when $h = 12$ and $i = 4$

3. If $p = q - r$, find r when $p = 11$ and $q = 20$

4. If $t = 4rs$, find s when $t = 24$ and $r = -2$

5. If $y = \dfrac{x}{z}$, find x when $z = 4$ and $y = 3$

6. If $l = m + 6n$, find n when $l = 15$ and $m = 3$

7. If $t = u - 3v$, find v when $t = 12$ and $u = 18$

8. If $x = y - z$, find z when $x = -16$ and $y = 4$

9. If $p = 6q + r$, find r when $p = 33$ and $q = 4$

10. If $a = \dfrac{b}{c}$, find b when $a = 11$ and $c = 2$

11. If $l = 2mn$, find m when $l = 24$ and $n = 3$

12. If $t = 3u + v$, find u when $t = 10$ and $v = -4$

In questions 13 to 17, several alternative answers are given. Write down the letter that corresponds to the correct answer.

13. If $p = q - r$, $p = 9$ and $r = 6$ then the value of q is

    A 3   **B** 15   **C** -3 **D** -15

14. If $d = ef$, $d = 18$ and $f = 3$ then the value of e is

    A 21   **B** 54   **C** 15   **D** 6

15. If $x = 6yz$, $y = 4$ and $x = 120$ then the value of z is

    A 5   **B** 12   **C** 110   **D** 2880

16. If $d = e + 4f$, $d = 20$ and $e = 6$ then the value of f is

    A 10   **B** $3\frac{1}{2}$ **C** 2   **D** 56

17. If $j = \dfrac{k}{l}$, $l = 3$ and $j = 12$ then the value of k is

    A 4   **B** 36   **C** 15   **D** $\frac{1}{4}$

CHANGING THE SUBJECT OF A FORMULA

The formula for finding the VAT due, $£T$, on a bill is given by

$$T = \frac{Br}{100}$$

where $£B$ is the total bill excluding VAT and $r\%$ is the rate at which VAT is added.
This is a formula for finding T, so T is called the *subject of the formula.*

Suppose we want a formula in order to find the value of B; this means that we want a formula in the form $B = ...$
i.e. a formula in which B is the subject.

We can do this by thinking of $T = \dfrac{Br}{100}$ as an equation to solve for values of B,

i.e. $$T = \frac{Br}{100}$$

Multiply both sides by 100 $$100T = Br$$

Divide both sides by r $$\frac{100T}{r} = B$$

i.e. $$B = \frac{100T}{r}$$

This process is called *changing the subject of a formula.*

Since changing the subject of a formula involves 'solving' the formula for the required letter, the methods used for solving linear equations apply, i.e. remove the fractions and brackets; collect the terms containing the required letter on one side; collect all other terms on the other side; divide both sides by the number (or bracket) in front of the required letter.

ONE OPERATION

We treat the original formula as an ordinary equation and solve it in the usual way.

EXERCISE 8f

Make x the subject of the formula $y = x + z$

$$y = x + z$$

Take z from each side $\quad y - z = x$

i.e. $\quad\quad\quad\quad\quad\quad\quad\quad x = y - z$

1. Make q the subject of the formula $p = q + r$

2. Make h the subject of the formula $g = 7 + h$

3. Make B the subject of the formula $A = B + 3C$

4. Make b the subject of the formula $y = 2a + b$

Make x the subject of the formula $y = x - z$

$$y = x - z$$

Add z to each side $\quad y + z = x$

i.e. $\quad\quad\quad\quad\quad\quad\quad\quad x = y + z$

5. Make m the subject of the formula $l = m - 4$

6. Make q the subject of the formula $p = q - r$

7. Make z the subject of the formula $x = z - 5y$

8. Make b the subject of the formula $a = b - cd$

Make b the subject of the formula $A = lb$

$$A = lb$$

Divide both sides by l $\dfrac{A}{l} = b$

i.e. $b = \dfrac{A}{l}$

---

9. Make m the subject of the formula $F = ma$

10. Make q the subject of the formula $p = 8q$

11. Make x the subject of the formula $y^2 = 4ax$

12. Make r the subject of the formula $C = 2\pi r$

Make Y the subject of the formula $X = \dfrac{Y}{7}$

$$X = \dfrac{Y}{7}$$

Multiply both sides by 7 $7 \times X = {}^{1}\!\!\not{7} \times \dfrac{Y}{\not{7}_{1}}$

$$7X = Y$$

i.e. $Y = 7X$

---

13. Make n the subject of the formula $m = \dfrac{n}{6}$

14. Make z the subject of the formula $y = \dfrac{z}{5}$

15. Make q the subject of the formula $P = \dfrac{q}{r}$

16. Make F the subject of the formula $N = \dfrac{F}{u}$

In each question from 17 to 25, make the letter in the bracket the subject of the formula.

17. $D = ST$ (T) **20.** $E = Ri^2$ (R) **23.** $y = x - 5$ (x)

18. $y = mx + c$ (c) **21.** $y = mx$ (x) **24.** $C = 2\pi r$ (π)

19. $p = a + b + c$ (a) **22.** $A = bh$ (h) **25.** $A = \pi r^2$ (π)

In questions 26 to 30, several alternative answers are given. Write down the letter that corresponds to the correct answer.

26. If $V = u + v$, the formula with u as the subject is

A $u = v + V$ **B** $u = v - V$ **C** $u = V - v$ **D** $u = \dfrac{V}{v}$

27. If $s = \dfrac{d}{t}$, the formula with d as the subject is

A $d = st$ **B** $d = \dfrac{s}{t}$ **C** $d = s - t$ **D** $d = s + t$

28. If $p = q - r$, the formula with q as the subject is

A $q = p - r$ **B** $q = \dfrac{p}{r}$ **C** $q = r - p$ **D** $q = p + r$

29. If $A = \pi r l$, the formula with l as the subject is

A $l = A - \pi r$ **B** $l = \dfrac{A}{\pi} - r$ **C** $l = \pi r A$ **D** $l = \dfrac{A}{\pi r}$

30. If $V = abc$, the formula with c as the subject is

A $c = V - ab$ **B** $c = \dfrac{V}{ab}$ **C** $c = V - a - b$ **D** $c = \dfrac{ab}{V}$

MIXED QUESTIONS

EXERCISE 8g

1. If $C = 2x + y$

    a) find C when $x = 5$ and $y = 9$

    b) find C when $x = 1.7$ and $y = 9.8$

    c) find y when $C = 12$ and $x = 4$

    d) make y the subject of the formula

    e) use the formula found in (d) to find y when $C = 15$ and $x = 3$

2. If $Q = 2a + b$

    a) find Q when $a = 3.5$ and $b = 6$

    b) find b when $Q = 25$ and $a = 9$

    c) find a when $Q = 13$ and $b = -5$

    d) make b the subject of the formula

    e) use the formula found in (d) to find b when $Q = 25$ and $a = 9$. Does your answer agree with the answer to (b) ?

    f) make a the subject of the formula.

    g) suggest a way of using the answer to (c) to check that your answer to (f) is correct.

3. If $2s = a + b + c$,

    a) find s when $a = 6$, $b = 7$ and $c = 8$

    b) find s when $a = 2.4$, $b = 3.6$ and $c = 4.8$

    c) find c when $s = 16$, $a = 11$ and $b = 12$

    d) make a the subject of the formula

    e) use the formula found in (d) to find a when $s = 12$, $b = 9$ and $c = 10$.

TWO OR MORE OPERATIONS

Sometimes more than one step is needed to change the subject of the formula.

In particular, suppose that the formula is $y = a - b$ and that we wish to make b the subject. We do not want b to be negative in the new formula so we need to add b to each side

i.e. $$y + b = a$$

We can then proceed as before and take y from each side

$$b = a - y$$

EXERCISE 8h

Make z the subject of the formula $x = 7 - z$

$$x = 7 - z$$

Add z to each side $x + z = 7$

Take x from each side $z = 7 - x$

1. Make a the subject of the formula $c = 9 - a$

2. Make x the subject of the formula $s = 4 - x$

3. Make P the subject of the formula $Q = 100 - P$

4. Make k the subject of the formula $h = m - k$

Make b the subject of the formula $a = 4b + c$

$$a = 4b + c$$

Take c from each side $\qquad a - c = 4b$

Divide both sides by 4 $\qquad \dfrac{a - c}{4} = b$

i.e. $\qquad\qquad\qquad\qquad b = \dfrac{a - c}{4}$

Note that this could be written $b = \frac{1}{4}(a - c)$

---

5. Make x the subject of the formula $y = 2x + z$

6. Make a the subject of the formula $c = 2a - b$

7. Make b the subject of the formula $P = 2l + 2b$

8. If $x = 5a + 3b$, give b in terms of x and a.

In each question from 9 to 16, make the letter in the bracket the subject of the formula.

9. $y = mx + c$ (x)

10. $P = 2a + 2b$ (a)

11. $a = 3b - c$ (c)

12. $x - y + 4 = 0$ (x)

13. $a = 3b - c$ (b)

14. $x - y + 4 = 0$ (y)

15. $P = 2a + 2b$ (b)

16. $y = mh - k$ (k)

In questions 17 to 20, several alternative answers are given. Write down the letter that corresponds to the correct answer.

17. If $y = 2x + 3$, the formula with x as the subject is

A $x = \frac{1}{2}(y - 3)$ **B** $x = 2y + 3$ **C** $x = 2y - 3$ **D** $x = \frac{1}{2}y - 3$

18. If $p = q - r$, the formula with r as the subject is

    A $r = p + q$ **B** $r = p - q$ **C** $r = q - p$ **D** $r = \frac{q}{p}$

19. If $x = 3z - y$, the formula with z as the subject is

    A $z = 3(x + y)$ **B** $z = \frac{1}{3}(x - y)$ **C** $z = \frac{1}{3}x + y$ **D** $z = \frac{1}{3}(x + y)$

20. If $a = 4b - c$, the formula with c as the subject is

    A $c = a - 4b$ **B** $c = \frac{4b}{a}$ **C** $c = 4b - a$ **D** $c = 4ab$

FORMULAE CONTAINING FRACTIONS

The first step is to get rid of fractions by multiplying both sides by a suitable number.

EXERCISE 8i

Make q the subject of the formula $p = \frac{qr}{6}$

$$p = \frac{qr}{6}$$

Multiply both sides by 6 $6 \times p = \cancel{6} \times \frac{qr}{\cancel{6}}$

$$6p = qr$$

Divide both sides by r $\frac{6p}{r} = q$

i.e. $q = \frac{6p}{r}$

1. Make a the subject of the formula $C = \frac{a}{4}$.

2. If $x = \frac{y}{3}$, write y in terms of x.

3. If $p = \frac{4}{r}$, make r the subject of the formula.

4. Make z the subject of the formula $w = \dfrac{z}{a}$.

5. If $3a = \dfrac{b}{4}$, make b the subject of the formula.

6. If $\dfrac{x}{2} = \dfrac{y}{3}$ make y the subject.

7. Make up the subject of the formula $\dfrac{1}{V} = \dfrac{p}{K}$.

If $x = \dfrac{y}{3} + z$, make y the subject of the formula

$$x = \frac{y}{3} + z$$

Multiply both sides by 3 $\qquad 3 \times x = \overset{1}{\cancel{3}} \times \dfrac{y}{\underset{1}{\cancel{3}}} + 3 \times z$

$$3x = y + 3z$$

Take $3z$ from each side $\qquad 3x - 3z = y$

i.e. $\qquad\qquad\qquad\qquad\quad y = 3x - 3z$

---

8. Make x the subject of the formula $y = 3 + \dfrac{x}{2}$.

9. If $p = \dfrac{q}{2} + \dfrac{3}{2}$, give q in terms of p.

10. If $a = \dfrac{b+c}{2}$, make b the subject of the formula.

11. Make y the subject of the formula $3x = \dfrac{2y}{3} + 2$.

12. If $4 = \dfrac{y}{x} + 3$, give y in terms of x.

THE nTH TERM OF A SEQUENCE

In a sequence the terms occur in a particular order, i.e. there is a first term, a second term and so on. The value of each term depends upon its position in that order. (This is the difference between a sequence of numbers and a set of numbers which can be in any order.)

The letter n is used for a natural number so we can refer to the nth term of a sequence in the same way as we refer to the 4th term or the 8th term.

If we are given a formula such as

$$n\text{th term} = n(n+1)$$

then we can find any term of the sequence by giving n a numerical value.

In this case, the first term is found by substituting 1 for n in $n(n+1)$,

i.e.   1st term $= 1 \times 2 = 2$

Similarly,   2nd term $= 2 \times 3 = 6$ (substituting 2)

                         3rd term $= 3 \times 4 = 12$

                         . . . .

                         10th term $= 10 \times 11 = 110$ and so on.

EXERCISE 8j

> The nth term of a sequence is given by the formula
> $$n\text{th term} = (n-1)^2$$
> Give the first two terms and the eighth term of the sequence.
>
> $n = 1$ 1st term $= (1-1)^2 = 0$
>
> $n = 2$ 2nd term $= (2-1)^2 = 1^2 = 1$
>
> $n = 8$ 8th term $= (8-1)^2 = 7^2 = 49$

Write down the first four terms and the seventh term of the sequence for which the nth term is given.

1. $2n + 1$ **4.** n^2 **7.** $3 + 2n$

2. $2n - 1$ **5.** $(n-1)(n+1)$ **8.** $\dfrac{1}{n}$

3. 2^n **6.** $n + 4$ **9.** $\dfrac{n}{n+1}$

10. The flow chart gives the terms of a sequence.

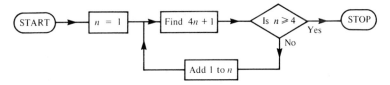

a) Write down the first four terms of the sequence.

b) How would you change the flow chart if you wanted the first six terms.

c) Write down the nth term of the sequence.

d) Draw a flow chart that will give the first 20 terms of the sequence whose nth term is $2n - 1$.

11. This BASIC program prints out the first four terms of the sequence given in the flow chart in question 9.

```
10  FOR N = 1 TO 4
20  PRINT 4*N+2
30  NEXT N
```

a) What does * mean in line 20 ?

b) How would you change the program to give the first 20 terms of the sequence ?

c) Write a program that gives the first 20 terms of the sequence whose nth term is $n^2 + 1$.

FINDING A FORMULA FOR THE nTH TERM

When the pattern in a sequence is known, an expression for the nth term can often be found.

Consider the sequence   2, 4, 6, 8, ...

We need to find the relationship between each term and the number, n, that gives its position. It is helpful to start by making a table of values of n and the corresponding terms in the sequence.

n	1	2	3	4	...
nth term	2	4	6	8	...

The pattern here is that each term is twice its position number, so the 10th term will be 2×10 and the nth term is $2n$.

Now we can check that this does give the correct sequence, i.e.
if $n = 1$, 1st term $= 2 \times 1 = 2$; if $n = 2$, 2nd term $= 2 \times 2 = 4$, and so on.

166

166

Chapter 8

EXERCISE 8k

Find, in terms of n, an expression for the nth term of each of the following sequences.

1. 3, 6, 9, 12, ...   **3.** 2, 3, 4, 5, ...   **5.** 4, 8, 12, 16, ...

2. $-1, -2, -3, -4, \ldots$ **4.** 0, 1, 2, 3, ...   **6.** 2, 4, 8, 16, ...

Find a formula for the nth term of the sequence 1, 4, 7, 10, ...

n	1	2	3	4
nth term	1	4	7	10

(The terms increase by 3 each time, so multiples of 3 are involved.)

$3n$	3	6	9	12

(These are each 2 more than the given terms, so take 2 from $3n$.)

$$n\text{th term} = 3n - 2$$

(Check that this fits all the given terms.)

$n = 1$ 1st term $= 3 \times 1 - 2 = 3 - 2 = 1$

$n = 2$ 2nd term $= 3 \times 2 - 2 = 6 - 2 = 4$

$n = 3$ 3rd term $= 3 \times 3 - 2 = 9 - 2 = 7$

$n = 4$ 4th term $= 3 \times 4 - 2 = 12 - 2 = 10$

Find an expression for the nth term of each of the following sequences.

7. 7, 9, 11, 13, ...   **10.** $1 \times 3, 2 \times 4, 3 \times 5, \ldots$

8. 0, 3, 6, 9, 12, ...   **11.** 1, 8, 27, 64, ...

9. $\frac{1}{3}, \frac{1}{4}, \frac{1}{5}, \frac{1}{6}, \ldots$ **12.** 3, 2, 1, 0, $-1, \ldots$

13.

One of the races at a school sports day is set out with bean bags placed at 1 metre intervals along the track.

A competitor starts at S, runs to the first bag, picks it up and returns it to S. Then she runs to the second bag, picks it up and returns it to S, and so on.

How far has a competitor run when she has returned

a) 1 bean bag   b) 4 bean bags   c) n bean bags ?

MIXED EXERCISES

EXERCISE 8l

1. If $y = mx + c$, find y when $m = -6$, $x = -2$ and $c = 3$.

2. If $E = Ri^2$ find R when $i = 3$ and $E = 72$.

3. If $x = z - y$, make z the subject of the formula.

4. The surface area, A cm², of a sphere of radius a cm is given by the formula $A = 4\pi a^2$. Find the surface area of a sphere of radius 6 cm.

5. A joint of meat needs to be cooked for 40 minutes for each kilogram of its weight, plus 30 minutes extra. Make a formula for the time, t minutes, needed to cook a joint of M kilograms.

6. If $p = a + 2b$, give b in terms of a and p.

7. Write down the third and tenth term of the sequence whose nth term is $3n - 4$.

EXERCISE 8m

1. If $S = \dfrac{a}{1-r}$, find S when $a = \frac{2}{3}$ and $r = \frac{1}{2}$.

2. If $v = rw$, find w when $v = -9$ and $r = -2$.

3. If $a = 3b + c$, make b the subject of the formula.

4. A quarterly gas bill, £B, for x kilowatt hours is given by the formula $B = 0.02x + 12$. Find the bill for 4000 kilowatt hours.

5. A weekly magazine costs xp and a daily newspaper costs yp. Make a formula for the total cost, Cp, of 6 newspapers and one magazine.

6. If $x = \dfrac{y}{z}$, give z in terms of x and y.

7. Find, in terms of n, an expression for the nth term of the sequence
$\dfrac{1}{2}, \dfrac{2}{3}, \dfrac{3}{4}, \dfrac{4}{5}, \ldots$

EXERCISE 8n

In this exercise, several alternative answers are given. Write down the letter that corresponds to the correct answer. Questions 1 to 5 concern the formula $v = u + at$

1. When $u = 6$, $a = 2\frac{1}{2}$ and $t = 9$, the value of v is

   A $37\frac{1}{2}$ **B** $17\frac{1}{2}$ **C** $76\frac{1}{2}$ **D** $28\frac{1}{2}$

2. When $v = 24$, $a = -3$ and $t = -4$, the value of u is

   A 3 **B** 12 **C** 36 **D** 2

3. When $v = 36$, $u = 4$ and $t = 8$, the value of a is

   A 3 **B** 5 **C** 4 **D** 24

4. The formula with t as the subject is

   A $t = a(v-u)$ **B** $t = v-u-a$ **C** $t = \dfrac{v}{u} - a$ **D** $t = \dfrac{v-u}{a}$

5. The formula with u as the subject is

   A $u = v - at$ **B** $u = v + at$ **C** $u = \dfrac{v}{at}$ **D** $u = vat$

6. The first four terms of a sequence are 2, 5, 10, 17, ... The nth term is

   A $2 + 3n$ **B** $n^2 + 1$ **C** $3n - 1$ **D** $n^2 - 1$

9 WORKING WITH PERCENTAGES

PERCENTAGES, FRACTIONS AND DECIMALS

The word 'per cent' literally means 'per hundred'.
Hence 5% means 5 per 100.

Now 5 per 100 can be expressed as the fraction $\frac{5}{100}$, and $\frac{5}{100}$ can be written as the decimal 0.05 or simplified to $\frac{1}{20}$

i.e. $5\% = \begin{cases} \dfrac{5}{100} \\ 0.05 \\ \dfrac{1}{20} \end{cases}$

A percentage can be written as a fraction by dividing by 100. Reversing this operation means that a fraction can be expressed as a percentage if the fraction is multiplied by 100.

For example $\qquad \frac{3}{8} = \frac{3}{8} \times \frac{100}{1}\%$

$\qquad\qquad\qquad\quad = 37.5\%$

and $\qquad\qquad 1.67 = 1.67 \times 100\%$

$\qquad\qquad\qquad\quad = 167\%$

EXERCISE 9a

Copy and complete the following table.

	Percentage	Fraction	Decimal
1.	20%		
2.	50%		
3.	10%		
4.	12%		
5.		$\frac{1}{4}$	
6.		$\frac{3}{5}$	

	Percentage	Fraction	Decimal
7.		$\frac{1}{8}$	
8.		$\frac{7}{20}$	
9.			0.75
10.			0.4
11.			0.15
12.			0.06
13.	32%		
14.		$1\frac{1}{2}$	
15.			1.02
16.	21.5%		
17.			0.015
18.	$7\frac{1}{2}\%$		
19.		$\frac{7}{40}$	
20.	120%		

21. Express 58% as a fraction.

22. Express $\frac{9}{20}$ as a percentage.

23. Express 0.84 as a percentage.

PERCENTAGES OF QUANTITIES

17% is the same as $\frac{17}{100}$

So, finding 17% of £10 is equivalent to finding $\frac{17}{100}$ of £10

i.e. $$17\% \text{ of } £10 = \frac{17}{100} \times £10$$

$$= £1.70$$

In the same way, we know that $50\% = \frac{1}{2}$,

so $$50\% \text{ of } £10 = \frac{1}{2} \text{ of } £10$$

$$= £5$$

EXERCISE 9b

1. Find 15% of £24.

2. The bus fares in Extown are going up by 10%. What will be added to a fare of 30 p ?

3. Find 9% of 3 m.

4. A curtain, of length 3 m, shrinks by 5% when washed. By how many centimetres does it shrink ?

5. A union asks for a wage increase of 8%. How much extra would this give a worker on a weekly wage of £240 ?

6. 6% of an employee's monthly pay is deducted for pension contributions. A. Smith's monthly pay is £800. How much does A. Smith pay towards his pension each month ?

7. A clothes shop has this notice in its window: SALE 25% reduction on all marked prices. What is the reduction on a pair of jeans priced at £25.20 ?

8. A motor accessory shop quotes all prices exclusive of VAT. VAT is charged at $17\frac{1}{2}$% of the marked price. How much VAT has to be paid on a bottle of antifreeze priced at £5.20 ?

9. A mail-order firm offers 10% commission on all goods supplied through the catalogue. How much commission is payable on an order of value £167 ?

10. An airline company gives a 30% reduction on airfares for children. What is the reduction on an airfare of £170 ?

ONE QUANTITY AS A PERCENTAGE OF ANOTHER QUANTITY

To find 2 cm as a percentage of 25 cm, we first express 2 cm as a fraction of 25 cm,

i.e.   2 cm is $\frac{2}{25}$ of 25 cm

Then, changing the fraction to a percentage gives

$$2 \text{ cm is } \frac{2}{25} \times 100\% \text{ of } 25 \text{ cm}$$

i.e.   2 cm is 8% of 25 cm

To find one quantity as a fraction, or as a percentage, of another quantity, the two quantities must be expressed in the same unit. If this is not the case, one of the units must be changed. It is usually better to change the larger unit to the smaller. For example, to find 5 p as a percentage of £ 2 we express £ 2 as 200 p.

then $\qquad$ 5 p is $\frac{5}{200} \times \frac{100}{1}\%$ of £ 2

i.e. $\qquad$ 5 p is $2\frac{1}{2}\%$ of £ 2

EXERCISE 9c

A pair of jeans were 96 cm long when new. They were 90 cm long after the first wash. By what percentage of their original length had they shrunk ?

Original length $= 96$ cm

'Washed' length $= 90$ cm

Shrinkage $= 6$ cm

$\therefore$ Shrinkage $= \frac{6}{96}$ of original length

$= \frac{6}{96} \times \frac{100}{1}\%$ of original length

$= 6\frac{1}{4}\%$ of original length.

1. In a group of 120 people, 18 were over sixty years old. What percentage of the group were over sixty ?

2. A sports stadium can seat 3000 spectators. Find the percentage of seats filled when 2400 people are seated.

3. In an examination, Gita got 9 out of a possible total of 15. What percentage of the total mark did Gita get ?

4. John paid a deposit of £ 50 on a bike. The cash price of the bike was £ 250. What percentage of the cash price did John pay as a deposit ?

5. From a total workforce of 500, the management made 20 people redundant. What percentage of the workforce was made redundant ?

6. During a sale, a clothes shop offered '£5 off the marked price of all stock'. Find the percentage reduction on a shirt with a marked price of £20.

7. In a consignment of 2500 boxes of chocolates, 250 boxes were damaged. What percentage of the consignment were not damaged ?

8. At the start of the school year, there were 200 copies of 'Jane Eyre' but at the end of the year there were only 190 copies. What percentage of the copies were 'lost' ?

9. An apprentice is paid £60 a week and has to pay £12 a week on fares. What percentage of his pay is spent on fares ?

10.

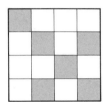

Find, to the nearest whole number, the percentage of the diagram that is unshaded.

11. When train fares increase, the cost of John Smith's journey to work increases from £1 a day to £1.20 a day. Find the increase as a percentage of the old fare.

12. In the budget, the excise duty on petrol is increased so that a litre of petrol goes up in cost by 3p. What percentage is this increase of 3p on petrol which previously cost 50p a litre ?

13.

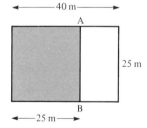

The plan shows a plot of land divided into two parts by a fence **AB**. Find the area of the unshaded part as a percentage of the area of the whole plot.

14.

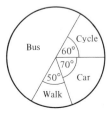

The pie chart illustrates the results of a survey on the method of transport of a group of pupils coming to school. What percentage of the total surveyed came by cycle ?

15.

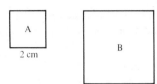

Square A is enlarged to square B so that the lengths of the sides of square B are twice those of square A. Find the area of A as a percentage of the area of B.

PERCENTAGE CHANGE

Most quantities that we deal with in our lives change as time passes. For example, the cost of goods and services changes (nearly always upwards). The number of people living in a certain area changes. The number of new cars sold each month changes.

These changes are usually expressed as percentages. We are all familiar with news items such as

'Bus fares increase by 5%'
'Retail prices index up by $\frac{1}{2}$%'
'Workforce reduced by 5%'
'Population of borough down by 15%'

When a quantity increases or decreases, the change is always expressed as a percentage of the *original* quantity, i.e. the quantity before the change occurred.

For example, if a bus fare changes from 20 p to 22 p, the increase is 2 p.

To find the percentage increase, we find 2 p as a percentage of 20 p.

$$2\,p = \tfrac{2}{20} \times 100\% \text{ of } 20\,p$$

$$= 10\% \text{ of } 20\,p$$

So the bus fare has increased by 10%.

Similarly, if a bike that cost £650 is sold two years later at a loss of 30%, then the loss is 30% of £650.

i.e.   the loss is $\frac{30}{100} \times £650$

$$= £195$$

Understanding statements about percentage changes requires knowledge of the language used.

Some of the words used when there is an *increase* are

appreciation, inflation, gain, profit, surcharge

Some of the words used when there is a *decrease* are

depreciation, discount, reduction, loss

Careful reading of a statement is also necessary. Some statements, such as news headlines, can be misleading at first sight. Here is a familiar one:

'Inflation Down'

Some people take this to mean that prices have gone down. That is not what it means. All that can be said is that prices have *risen* by a *smaller amount* than previously.

EXERCISE 9d

1. Train fares are to be increased by 6%. Find the extra that will have to be paid on a fare of £8.50.

2. A sale advertises '10% off all marked prices'. Find the discount on a radio with a marked price of £29.50.

3. A holiday brochure states that there is a surcharge of 10% on the price of all package holidays during August. Find the surcharge on a holiday priced at £450.

4. A bulk-buying warehouse offers a discount of 5% on purchases over £100. Find the discount on a bill of £150.

5. A sale ticket reads: Original price £5.00
   Sale price £4.00
   Find the reduction as a percentage of the original price.

6. In a supermarket the cost of a 250 g jar of coffee has gone up from £3.90 to £4.29. Find the percentage increase in price.

7. Mike Stevens bought a motor bike for £1500 and sold it a year later for £1000. Find his percentage loss.

8. A trainee hairdresser is paid £40 a week. After six months the pay is increased to £50 a week. Find the percentage increase.

9. Two shops stock the same make and model of scientific calculator. Shop A offers £1 off m.r.p. Shop B offers 10% discount on m.r.p. (m.r.p. means the manufacturers recommended price.) If the m.r.p. is £9.60 which shop offers the better buy and by how much ?

10. A square with sides 4 cm long, is drawn on a sheet of paper. This is then enlarged by a photocopier so that the lengths of the sides of the square are increased by 50%. Find

a) the lengths of the sides of the square on the copy

b) the area of the square on the copy

c) the percentage increase in the area of the square after enlargement.

FINDING THE CHANGED AMOUNT

When a quantity, A, is increased by 30%
then the new quantity is   100% of A + 30% of A

$$= 130\% \text{ of A.}$$

When a quantity, B, is decreased by 30%
then the new quantity is   100% of B − 30% of B

$$= 70\% \text{ of B.}$$

EXERCISE 9e

A hotel offers a 60% reduction on its adult rate for a child under two years of age. If the cost for 1 adult for 1 night is £47, find the rate for a child under two years old.

The nightly rate for a child $= (100 - 60)\%$ of £47

$$= 40\% \text{ of } £47$$

$$= \frac{40}{100} \times £47$$

$$= £18.80$$

The value of Jane Brown's house was £50 000 when she bought it three years ago. The value of the house increased by 30% during the three years. Find the value of the house now.

$$\text{Present value of house} = (100 + 30)\% \text{ of } £50\,000$$

$$= 130\% \text{ of } £50\,000$$

$$= \frac{130}{100} \times £50\,000$$

$$= £65\,000$$

1. A builders' merchant offers a discount of 10% for payment in cash. How much has to be paid in cash for a bill of £250 ?

2. An airline gives a 20% reduction on fares for children between the ages of 2 and 11 years. Find the child fare when the adult fare is £120.

3. Jill Jones buys a car for £2500 and sells it two years later at a loss of 60%. Find the price at which Jill sold her car.

4. A photocopier is set so that all lines on copies are 20% shorter than lines on the originals. A rectangle is 10 cm long on an original. Find the length of the rectangle on the copy.

5. A pair of curtains were 2 m long when new. After washing they shrunk by 5% of their length. Find the length of the curtains after they had been washed.

6. A builders' merchant quotes prices exclusive of VAT. VAT is added at $17\frac{1}{2}\%$ of the marked price. Find the cost, inclusive of VAT, of a tin of paint marked at £3.60.

7. The prices quoted in a holiday brochure are subject to a surcharge of 12% if single rooms are requested. Find the cost, for single room accommodation, of a holiday priced at £340.

8. The hourly rate for a cashier is £2.50. If this is increased by 6%, find the new hourly rate.

9. Between January 1990 and January 1991 prices increased by 5% on average. If a man earned £240 a week in January 1990, what should he be earning in January 1991 if his pay is to keep in line with price increases ?

10. A photocopier is set to enlarge originals by 30% (i.e. lengths of lines on the copies are 30% longer than lines on the original.) An original shows the plan of a house: this is a rectangle measuring 30 cm by 50 cm. What are the dimensions of this rectangle on the copy?

MIXED EXERCISES

EXERCISE 9f

1. On booking a holiday, a deposit of 25% of the cost is asked for. Find the deposit for a holiday costing £780.

2. A man is paid £130 a week. His pay is then increased by 8%. Find his new weekly pay.

3. Copy and complete the following bill:

	£
10 brackets at £1.50 each 2 uprights at £6.00 each	
Total	
VAT at $17\frac{1}{2}$%	
To pay	

4. In an English test, Peter got 17 out of 25. Find his mark as a percentage of the total.

5. 90 pupils sat a history examination and 27 of them got 75% or more. Find the percentage of pupils taking the examination who got 75% or more.

6.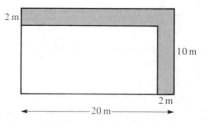

The diagram shows a rectangular garden. The unshaded area is grass.

Find   a) the area of the garden
          b) the area of the grass
          c) the percentage of the area of the garden that is grass.

7. In a mathematics test, Mushad got 35 out of 60 and Devon got 60%. Who got the higher mark?

8.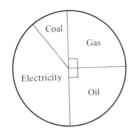

The pie chart shows the fuel used for heating by 36 households. Find the percentage of households using gas.

9. Mr Smith's weekly pay is £150 and 15% of this is deducted for National Insurance, pension and income tax. Find his pay after deductions.

10. A school made £3000 at a summer fair. It was decided to give 60% of this to charity and the rest to the school fund. How much did the school fund receive ?

11. A radio cassette player is priced at £42. Discount store A is offering it at £5 off. Discount store B is offering it at 5% discount. Which store offers the better price and by how much ?

12. A shop has a sale offer of 10% discount on all marked prices. A particular type of lampshade has a marked price of £20. I buy two of these lampshades. How much do I pay for them ?

13. A group of people were asked how they got to work. The results are shown in the table.

Method of transport	Walk	Bike	Bus	Train	Car
Number of people	10	5	8	15	2

a) How many people were interviewed ?

b) What percentage of the group walked to work ?

14. A dealer bought a motor bike for £300 and sold it for £450. Find his profit and express his profit as a percentage of the price the dealer paid for the motor bike.

15. The cost of a package holiday to Italy was £300 per adult. A reduction of 15% of this price was given for each child. Find the total cost for a family of two adults and two children.

16. Company A made a takeover bid for Company B. Company B had 250 000 shares and A had to own 51% of these shares to gain control of B. Company A offered to pay £1.20 for each of B's shares.

a) How many of B's shares did A have to own ?

b) If Company A had to buy all these shares, how much would the takeover cost A ?

17. Two building societies each offer a £1000 five year bond. Society A offers to increase your investment by $\frac{1}{5}$ after five years. Society B offers a return of 24% on the amount invested after five years. If £5000 is invested for the full five years, which society gives the better return and by how much?

18.

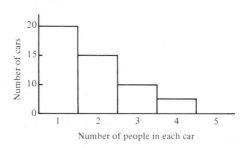

Number of cars

Number of people in each car

The bar chart illustrates the results of a survey on the number of people in each car. Find

a) the number of cars in the survey

b) the percentage of cars with one person in them

c) the percentage of cars with more than two people in them.

19.

A gardener plants cabbage seedlings 50 cm apart. The distance between the first and last seedling in the row is 4 m.

a) How many seedlings can be planted in 1 row?

b) If the space between the seedlings is reduced to 40 cm, find the new number of seedlings that can be planted in the same row.

c) Find, to the nearest whole number, the percentage increase in the number of seedlings that can be planted in the row when the spacing is reduced from 50 cm to 40 cm.

20. Mr and Mrs Black bought a house in January 1989 and paid £40000 for it. The value of the house increased by 10% from January 1989 to January 1990.

a) Find the value of the house in January 1990.

b) From January 1990 to January 1991 the house decreased in value by 10% of its value in January 1990. Find its value in January 1991.

21. A motor bike costs £500 when new. Each year its value decreases by 10% of its value at the beginning of that year. Find the value of the motor bike when it is   a) 1 year old   b) 2 years old.

22. Copy and complete the following bill.

	£
2 bags cement	15.00
30 paving stones	60.00
2% trade discount:	
VAT at $17\frac{1}{2}$%	
Payment due	

EXERCISE 9g

Each question is followed by several alternative answers. Write down the letter that corresponds to the correct answer.

1. 20% of £200 is

   A £20   **B** £4   **C** £80   **D** £40

2. 75% is equivalent to

   A 7.5   **B** $\frac{3}{4}$ **C** $\frac{1}{4}$ **D** $\frac{1}{75}$

3. 34 out of 50 as a percentage is

   A 34%   **B** 50%   **C** 68%   **D** 150%

4.

The area of the diagram that is shaded as a percentage of the whole area is

   A $\frac{1}{4}$%   **B** 25%   **C** 75%   **D** 50%

5. When £100 is increased by 20%, the new value is

   A £120   **B** £80   **C** £200   **D** £20

6. A jumble sale made £400. 25% of the proceeds was given to charity. The amount given to charity was

   A   £100   **B**   £25   **C**   £300   **D**   £50

7. A 10% reduction was made on the marked price of all goods. The reduction on an article marked at £50 was

   A   50 p   **B**   10 p   **C**   £5   **D**   £10

8. A cassette player cost £100 when bought and was sold one year later for £90. The percentage loss was

   A   9%   **B**   10%   **C**   90%   **D**   1%

9. In an advertisement, the price of a chair is given as £50 plus $17\frac{1}{2}$% VAT. The total cost of the chair is

   A   £65   **B**   £42.50   **C**   £50   **D**   £58.75

10. Which of the following is in descending order of size ?

   A   24%, 0.23, $\frac{1}{4}$ **C** $\frac{1}{4}$, 0.23, 24%

   B   0.23, $\frac{1}{4}$, 24%   **D** $\frac{1}{4}$, 24%, 0.23

10 DEALING WITH MONEY

Most of us need to borrow money at some time in our lives. When we buy goods or services and pay for them over several months or years, we have obtained credit, i.e. borrowed money. There are many ways of borrowing money and almost as many names for the different types of loan.

MORTGAGES

Money borrowed to pay for property such as a house or flat is called a mortgage. Mortgages are available from building societies, banks and some local authorities.

A mortgage is a long-term loan repayable, usually monthly, over several years. The charge for the loan is called the interest. Mortgage interest rates are often mentioned in news programmes. They are newsworthy because they go up and down frequently and because repayments form a large part of many people's expenditure.

The special features of a mortgage are that the deeds of the property (the papers giving details of ownership) are held by the lender for the duration of the mortgage. During this time the lender has certain rights over the property and can impose conditions on how the property is used.

When asking for a mortgage, most people are interested in the size of the monthly repayments. These are normally quoted per £1000 borrowed and vary with the interest rate and the number of years over which the loan is to be repaid.

EXERCISE 10a

A building society offers a twenty-year mortgage for monthly repayments of £11.50 per £1000 borrowed. What are the monthly repayments on a mortgage of £25 000 ?

Monthly repayment on £1000 = £11.50

Monthly repayment on £25 000 = £11.50 × 25

= £287.50

1. The Brick Building Society offers a twenty-five year mortgage for monthly repayments of £14 per £1000 borrowed. What are the monthly repayments on a mortgage of £60 000 ?

2. The bank gives ten-year mortgages for monthly repayments of £15.20 per £1000 borrowed. What are the monthly repayments on a loan of £20 000 ?

3. Jane and Peter Smith borrow £15 000 from a building society. The repayments are £10.62 per month per £1000 borrowed. Calculate their monthly repayments.

4. The Greenshire Council grants a woman a mortgage of £50 000 to buy a house. Calculate the monthly repayments if the council charges £11.68 per £1000 per month.

5. The Redbrick Building Society gives Mr and Mrs Leung a mortgage of £30 000. The repayments are £12.15 per £1000 borrowed per calendar month. Calculate

    a) the monthly repayment

    b) the yearly repayment

    c) the total repaid over the full 25-year term of the mortgage.

Jim Green wants to buy a house costing £70 000. His bank agrees to give him an 80% mortgage. How much will the bank lend Jim Green ?

(An 80% mortgage means that a loan of 80% of the purchase price is given.)

$$80\% \text{ of } £70\,000 = £\frac{80}{100} \times 70\,000$$

$$= £56\,000$$

The bank will lend £56 000

---

6. Claire Peters obtains a 95% mortgage on a flat whose purchase price is £25 000.

    a) How much does Claire borrow ?

    b) How much does Claire have to pay towards the cost herself ?

7. The bank gives Mr and Mrs Nokes a 90% mortgage on a house costing £42 000

a) What amount of money does the bank lend?

b) How much extra money has to be found by Mr and Mrs Nokes?

8. Mr & Mrs Shah buy a house costing £120 000. They obtain a 70% mortgage on which the repayments are £12.20 per month per £1000 borrowed. Find

a) the amount borrowed

b) the monthly repayments.

BANK LOANS

A bank loan is a straightforward loan of money for a fixed term (typically two to five years) with fixed monthly repayments. The goods and services that you buy with the money are yours from the start although the bank manager will want to know what you intend doing with the money. However, in case repayments are not kept up, some form of security is usually required. This can be the deeds of a house, share certificates or a guarantee by another person or company.

EXERCISE 10b

1. Lisa Davis is given a bank loan of £500 to be repaid in 24 monthly instalments of £27.50. What is the total amount that Lisa has to repay?

2. The monthly repayments for a 3-year bank loan of £2000 are £81.20. Find the amount paid in 1 year and the amount paid over the full three-year term of the loan.

3. The table shows the monthly repayments and the total repaid for a bank loan of £500 for 2, 3, 4 or 5 years.

Loan £500	2 yrs	3 yrs	4 yrs	5 yrs
Monthly payments	25.67	19.00	15.81	14.04
Total paid	616.08	684.00	758.88	842.40

Use the table to find

a) the monthly repayments on a loan of £500 for 3 years

b) the total repaid if the loan is for 5 years

c) the extra cost of a bank loan of £500 for 4 years compared with paying cash.

CREDIT SALES

Many people find that they cannot pay cash for expensive items such as cars, furniture, washing machines and cookers. These are frequently bought using a form of credit called a credit sale.

In a credit sale the goods belong to the purchaser from the time of purchase.

Credit agreements often require a deposit, or down payment, together with equal monthly repayments over a period of time. The repayment period can be from 3 months up to 2 or 3 years.

Credit sales are sometimes 'free', i.e. the total repayment is the same as the cash price, and the repayment period is often short. Usually, however, the total repayments are more, often a lot more, than the cash price. The difference between the credit price and the cash price is the cost of using an article before it has been paid for in full.

The cost of any form of credit, including mortgages and bank loans, must be published. By law, the cost is shown as a percentage, called the annual percentage rate (APR).

EXERCISE 10c

The cash price of a freezer is £540. The credit sale terms are a deposit of £100 together with 24 monthly repayments of £21.15. Find the credit sale price and the amount saved by paying cash.

$$\text{Deposit} = £100$$

$$\text{Repayments} = 24 \times £21.15$$

$$= £507.60$$

$$\text{Credit sale price} = £100 + £507.60$$

$$= £607.60$$

$$\text{Amount saved by paying cash} = £607.60 - £540$$

$$= £67.60$$

1. A motorbike has a cash price of £820. The credit sale terms are a deposit of £200 together with 24 monthly repayments of £31.50. Find the credit sale cost and the difference between this and the cash price.

2. The cash price of a stereo radio/cassette player is £60. The credit sale terms are a down-payment of 25% of the cost price together with six monthly repayments of £8.25. Find

a) the down-payment   b) the total credit sale price.

3. A carpet is offered for sale at a cash price of £850 or on credit terms of 12 monthly payments of £81.50. Find the difference between the cash price and the credit price.

4. A second-hand car is offered for sale either for £850 cash or on credit sale terms of 20% deposit plus 18 monthly payments of £80.50. Find

a) the deposit   b) the credit sale price.

5. A washing-machine is offered for sale either for a cash price of £250 or on credit terms of 25% deposit plus six monthly payments of £34.38. Find   a) the deposit   b) the credit price
c) the difference between the cash price and the credit price.

6. Mr Spiro wants to buy a new car costing £15000, but cannot afford to pay cash. The following options for paying are available:
  1. A bank loan of £15000 repayable over 36 months at £562.76 per month
  2. A credit sale agreement requiring a deposit of £3750 together with 30 monthly payments of £508.34.

a) Find the cost of the car if bought using the bank loan.

b) Find the total cost of the credit sale agreement.

7. A home video camera has a marked price of £450. A 5% discount is given for paying cash. Credit terms on offer are a deposit of one third of the marked price together with 12 monthly payments of £31.50.

a) Find the cash price of the camera.

b) Find the total credit cost of the camera.

c) How much more does the camera cost if bought on credit?

8. The roof of a house needs retiling and the cost of the job is £3000. The house owner finds a finance house which will lend 75% of the cost to be repaid over three years at £87.80 a month. Find

a) the amount that the owner borrows

b) the total paid by the owner for the repair.

9.

```
┌─────────────────────────────┐
│          £650               │
│       Credit terms:         │
│  Deposit _____ £97.50     │
│  12 monthly                 │
│  payments _____ £58.90    │
└─────────────────────────────┘
```

This sales ticket is on a matching set of 1 settee and 2 chairs.

a) Find the total credit price.

b) What is the deposit as a percentage of the cash price ?

10. A department store offers its own credit terms on any item it sells over a price of £ 100. The credit terms are: a deposit of one quarter of the price, the balance to be increased by 20% and then divided by 12 to give the monthly repayments.
The cost of supplying and fitting a range of kitchen units is £ 1000. The purchaser decides to use the shop's credit terms. Find

a) the deposit to be paid

b) the balance plus 20% of the balance

c) the monthly repayments.

CREDIT CARDS

Credit cards like Access and Visa operate in a different way from traditional forms of credit. Each card-holder is given a credit limit. Suppose that the credit limit is £ 500. This means that the card can be used to pay for goods and services up to a total value of £ 500.

A statement is issued each month detailing expenditure and demanding a minimum payment towards the debt. This minimum payment is usually £ 5 or 5% of the debt, whichever is the greater. The card-holder must pay at least the minimum figure but may pay more, or even pay the full debt in which case there is no charge. If part payment is made, there is a charge of about 2% per month on the debt. (This sounds low, but 2% per month is 26.8% per annum!)

Other cards, like American Express, or some department store cards, operate in a similar way to credit cards except that the full amount has to be paid each month. These are called *charge cards*.

EXERCISE 10d

> My monthly credit card statement shows my debt as £485. The minimum payment is £5 or 5% of the debt, whichever is greater. What must I pay ?
>
> $$5\% \text{ of } £485 = £\frac{5}{100} \times 485$$
>
> $$= £24.25$$
>
> £24.25 > £5
>
> I must pay £24.25

1. Mrs Jones' credit card statement showed that she owed the company £124.50. The minimum payment demanded was £5 or 5% of the debt whichever was greater. Find the minimum payment.

2. Mr Siddons owes the credit card company £65.20. Find the minimum payment he must make if it is 5% of the debt or £5, whichever is greater.

3. Anna Smith uses her credit card to buy a moped costing £350. The first month she pays the minimum of 5% of the debt to the credit card company. Find her first payment.

4. John Allan's credit limit is £700. He uses his card to pay for goods of total value £452.00. He then presents his card to pay for a garage bill of £320.00. Will the credit card company authorise this payment ?

5. Peter Davis has a credit limit of £600. He has not kept a record of bills he has paid for with his card and when he offers his card in settlement of a garage bill for £210, the credit card company will only authorise payment of £150. Find

   a) the amount Peter has to pay the garage in cash

   b) the amount Peter owed the credit card company before paying the garage.

6. My credit limit is £400. My last statement was for £280 and I paid the company £150 of this debt. Can I now use my card to pay a bill for £300 ?

7. Peter Watson's credit limit is £300. His last statement was for £112 and he paid 75% of this. Can he now use his card to pay a bill for £205 ?

INSURANCE

When we own valuable property it is sensible to insure it against theft, loss, fire, etc.

If a car or motor cycle is driven on public roads the driver must, by law, be insured against third party damage. Third party damage means damage inflicted by us on other people or their property.

All property is at risk of damage or loss but relatively few people suffer. Insurance works by spreading the cost of loss among all who are insured.

The cost of insurance is called a *premium,* usually payable yearly, and is given in the form '50p per £1000 insured value'.

Premiums vary according to the risk to be covered and the nature of the article insured. Houses cannot be lost or stolen so insurance premiums for buildings are relatively low. Higher premiums are charged for the contents of a house as these are at greater risk than the building. Valuable articles that are likely to be taken out of the house are at an even higher risk of loss. These can be covered by an 'all risks policy'. Such items include jewellery, musical instruments, cameras and portable hi-fi sets.

EXERCISE 10e

> An insurance company quotes a premium of £1.20 per £1000 value for insuring a house. The value of the house is £84000. Find the premium to be paid.
>
> $$Premium = £1.20 \times 84$$
> $$= £100.80$$

1. An insurance company quotes a premium of £1.90 per £1000 value for insuring a house worth £60000. Find the premium to be paid.

2. The premium for insuring the contents of a house is £2.50 per £1000 value. Find the premium to be paid on contents worth £7000.

3. An 'all risks' policy for a camera of value £450 quotes a premium of £5 per £100 value. Find the premium to be paid.

4. An 'all risks' policy for insuring a clarinet worth £250 quotes a premium of £1.50 per £100 value. Find the premium to be paid.

5. The premium for insuring a building worth £150000 is 80p per £1000. Find the premium to be paid.

6. The table quotes premiums for a house contents insurance policy per £1000 value insured.

    Area A   £4.20
    Area B   £3.90
    Area C   £3.50

a) Find the premium paid on contents worth £6500 in Area A.

b) Find the premium paid on contents worth £6500 in Area B.

c) Find the premium paid on contents worth £10000 in Area C.

7. The premiums quoted for buildings and house insurance by a company are

	Building/£1000	Contents/£1000
Inner London	£2.50	£5.40
Outer London	£1.90	£3.80

The company has a miniumum premium of £50. Find

a) the premium for a building in Inner London that is worth £100000

b) the premium for contents of a flat in Outer London, worth £5000.

8. The premiums quoted for house contents insurance by a company are, per £1000 value,

    Metropolitan Areas   £5.60
    Suburbs and other towns   £4.90
    Country areas   £3.50

Find the premium to be paid on

a) contents worth £15000 in a metropolitan area

b) contents worth £20000 in a country area

c) contents worth £25000 in a suburban area.

9. Ann and Peter Smith work out that the value of the contents of their house is £15000. This includes a piano worth £1000 and a gold watch worth £500. The insurance premium for their contents is quoted at £4.25 per £1000 value. One condition of their insurance is that any item whose value is greater than 5% of the total value insured must be listed separately.

a) Find the premium to be paid.

b) State which items have to be listed separately.

10. A buildings insurance policy covers loss and damage to the fabric of a house and any fixtures and fittings (i.e. items that are built in and attached to the walls, etc.). The premium is £1.60 per £1000 value. A reduction of 2% on the premium is given if the policy-holder agrees to pay the first £500 worth of any claim. (This is called an 'excess'.)

Find the premium to be paid on a house worth £70000 if

a) the policy-holder does *not* want to pay the first £500 of any claim

b) the policy-holder does agree to pay the excess.

MOTOR INSURANCE

The cost of insurance for a car or motorcycle is a significant part of the cost of running it.

The minimum insurance cover required by law is third party liability. This means that you must be covered against damage caused to other people and their property. (It does not include any cover for yourself, your passengers or your vehicle.) Most people choose to be covered against more than the legal minimum and there are various ways of reducing the premium. One way is to agree to pay the first £100 of any claim. Another is to restrict the people allowed to drive the vehicle. Most motor policies give a discount on premiums if no claims have been made; this discount is called a *no claims bonus* or *no claims discount* (NCD).

EXERCISE 10f

The insurance premium for John's motorcycle is £480, but he is given a 30% no claims bonus. Find the premium he pays.

No claims bonus = 30% of £480

$$= £\frac{30}{100} \times 480$$

$$= £144$$

Premium paid = £480 − £144

$$= £336$$

1. The insurance premium for comprehensive cover on John's medium-sized family car in London is £900. John qualifies for a 60% no claims bonus. Find the premium he actually pays.

2. Mr Andrews buys a new car. He is quoted a premium of £700 for comprehensive insurance. A discount of 5% of the premium is given if no one under 25 years old is allowed to drive the car. Find the premium Mr Andrews pays if he agrees to this restriction on those allowed to drive the car.

3. The premium for insuring Angela's motor cycle is £450. There is a reduction of 40% of the premium if no one but Angela is allowed to drive the bike. Find the premium Angela has to pay if she accepts the condition that she is the only person insured to drive it.

4. Because of an accident, John had to make a claim on his motor bike insurance. His basic premium was £450. When the renewal notice for the next year arrived he was given a no claims bonus reduction of only 30%. If John had not made a claim he would have been entitled to a 60% no claims bonus. Find

   a) the amount John actually had to pay

   b) the amount John would have had to pay if he had not made a claim.

5. Copy and complete the following renewal notice for a car insurance policy.

A & B Insurance Co.

Policy holder: A. Christos

Vehicle insured: Renault 5: reg no. STP 4B

Cover: Third party, fire & theft: gross premium	£	£
		250
40% no claims bonus	☐	
5% reduction for £50 excess	☐	
Renewal premium		☐

6. David's parents bought him a car on condition that he paid for all other expenses. The other costs involved in running the car for one year were: insurance £230, road tax £110, repairs and maintenance £130, petrol £482.

   a) What were David's running costs for the year?

   b) How much a week did David's car cost him?

7. Eleni's parents bought her a car on condition that she paid the running expenses herself. For the first year these were:
insurance £297, road tax £110, new battery £36, service bill £120, petrol £325.

a) Find the cost of running the car for the first year.

b) How much a week did it cost Eleni ?

8. When Rajit's renewal notice for his motor bike insurance policy came, the basic premium was £170. Rajit qualified for a 40% no claims bonus. He also decided to reduce the premium by agreeing to pay the first £100 of any claim. This gave him a further reduction of 5% of the basic premium. How much did he have to pay ?

9. An insurance company quotes a basic yearly premium of £450 for comprehensive insurance on a car. If no claims are made on the policy there is a 20% no claims bonus on the basic premium for the first renewal, a 40% no claims bonus on the basic premium for the second renewal and a maximum 60% no claims bonus for subsequent renewals.

Assuming that the basic premium does not change, find the amount that has to be paid to renew the policy after

a) 1 year   b) 2 years   c) 3 years.

10. Amy decides to reduce the cost of her insurance premium on her car as much as possible. The basic premium is £210 for third party cover. In addition she qualifies for a 40% no claims bonus. By agreeing to pay the first £50 of any claim she gets a further 3% reduction on the basic premium. Also by nominating herself as the only driver of the car, she is given 10% reduction on the basic premium. How much does Amy have to pay for her car insurance ?

MIXED EXERCISE

EXERCISE 10g

1. The 'X' Building Society offers a mortgage for monthly repayments of £10.96 per £1000 borrowed. Find the monthly repayments on a mortgage of £50000.

2. A building society offers to give an 80% mortgage on a house costing £60000. How much is the society prepared to lend on the house ?

3. A bank loan of £2000 has to be repaid by 36 monthly instalments of £87.20. Find the total repaid over the full term of the loan.

4. The cash price of a car is £5000. The credit sale terms are a deposit of £1000 plus 24 monthly repayments of £209. Find the difference between the cash price and the credit sale cost of the car.

5. A carpet supplier offers credit terms of 25% deposit plus six monthly repayments of £59 for the supply and fitting of a carpet for which the cost is £440. Find   a) the deposit   b) the total credit cost.

6. An insurance company quotes a premium of £2.20 per £1000 insured value for a contents policy. Find the premium on contents valued at £20 000.

7. The premium quoted for insuring a trombone worth £1500 is 50p per £100 for cover against loss or damage in the owner's home or when in use elsewhere in the country. If cover is required when the trombone is left unattended in a car, the premium is 75p per £100. Find the extra cost of covering the trombone when it is left in a car.

8. Mr Brown's basic insurance premium for his car is £300 for third party cover. He is entitled to a 30% no claims bonus. Find the premium that Mr Brown pays.

9. Copy and complete the following invoice.

A & B Builder's Merchants

	£
10 m of 15 mm copper tube at 80 p per m	
1 × 15 mm stopcock	2.75
5 % discount	
VAT at $17\frac{1}{2}$%	
Total	

10. Copy and complete the following list itemising the cost of running Peter's car for a year.

	£
Capital Depreciation	500.00
Road Tax	110.00
Insurance: gross premium £250	
less 60% no claims bonus	
Service	150.00
Petrol: 800 litres at 40 p per litre	
Total	

11 PERSONAL FINANCE

We all require money to pay for our everyday needs. We must have money to buy food and clothes, to pay the rent or the mortgage, to settle our electricity and gas accounts, etc.

Most people obtain their money by working, but for those unable to work, social security payments provide a basic sum.

HOURLY PAY

Many workers, for example shop assistants and production workers in a factory, are paid for their work by the hour. The hourly rate, or flat rate, is paid for each hour worked up to an agreed number of hours each week, i.e. the basic working week. Any extra hours worked are usually paid at a higher overtime rate. This rate may be paid at 'time-and-a-quarter' or 'time-and-a-half' and sometimes, for instance at weekends, may even be paid at 'double-time', i.e. at twice the basic rate.

EXERCISE 11a

Last week Fred Wills worked 48 hours, 12 of which were overtime. If the basic hourly rate is £6 and overtime is paid at time-and-a-quarter, find his gross wage for the week.

Basic working week $= (48 - 12)$ hours $= 36$ hours

Payment for 36 hours at £6 per hour $= 36 \times £6$

$$= £216$$

Overtime rate at time-and-a-quarter is £6 × £1.25 $= £7.50$

Payment for 12 hours overtime at £7.50 per hour $= 12 \times £7.50$

$$= £90$$

∴ gross wage for the week $= £216 + £90$

$$= £306$$

1.   Jean works a 40-hour week and is paid £3.50 per hour. Calculate her weekly basic pay.

2.   George is paid £4.50 per hour for a basic working week of 38 hours. Calculate his gross weekly wage.

3.   Angela works $37\frac{1}{2}$ hours each week for an hourly rate of £6. Find her gross weekly basic pay.

4.   Wayne worked 45 hours last week, 9 of which were overtime at time-and-a-half. If the basic hourly rate is £5, find his gross pay for the week.

5.   Amer Rae's basic hourly rate of pay is £4.20. How much will he earn in a week when he works for 42 hours, 7 of which are overtime at time-and-a-quarter?

6.   Peter Smith earns £144 for a basic working week of 36 hours. What is his basic hourly rate? If overtime is paid at time-and-a-quarter, how much does he earn for each hour of overtime worked? How much extra does he earn for $5\frac{1}{2}$ hours overtime?

7.   Sarah Comerford's time-sheet for a week is shown below.

Name Sarah Comerford				
Works No. 132				
Week No. 37				
Day	AM		PM	
	in	out	in	out
Monday	7.00	12.00	12.59	3.32
Tuesday	7.02	12.01	1.00	3.30
Wednesday	7.00	12.03	1.00	3.30
Thursday	6.58	12.00	1.15	3.31
Friday	7.00	12.01	1.00	3.32

Use this card to answer the following questions:

a) What time is 'clocking-on' time?

b) What time does work end for the day?

c) How long is the lunch break?

d) How long should Sarah work   i) each morning   ii) each afternoon?

e) On which day did Sarah have an extended lunch break?

f) How long is the basic working week?

g) Calculate her gross wage when she works a full week if the basic hourly rate is £6.

8. Anne White earns £171.36 when her basic hourly rate of pay is £4.76. How many hours does she work? How much per hour is she paid for overtime if the overtime rate is double-time? How much would she receive for working $9\frac{1}{2}$ hours overtime?

9. Tom and Arthur Bell work in different factories.
Tom is paid £8.40 per hour for a basic working week of 35 hours and receives time-and-a-half for any overtime.

Arthur is paid £9 per hour for a basic working week of 39 hours and receives double-time for any overtime. Find

a) Tom's basic weekly wage

b) Tom's overtime rate per hour

c) Arthur's basic weekly wage

d) Arthur's hourly overtime rate

e) which receives the greater gross pay in a week when they both work for 44 hours.

10. John Perry's time-sheet for a week is shown below. He works a basic five-day week and some overtime and finishes early on pay day.

Name John Perry				
Works No. 454				
Week Ending 18-10-1991				
Day	AM		PM	
	in	out	in	out
Monday	7.28	12.30	1.30	3.30
Tuesday	7.30	12.30	1.28	3.31
Wednesday	7.29	12.31	1.30	5.00
Thursday	7.30	12.31	1.29	3.00
Friday	7.31	12.30	1.30	3.30
Saturday	7.30	12.00		
Sunday	—	—		

Use this card to answer the following questions:

a) What time is 'clocking-on' time?

b) Was he late on any morning?

c) What is the length of a normal working day?

d) How long is allowed for lunch?

e) What time is 'clocking-off' time?

f) On which week-day does the factory close down early?

g) On which week-day(s) did he work overtime?

h) How much overtime did he work?

i) Which day is pay-day?

j) Calculate his gross wage if the basic hourly rate is £5.40 and overtime is paid time-and-a-half.

11. Helen Miles works for 38 hours and gets paid £136.80. How much per hour is this? Any work she does in excess of 38 hours is paid at time-and-a-half. What is her hourly overtime rate? How much will she earn in a week when she works for 49 hours?

12. Visit the local Jobcentre and make a note of the different jobs available. For each job find

a) the number of hours in a basic working week

b) the hourly rate of pay

c) the possibility of overtime and the rate at which it is paid.

COMMISSION

Some workers, such as salesmen and representatives, are paid in a different way. They are given a fairly low basic wage but they also get commission on every order they secure. The commission is usually a percentage of the value of the order.

EXERCISE 11b

In addition to a basic weekly wage of £40 Miss Black receives a commission of 1% for selling second-hand motor cars. Calculate her gross wage for a week when she sells cars to the value of £15 000.

$$\text{Basic wage} = £40$$

$$\text{Commission on } £15\,000 \text{ at } 1\% = \frac{1}{100} \times £15\,000$$

$$= £150$$

$$\therefore \quad \text{gross wage for the week} = £40 + £150$$

$$= £190$$

1. Calculate the commission earned on sales of

    a) £5000 at 5%   b) £6500 at $2\frac{1}{2}$%.

2. A salesman receives a basic wage of £50 per week plus commission at 6% on the value of the goods he sells. Find his income in a week when sales amount to £13 000.

3. Tom Hannah receives a basic wage of £55 per week and receives a commission of $2\frac{1}{2}$% on all sales over £500. Find his income for a week when he sells goods to the value of £5800.

4. Sue Renner receives a basic wage of £40 per week plus a commission of 2% on her sales. Find her income for a week when she sells goods to the value of £7200.

5. Penny George is paid a basic wage of £35 per week plus a commission of $1\frac{1}{2}$% on her sales over £1000. Find her income for a week when she sells goods to the value of £9300.

6. Alan McKay is paid a basic wage of £50 per week plus a commission of 3% on all sales over £800. Find his income for a week when he sells goods to the value of £7400.

7. In addition to a weekly wage of £70 Olive MacCarthy receives commission of $1\frac{1}{2}$% on the sales of antique furniture. Calculate her gross wage in a week when she sells furniture to the value of £8500.

8. Steve Axe sells double glazing. Apart from a basic wage of £75 he is paid commission at the following rates:

Up to £1000	none
From £1001 to £5000	5%
Above £5000	3%

    Calculate his income in a week when he sells double glazing to a value of £9500.

9. Look through the Job Opportunities columns of your local newspaper. Do any of the jobs offer payment by commission?

PIECE-WORK

Some workers are paid according to the amount of work they do. In a factory, for instance, the amount a person earns can be based on the number of components made in a shift. This type of payment is called *piece-work*.

Sometimes the worker's earnings are made up partly of a piece-work payment and partly of a basic wage.

EXERCISE 11c

Don Smith receives a guaranteed weekly wage of £160 plus a bonus of 40p for every circuit board he completes each day after the first twenty. During a particular week the number of boards he produced are as follows:
Monday 53, Tuesday 48, Wednesday 55, Thursday 51, Friday 47.
Calculate his gross wage for the week.

Guaranteed weekly wage = £160

Bonus payments are paid on (33 + 28 + 35 + 31 + 27)
i.e. 154 circuit boards

Bonus payment = 154 × 40 p

= 6160 p

= £61.60

Gross weekly pay = £160 + £61.60

= £221.60

1. John Perkins gets paid 20p for each article he completes up to 100 per day. For every article above this figure he receives 25p. In a particular week his production figures are

Mon	Tues	Wed	Thurs	Fri
216	192	234	264	219

a) How many articles does he produce in the week ?

b) For how many of these is he paid 20p each ?

c) For how many of these is he paid 25p each ?

d) Find his earnings for the week.

2. The table shows the number of electric light fittings produced by five factory workers each day for a week.

	Mon	Tues	Wed	Thurs	Fri
Ms Arnold	34	38	34	39	41
Mr Beynon	37	40	37	44	—
Miss Capstick	35	40	43	37	39
Mr Davis	42	45	40	52	46
Mrs Edmunds	39	38	37	35	42

The rate of payment is: 55 p for each fitting up to 20 per day and 95 p for each fitting above 20 per day.

a) How many fittings does each person produce in the week ?

b) For each person find
   (i) how many fittings are paid at 55 p each
   (ii) how many fittings are paid at 95 p each ?

c) Find each person's income for the week.

d) On which day of the week does this group of workers produce the greatest number of fittings ?

3. The table shows the number of car components assembled by a group of factory workers during a five day week.

	Mon	Tues	Wed	Thurs	Fri
John Aitkin	142	150	152	154	145
Edna Owen	125	153	153	147	138
Mair Prince	156	144	147	152	152
Len Brown	137	156	160	139	150
Helen Peters	140	154	154	152	148

Each employee is paid 36 p per component per day up to 100, and 48 p for each component above this figure.

a) How many components does each worker produce in the week ?

b) How much does each person earn in a week
   (i) at the lower piece rate   (ii) at the higher piece rate   (iii) in total ?

c) Arrange the workers in rank order by wages.

d) Which day of the week produces   (i) the greatest number of components
   (ii) the least number of components ?

4. Jonathan Green wishes to earn money to buy a bicycle costing £ 127.50 by washing cars at 50 p a time.

a) How many cars must he wash ?

b) How many days would it take him if he washes 15 each day ?

5. A team of twelve factory workers assembles front brake units for lorries. For each unit they produce in a day, up to 150 units, the team receives a bonus payment of 30 p; above this figure they receive 40 p. Find the average bonus payment per worker for a week in which the number of units produced is

Mon	Tues	Wed	Thurs	Fri
320	385	344	396	354

6. Can you find any jobs advertised at your local Jobcentre or in your local newspaper where the method of payment is piece-work ?

SALARIES

Many professional people, for example, civil servants, teachers and managers, are paid a fixed yearly amount called their salary. The salary is usually divided into twelve equal parts and paid each calendar month.

EXERCISE 11d

In each of the following questions, calculate

a) the employee's monthly salary

b) the employee's weekly salary.

	Employee	Annual salary
1.	David Sinclair	£ 6600
2.	Norma Collins	£ 17 808
3.	Tracey Bell	£ 7650
4.	Linda Grant	£ 14 772
5.	Tom King	£ 22 335

In each of the following questions, calculate the employee's annual salary.

	Employee	Monthly salary
6.	Angela Prout	£ 654
7.	John Hall	£ 840
8.	Majid Khan	£ 1136
9.	Peter Lear	£ 1476
10.	Olive Lewis	£ 1572

WAGE INCREASES

How often have you read headlines in newspapers that say such things as 'Civil Servants get 4.5%' or 'Bank Employes seek 8%'? Wage claims and awards are usually given in percentages, but percentage rises do not always seem to be fair. If a rise of 10% is awarded, a person who earns £500 a week will get an extra £50 per week whereas another person earning £100 per week will only get £10. Can you think of a fairer way of awarding pay rises? Can you justify percentage increases?

EXERCISE 11e

Peter James earns £189 per week and receives a 12% increase. Find
a) the cash value of the increase   b) his new weekly wage.

a) Increase in his weekly wage $= \dfrac{12}{100} \times £189$

$= £22.68$

b) New weekly wage $= £189 + £22.68$

$= £211.68$

Calculate, for each of the people listed below,
a) their weekly wage rise
b) their new weekly wage.

	Name	Present weekly wage	Percentage increase
1.	Joan Baber	£160	20%
2.	Peter Barker	£170	10%
3.	Sue Potter	£130	12%
4.	John James	£150	8%
5.	Gordon Peters	£400	6%
6.	Barbara Blake	£170	$7\frac{1}{2}\%$

Name	Present weekly wage	Percentage increase
7. Helen Fisher	£145	4%
8. Derek Gray	£200	5%
9. Haley Waters	£560	$3\frac{1}{2}$%
10. Rachel Walker	£680	12%

11. Kay Norman earns £260 per week. She has a choice of an increase of £30 per week or having her wage increased by 12%. Which should she take?

12. Arthur Wells earns £270 per week. He is offered a wage increase of 8.5% or £25 per week. Which should he take?

13. Has any group of workers been awarded a pay rise recently? What percentage was it? How much should their basic weekly wage increase? Do you know what the job entails? Do you think that the new rate is a fair rate for the job?

NATIONAL INSURANCE CONTRIBUTIONS (NIC)

The state pays workers when they are unemployed or sick. It provides old age pensions when they retire, and finances the National Health Service which is able to look after almost all our medical needs. To do this the Government collects National Insurance (NI) contributions from all employers, employees and self-employed persons. The rates vary according to the decision of the Chancellor of the Exchequer. At the time of writing (July 1992) people earning less than £226 per month pay nothing but as soon as £226 or more is earned 2% on the *first* £226 has to be paid.

EXERCISE 11f

1. John Hibbs earns £95 a week and has 3% deducted for national insurance contributions. Find his NI contributions.

2. Pam Symes earns £120 a week and has 5% deducted for national insurance contributions on all her earnings above £50. How much will she pay in NI contributions?

3. Len White earns £186 a week. National insurance contributions on his wages are calculated as follows: £0 to £50, no payment, £51 to £200 at 5%. Calculate Len White's contributions for the week.

National insurance contributions are calculated at the rates given in the table

Gross earnings per month	NI contribution payable
less than £226	0%
£226	2% i.e. £4.52
£227 to £1690	£4.52 + 9% of gross earnings above £226
over £1690	£136.28

Use this information to calculate Peggy Shaw's NI contributions if she earns £1400 each month.

NI contribution due on first £226 is £4.52

NI contribution due on remaining £1174 is $\frac{9}{100} \times £1174 = £105.66$

∴ total NI contribution due $= £4.52 + £105.66$

$$= £110.18$$

Use the national insurance rates given in the worked example to calculate the national insurance contribution paid by each of the following employees.

4. John Newbold who earns £1000 per month

5. Betty Norman who earns £1200 per month

6. Jim Williams who earns £950 per month

7. Wendy Cowley who earns £1740 per month

Use the national insurance rates given in the table below to calculate the national insurance contributions paid by the employees listed in questions 8 to 11.

Gross earnings per week	NI Contributions Payable
less than £52	0%
£52	2% i.e. £1.04
£53 to £390	£1.04 + 9% of gross earnings above £52
over £390	£31.46

8. Lisa Bingham who earns £90 each week

9. Malcolm Hunt who earns £145 each week

10. Walter Bridges who earns £240 each week

11. Penny Scott who earns £600 each week

12. Mary Rees pays national insurance contributions at the reduced rate of 4% on her weekly wages above £50. (By choosing to do this she cannot claim unemployment or sickness benefit.) Find her NI contributions if she earns £146 each week.

13. Use the data given in question 12 to calculate Mary Rees' NI contributions when her weekly wage rises to £195.

14. Philip Johnson works for a company that operates its own pension scheme. As a result his monthly NI contributions are calculated as follows: 9% of the first £200 plus 6.85% of the balance up to £1200. How much will he pay if his monthly salary is £1400?

15. Because Doug Sinclair is contracted out of NI contributions he pays at the reduced weekly rate of 2% on the first £50 and 5% on the remainder. How much does he pay in contributions if his weekly pay is £125?

16. Lee Summers pays national insurance contributions at the reduced rate of 4% on his weekly income above £55. Find his NI contributions if he earns £167 each week.

17. Use the data given in question 16 to calculate Lee Summers' NI contributions when his weekly wage increases by £18 per week.

18. Thornes Engineering operates its own pension scheme. As a result, employees' NI contributions are calculated as follows: 9% of the first £220 plus 6.85% of the balance up to £1350. How much will an employee pay whose monthly salary is £1650?

INCOME TAX

Every person with an income above a certain figure, whether the income is earned, from a pension or in the form of interest, must pay income tax. Everyone is allowed to keep some income, called allowances, without paying tax. All further income is taxable income and tax is paid on it at a certain percentage. For most people the first band (say £2000) of the taxable income is taxed at 20% while the remainder is taxed at the standard rate, which at present is 25%. People with high incomes pay tax at 40% on their taxable income above approximately £25000. The Chancellor of the Exchequer in his annual budget is likely to vary these rates, and the bands to which they apply, according to the financial and economic needs of the country.

EXERCISE 11g

Olive Green earns £8000 p.a. and has allowances of £3425. Calculate her annual income tax bill if the first £2000 of her taxable income is taxed at 20% and any remaining taxable income is taxed at 25%.

$$\text{Taxable income} = \text{Gross income} - \text{Allowances}$$
$$= £8000 - £3425$$
$$= £4575$$
$$\text{Tax on £2000 at 20\%} = \frac{20}{100} \times £2000$$
$$= £400$$
$$\text{Tax on £2575 at 25\%} = \frac{25}{100} \times £2575$$
$$= £643.75$$
$$\text{Total tax paid} = £400 + £643.75$$
$$= £1043.75$$

1. Complete the table.

Name	Gross income	Allowances	Taxable income
J. Peters	£9000	£2500	
E. John		£1730	£6421
P. Brown	£15430	£3784	
M. Jacob	£24380		£19850
A. Khan		£4731	£8264
C. White	£12670		£9437

2. Find the tax due for each of the employees named in question 1 if the first £2000 of taxable income is taxed at 20% and the remaining amount of taxable income is taxed at 25%.

3. Complete the table.

Name	Gross pay per calendar month	Annual allowances	Annual taxable income
R. Lee	£ 324	£ 1200	
M. Davis	£ 640	£ 2240	
S. Axe	£ 468	£ 2970	
J. Brewer	£ 836	£ 4320	
E. Evans	£ 1200	£ 3600	

4. Find a) the annual income tax bill
           b) the tax due per calendar month,
for the employees named in question 3, assuming that the first £ 2000 p.a. is taxed at 20 % and the remainder at a standard rate of 25 %.

For questions 5 to 10 complete the table assuming that the first £ 3000 p.a. of taxable income is taxed at 20 % and the remaining taxable income is taxed at 25 %.

	Name	Gross weekly pay	Annual non taxable allowances	Gross annual income	Annual taxable income	Weekly income tax payment	Weekly income net of income tax
5.	S. Wilcox	£ 100	£ 4200				
6.	E. Cole	£ 130	£ 3945				
7.	I. Tucker	£ 170	£ 4536				
8.	J. Parry	£ 185	£ 2674				
9.	P. Lewis	£ 240	£ 4333				
10.	C. Snook	£ 350	£ 3780				

GROSS AND NET WAGES

The total amount you earn in a week or a month is called your *gross* wage. Your 'take-home' pay is usually considerably less since there can be deductions for income tax, national insurance contributions, pension funds, etc. When all the agreed deductions have been subtracted from your gross wage, what remains is called your *net wage* or *take-home pay*.

We have already considered national insurance contributions and income tax. These, together with the employees pension contributions, make up the greater part of any deductions.

EXERCISE 11h

Edward Beynon earns £350 per week. He pays £27.86 in national insurance contributions, £21 towards his pension fund and his income tax payments amount to £61.50. Calculate his take-home pay.

$$\text{Total deductions} = £27.86 + £21 + £61.50$$
$$= £110.36$$

$$\text{Net pay} = \text{Gross pay} - \text{deductions}$$
$$= £350 - £110.36$$
$$= £239.64$$

Copy and complete the following table which gives details of the pay earned by several employees of a large firm during one week last January.

	Employee	Gross pay	NIC	Deductions Income tax	Pension fund	Net pay
1.	ATKINS	£95	£4.91	£6.64	£5.70	
2.	CONTI	£110	£6.26	£5.46	£6.60	
3.	DALEY	£145	£9.41	£20.38	£8.70	
4.	GRIFFIN	£176	£12.20	£19.85	£10.56	
5.	HALL	£132	£8.24	£15.07	£7.92	
6.	JAMES	£204	£14.72	£31.59	£12.24	
7.	KELLY	£275	£21.11	£38.19	£16.50	
8.	O'KEEFE	£183		£21.39	£10.98	£137.80
9.	RYTON	£393	£31.46	£68.75		£269.21
10.	VILLIERS	£552	£31.46		£14.52	£397.04

11. Alan Vaughan earns £380 per week. He pays £30.56 national insurance contributions and 6% for his pension fund calculated on his gross income. If income tax amounts to £60.21 calculate his net wage.

12. Nancy Swinbourne earns £156 per week. She pays 4% national insurance contributions, 6% for her pension fund, both calculated on her gross wage. If income tax amounts to £25.46 calculate her take-home pay.

13. Harold Fitt earns £320 per week. His deductions are calculated as follows:

National insurance contributions: £25.57
Pension fund: 6% of his gross wage
Income tax: 25% of the amount by which his gross wage is more than £50.

Calculate his net weekly wage.

SAVINGS

Few people can afford to pay for major things, like motor cars or holidays, from their weekly or monthly earnings. Usually the only way to pay for these things is by saving the money or by borrowing it. We consider next some of the most popular ways of saving.

BUILDING SOCIETIES

Building Societies have been helping people to buy their own homes for more than two hundred years. They collect money from those who wish to save and lend it to those who wish to borrow to buy a home, i.e. take out a mortgage. By charging the borrower a slightly higher rate of interest than they pay to the lender they are able to maintain their offices and pay their staff.

The main reasons why people like saving with a building society are:
a) if you save with them you stand a better chance when you wish to borrow
b) they are open for normal business hours, including Saturday mornings
c) they often pay higher rates of interest to savers than banks do
d) it is very easy both to put money into your account and to take it out.

You can open an ordinary share account with as little as £1. There are several other kinds of accounts that pay better rates of interest than the ordinary account but they may require 7 days, or even longer, notice of withdrawal before you can get your money out.

When you open an ordinary share account you are given a pass book which records all your dealings with the building society.

EXERCISE 11i

A page from Lee Andrews' Ordinary Share Account with the Hally Building Society is shown below. Use it to answer questions 1 to 13.

Date	Cashier's initials	Description	Withdrawn	Invested	Balance
		Balance brought forward			£ 421.81
06 JUL 91	WEA	CASH	£ 50.00		£ 371.81
09 JUL 91	WEA	CHEQUE	£ 312.00		£ 59.81
17 JUL 91	WEA	CHEQUE		£ 78.00	£ 137.81
17 JUL 91	WEA	CASH	£ 35.00		£ 102.81
10 AUG 91	WEA	CHEQUE		£ 750.00	£ 852.81
10 AUG 91	WEA	CASH	£ 200.00		£ 652.81
16 AUG 91	WEA	CASH	£ 320.00		£ 332.81
30 AUG 91	WEA	CHEQUE		£ 421.20	£ 754.01
30 AUG 91	WEA	CASH	£ 300.00		£ 454.01
02 SEP 91	WEA	CASH	£ 80.00		£ 374.01
18 SEP 91	WEA	CASH	£ 300.00		£ 74.01
23 SEP 91	WEA	CHEQUE		£ 472.53	£ 546.54
04 OCT 91	WEA	CASH	£ 300.00		£ 246.54
15 OCT 91	WEA	CHEQUE	£ 195.80		£ 50.74
30 NOV 91	WEA	CHEQUE		£ 642.50	£ 693.24
04 DEC 91	WEA	CASH	£ 80.00		£ 613.24
20 DEC 91	WEA	CHEQUE		£ 136.40	£ 749.64
20 DEC 91	WEA	CASH	£ 200.00		£ 549.64
31 DEC 91	—	Interest		£ 148.98	£ 698.62
08 JAN 91	WEA	CHEQUE	£ 237.40	£ 461.22	

1. What was the largest amount in the account at any one time during the period ?

2. How much was in the account on

    a) 10 August   b) 3 October   c) 25 December ?

3. What was the largest amount withdrawn on any one day ?

4. What was the largest amount paid into the account on any one day ?

5. How much interest is recorded on this page? Is the interest added to, or subtracted from, the balance ?

6. How many times did Lee Andrews withdraw cash from the account ? What was the total amount of cash withdrawn during the period ?

7. How many cheques were

    a) paid into the account   b) withdrawn from the account ?

8. What was the least amount in the account during the period ?

9. How much more would be carried forward to the next page than was brought forward to this page ?

10. How much was paid into the account during the last three months of the year ?

11. How much was withdrawn from the account during August and September ?

12. On how many days did Lee visit the building society ?
(Use the information given in the pass book and assume that no more than one visit was made on any one day.)

13. Lee Andrews' next eight transactions were:

        9 January — paid in a cheque for £64.58
        15 January — withdrew £100 in cash
        29 January — paid in a cheque for £374.43
        3 February — withdrew £250 in cash
        21 February — withdrew a cheque for £280 to pay the deposit for
                  a holiday
        28 February — paid in a cheque for £173.80
        3 March — withdrew £180 in cash
        25 March — withdrew £230 in cash

Show how you would expect the next page of the pass book to be written up.

14. What was the balance after the withdrawal on 25th March ?

NATIONAL SAVINGS

If you look through the numerous leaflets available at Post Offices you will find that they offer many different ways of saving.

Investing in National Savings has many advantages.

1. The investment is totally secure, i.e. you cannot lose your money.
2. The rate of interest is very competitive.
3. Depositing and withdrawing money is easy since this may be done at any Post Office.

National savings investments include Premium bonds, fixed rate and index-linked certificates, ordinary savings accounts and many others. The most popular of these are the National Savings Certificates, which are now considered.

NATIONAL SAVINGS CERTIFICATES

National Savings Certificates are of two types: Index-Linked Certificates, which provide full protection against inflation, plus extra interest, and the more common Guaranteed Certificates, which guarantee a fixed rate of interest, tax free, over a given number of years.

A recent issue allows any person to buy up to 400 units at £25 per unit. The value and yield of one unit, i.e. a £25 certificate, is given in the following table.

Year after purchase	Value at end of year	Yield for year tax free
1	£26.44	5.76%
2	£28.20	6.66%
3	£30.40	7.80%
4	£33.12	8.95%
5	£36.48	10.14%

The units may be cashed in at any time but, as the table shows, the rate of interest increases the longer the certificates remain invested.

EXERCISE 11j

Use the table given in the text to answer the questions that follow.

1. How many £25 units could I buy for £100 ?

2. How many £25 units could I buy for £450 ?

3. What would be the cost of buying 9 units ?

4. What would be the cost of buying 150 units ?

5. Find the value of 30 units after 3 years.

6. Find the value of 55 units after 4 years.

7. a) What is the purchase price of 35 units ?
b) How much are they worth when they are cashed in after 5 years ?
c) How much interest have they earned ?

8. How much extra interest would I receive by leaving 30 units in for 5 years rather than cashing them after 3 years ?

9. How much interest will be earned on 50 units invested for 5 years ?

10. How much interest will be earned on 30 units invested for 4 years ?

11. How much interest will be earned in 5 years by a lady who invests £2000 in these certificates ?

12. Tom received £2736 when he cashed his certificates after 5 years.

   a) How many units did he buy ?

   b) How much did he pay for them ?

   c) How much interest did he receive on them ?

13. Judith received £1337.60 when she cashed her certificates after 3 years.

   a) How many units did she buy ?

   b) How much did she pay for them ?

   c) How much interest was earned ?

MIXED EXERCISE

EXERCISE 11k

In this exercise several alternative answers are given. Write down the letter that corresponds to the correct answer.

1. Janet's basic rate of pay is £4 per hour. Overtime is paid at time-and-a-half. Her hourly overtime pay is

   A £5   **B** £4.50   **C** £8   **D** £6

2. Peter 'clocked in' at 7.35 and 'clocked out' at 4.05. He was allowed one hour for lunch. The number of hours he worked was

   A 7 h 20 min   **B** 8 hours   **C** $7\frac{1}{2}$ hours   **D** $8\frac{1}{2}$ hours

3. Alison Brown receives a basic wage of £80 per week and receives a commission of 3% on all sales over £1000. In a week when she sells goods to the value of £2000 her income for the week is

   A £110   **B** £140   **C** £380   **D** £60

4. Una earns £100 a week and receives a rise of 15% while Elsie, her sister, earns £300 a week but receives a rise of only 5%. Which of the following statements must be true ?

   A After their rises Una is better off than Elsie.

   B Una has a larger rise, in pounds, than Elsie.

   C They have exactly the same rise.

   D Elsie's rise is £6.40 a week more than Una's.

5. Roy pays income tax at 20% on everything he earns each week above £60. In a week when he earns £150 the amount of income tax he pays is

   A £90   **B** £18   **C** £30   **D** £15

12 HOUSEHOLD EXPENSES

ELECTRICITY BILLS

The unit of electricity is the kilowatt hour (kWh). It is the amount of electricity used in one hour by an appliance with a rating of 1 kilowatt. A 2 kW electric fire would use 1 unit in half an hour, whereas a 100 W bulb would operate for 10 hours on the same amount of electricity (1 kW = 1000 W). Every consumer has a meter which shows the total number of units used since the meter was installed. Most meters give a digital reading which is easily read, e.g.

0	4	3	5	2

The meter is usually read quarterly by an official of the electricity board. The bill, an example of which is shown below, shows the readings at the beginning and end of the quarter, the number of units used, the fixed or standing charge, the cost of each unit, and the total amount due.

M·E·B
MIDLANDS ELECTRICITY

Miss A Richards
12 Thorpe Road
WORCESTER
WR14 2GC

ACCOUNT DATE	CONSUMER REFERENCE No.
02 OCT 92	3231 479

VAT REGISTRATION No.

238	5679	21

METER READINGS			AMOUNT £
PREVIOUS	PRESENT		
50245	50828	Domestic Tariff	
		583 Units @ 8.46	49.32
		Quarterly charge	11.75

DATE OF	E INDICATES ESTIMATED READING. SEE REVERSE OF ACCOUNT	TOTAL AMOUNT	
QUARTER 4	C INDICATES CONSUMERS OWN READING. THE DATE SHOWN ON THE LEFT IS THE DATE WE RECEIVED YOUR READING	NOW DUE FOR PAYMENT	£ 61.07
	R INDICATES METER REMOVED		

PAYMENTS BY POST to MIDLANDS ELECTRICITY BOARD, P.O. BOX No. 18, KINGSWINFORD, WEST MIDLANDS, DY6 8BL. (further advice on methods of payment is given overleaf)

While electricity is a difficult form of energy to store, it is convenient to produce it continuously at the power stations, 24 hours a day. There are therefore times of the day when more electricity is produced than is normally required. The Electricity Boards are able to solve this problem by selling 'off-peak', or 'white meter', electricity to domestic users at a cheaper rate. Most of the electricity consumed in this way is for domestic heating. Off-peak electricity is sold at approximately half price.

EXERCISE 12a

At the beginning of a quarter Mr Smith's electricity meter reading was 51204 and at the end of the quarter it was 52572. How many units were used in the quarter ?

Number of units used was $52572 - 51204 = 1368$

Copy and complete the following table which shows the meter readings at the beginning and end of a quarter.

Name	Reading at beginning	Reading at end	Number of units used in the quarter
1. R. Bird	24683	24927	
2. A. Smith	51949	53208	
3. P. Brown	34927	36114	

How many units of electricity were used in the quarter by these customers ?

Name	Present reading	Previous reading
4. T. White	14294	13721
5. M. Stuart	37265	35407
6. C. Connelly	49386	48966

7. Complete the following table which shows the meter readings in the Short household for a year.

Date	Meter reading	Number of units used
2 February	46249	
5 May	47103	First quarter:
3 August	47615	Second quarter:
10 November	47979	Third quarter:
1 February	49233	Fourth quarter:

8. Complete the following table which refers to meter readings in the Jones household for a year.

Date	Meter reading	Number of units used in the specified quarter
10 January	53498	
7 April		First: 912
13 July		Second: 446
9 October	55450	Third:
12 January		Fourth: 1184

The Seaton household used 1192 units of electricity during the fourth quarter of the year. If electricity costs 7.25 p per unit and there is a standing charge of £ 11.54, find the cost of electricity for the quarter.

Cost of 1192 units at 7.25 p per unit $= 1192 \times 7.25\,\text{p}$

$$= 8642\,\text{p}$$

$$= £\,86.42$$

Total cost $=$ standing charge $+ £\,86.42$

$$= £\,11.54 + £\,86.42$$

$$= £\,97.96$$

Find the quarterly electricity bill for each of the following households.

	Household	Meter reading		Number of units used	Standing charge	Cost per unit
		At beginning of quarter	At end of quarter			
9.	Collins	47392	48964		£ 11.50	12 p
10.	Dando	15926	16911		£ 12.40	13 p
11.	Hayter	33464	34709		£ 15.00	9.5 p
12.	Jarvis	24355	25182		£ 18.30	11.5 p

Find the quarterly electricity bills for each of the following households. Assume in each case that there is a standing charge of £10, and that off-peak units are bought at half price.

	Name	Number of units used		Basic cost per unit
		At the basic price	Off-peak	
13.	G. Allen	800	900	10 p
14.	L. Dobson	1200	1000	9 p
15.	P. Walters	750	1100	8.5 p
16.	R. Young	645	850	7.65 p
17.	D. Woods	1540	3500	8.4 p

18. Mr Mudge's electricity bill was £54 including a standing charge of £9.45. If electricity costs 7.5 p per unit, how many units were used during the quarter ?

19. In the Shaw household the electricity bill for the quarter was £92.79. If they had used 875 units at 9.4 p each how much was the standing charge ?

20.

Appliance	Rating	Number of hours used in the week	Number of units used	Cost at 8.45 p per unit
Cooker	8 kW	5		
TV set	250 W	36		
Hi-fi	100 W	6		
Refrigerator	200 W	50		
Washing machine	2 kW	5		
Electric fire	3 kW	18		
Vacuum cleaner	500 W	2		
6 light bulbs	100 W	40 each		

The table given above shows the various appliances used in the Berry household and the period of time for which each was used during a particular week. Complete the table, giving each value in the last column correct to the nearest penny.

Find the total cost for a quarter of thirteen similar weeks if there is a standing charge of £9.85.

GAS BILLS

Many households use gas for cooking and heating. The amount of gas used is measured by volume and recorded in units by a meter, each unit being 100 cubic feet of gas.

In different areas, however, equal volumes of gas give different amounts of useful heat, so, to be fair, the Gas Boards charge for their gas in units of heat called *kilowatt hours* (kWh).

The way in which the number of kilowatt hours used is calculated from a meter reading in cubic feet is quite complicated. Fortunately it is worked out by the Gas Boards but, so that you can see how it is done, here is a summary of the procedure.

The volume of gas indicated by the meter has to be changed into kilowatt hours. This is done by the following formula which includes a conversion factor called the calorific value – a typical value is 38.2 megajoules per cubic metre.

$$\text{Number of kilowatt hours}$$
$$= \frac{\left(\begin{array}{c}\text{Number of cubic}\\\text{metres of gas}\end{array}\right) \times \left(\begin{array}{c}\text{Calorific value in}\\\text{megajoules per cubic metre}\end{array}\right)}{3.6}$$

For example, 271 units of gas are recorded as used by the gas meter, with a calorific value of $38.2\,\text{MJ/m}^3$, is equivalent to $8138\,\text{kWh}$. ($100\,\text{ft}^3 \approx 2.83\,\text{m}^3$)

A typical standing charge is now 10.30 p per day. This gives £9.48 for a quarter of 92 days. Various quarterly tariffs are available. An example using a standard credit tariff is given on the opposite page.

EXERCISE 12b

Copy and complete the following table which shows gas meter readings at the beginning and end of a quarter.

	Meter reading		
	At beginning of quarter	At end of quarter	Number of units used in the quarter
1.	000493	000625	
2.	002936	003107	
3.	000927	001043	
4.	005934	006258	

<table>
<tr><td colspan="2">British Gas</td><td>If you have an enquiry about this bill please ring</td><td>District
11</td></tr>
</table>

British Gas	If you have an enquiry about this bill please ring — District **11**

During normal office hours

VAT registration number
232 1770 91   1/2991

MR. A. N. OTHER
FLAT 1
NEWTOWN ROAD, NEWTOWN
ABC 124X

Customer reference number

Date of bill (tax point)
15 APR 92

Calorific value:
38.2   Mj/m²

Date of meter reading	Meter reading (see below for key –o) Present	Previous	Gas supplied 100s cubic feet	Cubic metres	kWh	Charges
14 APR	5862	5636	226	639.5	6785	106.25

STANDING CHARGE PERIOD 13.1.92 TO 14.4.92   9.48

92 DAYS AT 10.30p PER DAY

Tariff **STANDARD CREDIT**   Pence per 1.566 kWh

If the present meter reading is an estimate (E) and you would like us to use your own meter reading, please write your reading on the back of the bill and send it to us as soon as possible. Or telephone and tell us your reading. Thank you.

£   115.73

Key –o
to types of
meter reading
E Estimated reading
C customer's reading
X Exchange meter

5. Copy and complete the following table which refers to the gas meter readings in the Banks household for a year.

Date	Meter reading	Number of units used in the quarter
3 January	003342	
9 April	003498	First:
13 July		Second: 104
8 October	003734	Third:
5 January		Fourth: 198

During the winter quarter Mrs Leatt used 3986 kWh of gas. If gas costs 1.566 p per kWh and there is a standing charge of £9.48 find the quarterly bill.

$$\text{Standing charge} = £9.48$$

$$3986 \text{ kWh at } 1.566 \text{ p per kWh} = 3986 \times 1.566 \text{ p}$$

$$= £62.42$$

$$\text{Quarterly bill} = £9.48 + £62.42$$

$$= £71.90$$

Calculate the quarterly bill for each of the following households. (Assume that there are 92 days in a quarter.)

	Name	Number of kWh used	Daily standing charge	Cost of gas per kWh
6.	Collier	5800	10 p	1.5 p
7.	Green	10 100	12 p	1.6 p
8.	Morgan	5366	10.4 p	1.8 p
9.	Skipworth	6873	10.9 p	1.556 p
10.	Yacomeni	9048	12.6 p	1.672 p

Miss Swaines uses an average of 10 200 kWh each quarter (92 days). She can pay for this gas using

either a) CREDIT Tariff which charges 1.55 p per kWh plus a daily standing charge of 12 p

or b) the DOMESTIC PREPAYMENT Tariff which charges 2.5 p per kWh for the first 1500 kWh plus 1.37 p per kWh for additional kWh plus a daily standing charge of 6 p.

Which method of payment should she use?

a) If she uses the credit tariff

$$\text{cost of } 10\,200 \times 1.55\,\text{p per kWh} = 10\,200 \times 1.55\,\text{p}$$
$$= £\,158.10$$
$$\text{Standing charge} = 92 \times 12\,\text{p} = £\,11.04$$
$$\text{Total cost} = £\,169.14$$

b) If she uses the domestic prepayment tariff

$$\text{cost of first } 1500\,\text{kWh at } 2.5\,\text{p per kWh} = 1500 \times 2.5\,\text{p}$$
$$= £\,37.50$$

Cost of remaining 8700 kWh at 1.37 p per kWh

$$= 8700 \times 1.37\,\text{p} = £\,119.19$$
$$\text{Standing charge} = 92 \times 6\,\text{p} = £\,5.52$$
$$\text{Total cost} = £\,162.21$$

Method (b) costs £ 6.93 less than Method (a). It would therefore be better to use the domestic prepayment tariff.

For each of the following customers calculate which tariff is the cheaper and by how much. (Assume that there are 92 days in a quarter.)

	Customer	Number of kWh used	Credit tariff		Domestic Prepayment tariff		
			Standing charge per day	Cost per kWh	Standing charge per day	Price per kWh for initial kWh	Price per kWh for further kWh
11.	Pusey	8500	15 p	1.5 p	7 p	2.6 p for first 1500 kWh	1.4 p
12.	Kilminster	12 000	18 p	1.6 p	8 p	2.8 p for first 1500 kWh	1.5 p
13.	Wates	15 000	18.9 p	1.8 p	8.5 p	2.9 p for first 1000 kWh	1.5 p
14.	Young	13 800	20 p	1.7 p	9.2 p	2.6 p for first 2000 kWh	1.59 p
15.	Smith	9000	13.2 p	1.65 p	8 p	2.8 p for first 1500 kWh	1.52 p

	Customer	Number of kWh used	Credit tariff		Domestic Prepayment tariff		
			Standing charge per day	Cost per kWh	Standing charge per day	Price per kWh for initial kWh	Price per kWh for further kWh
16.	Urban	10 500	16.3 p	1.6 p	11 p	2.6 p for first 1500 kWh	1.35 p
17.	Zaraschi	12 000	20.2 p	1.9 p	10.3 p	2.8 p for first 1000 kWh	1.45 p
18.	Liszt	12 412	19.3 p	2.1 p	9.5 p	2.9 p for first 1800 kWh	1.52 p

POSTAGE

The Post Office offers all of us a wide range of services, the most important of which is the collecting and delivering of letters and parcels.

The rates (June 1992) for sending letters and parcels within the United Kingdom are given below but are likely to change from time to time.

Letters

Weight not over	First Class	Second Class
60g	24p	18p
100g	36p	28p
150g	45p	34p
200g	54p	41p
250g	64p	49p
300g	74p	58p
350g	85p	66p
400g	96p	75p
450g	£1.08	84p
500g	£1.20	93p
600g	£1.50	£1.15
700g	£1.80	£1.35
750g	£1.95	£1.40
800g	£2.05	Not admissible over 750g
900g	£2.25	
1000g	£2.40	
Each extra 250g or part thereof 60p		

Parcels

Weight not over	Price
1kg	£2.50
2kg	£3.15
4kg	£4.10
6kg	£4.65
8kg	£5.35
10kg	£6.25
30kg	£7.80

EXERCISE 12c

Use the tables given in the text to answer the questions that follow.

> Find the cost of posting
> a) six letters, each weighing under 100 g, by first-class letter post
> b) two parcels, each weighing under 6 kg, by parcel post.
>
> > a) Posting one letter, under 100 g, by first-class post costs 36 p.
> >
> > $\therefore$ cost of six such letters is $6 \times 36\,\text{p} = £2.16$
> >
> > b) Posting one parcel, under 6 kg, by parcel post costs £4.65.
> >
> > $\therefore$ cost of two such parcels is $2 \times £4.65 = £9.30$

Find the cost of posting

1. three letters, each weighing a little less than 60 g, by first-class letter post

2. six letters, each weighing a little less than 100 g, by second-class letter post

3. five letters, each weighing a little less than 300 g, by first-class letter post

4. four letters, each weighing a little less than 350 g, by second-class letter post

5. ten letters, each weighing a little less than 500 g, by first-class letter post

6. two letters, each weighing a little less than 400 g, by second-class letter post

7. three letters, each weighing 342 g, by second-class letter post

8. four letters, each weighing 84 g, by first-class letter post

9. a parcel, weighing 1400 g, by first-class letter post

10. two parcels, each weighing 1.1 kg

11. three parcels, each weighing 4 kg

12. five parcels, each weighing $5\frac{1}{2}$ kg

13. a letter weighing 213 g and a parcel weighing 5400 g, both by first-class letter post

14. four parcels, weighing respectively $2\,\text{kg}$, $3\frac{1}{2}\,\text{kg}$, $5\frac{1}{4}\,\text{kg}$ and $7\,\text{kg}$, by parcel post.

15. three letters, weighing $173\,\text{g}$, $195\,\text{g}$ and $347\,\text{g}$ respectively, by second-class letter post.

16. A publisher wishes to send urgently a book weighing $4\frac{1}{2}\,\text{kg}$ to a customer. What is probably the fastest way of getting it there? How much more expensive is it to send the book first-class letter rate than at parcel rate?

17. A mail order firm wishes to send advertising material to $10\,500$ prospective customers. If each envelope, plus its contents, weighs $160\,\text{g}$ how much does the firm save by using second-class rather than first-class postage?

18. A solicitor's office sends the following mail in a week:

> 86 letters, each under $60\,\text{g}$, by first-class post
> 14 letters, each under $200\,\text{g}$, by first-class post
> 6 letters, each under $350\,\text{g}$, by second-class post
> 4 parcels, weighing respectively $1\frac{1}{2}\,\text{kg}$, $2\frac{1}{4}\,\text{kg}$, $5\,\text{kg}$ and $4\frac{1}{2}\,\text{kg}$, by parcel post.

Find the postage bill for the week. What would this amount to in a full year of 52 similar weeks?

For questions 19 and 20 you will need information from your local Post Office.

19. a) How much does it cost to send newspapers or magazines by post?

b) What is the difference between surface mail and airmail?

c) Which counties qualify for the area parcel rate from your local Post Office?

20. What is   a) a registered letter   c) COD
                b) recorded delivery   d) data post?

UNIT PRICING

Assuming that goods are of the same quality, it is often difficult to know whether to buy three small tins of paint or one large tin; two small jars of coffee or one large jar.

To decide which is the better buy we can find the cost of one unit in each case,

e.g. find the cost per gram, of beans from two different sized tins

or   find the cost to paint one square metre, from two different tins of paint.

EXERCISE 12d

> Which is the lower unit price:
> 500 g of cheese for £ 1.20 or 400 g for £ 1 ?
>
> If 500 g of cheese costs £ 1.20
>
> the cost of 100 g is $\dfrac{120}{5}$ p = 24 p
>
> If 400 g costs £ 1
>
> the cost of 100 g is $\dfrac{100}{4}$ p = 25 p
>
> The lower unit price is therefore 500 g for £ 1.20.

In the following questions find the cost of one unit in each case and hence decide which is the better buy.

1. Butter at £ 1 per kg, or £ 2.94 for 3 kg

2. A tin of beans at 27 p for $15\frac{1}{2}$ oz, or a tin of beans at 21 p for $7\frac{1}{2}$ oz

3. Bread at 94 p for a large loaf, or 67 p for a small loaf, if the small loaf is $\frac{3}{5}$ the weight of the large loaf.

4. Envelopes at 40 p per dozen, or envelopes at 32 p for 10

5. Plants at 5 p each, or 50 p per dozen.

6. Plants at £ 2.40 per dozen, or £ 4.50 per box of 25

7. Meat at £ 8 for $2\frac{1}{2}$ lb, or meat at £ 11.80 for $3\frac{1}{4}$ lb.

8. Potatoes at 80 p for a 5 kg bag, or potatoes at £ 6.50 for a 50 kg bag

9. Paint at £ 8.50 for 5 litres, or paint at £ 3.50 for 2 litres

10. A tin of paint costing £ 4.30 that covers $20\,m^2$, or a tin of paint costing £ 3 that covers $14\,m^2$.

11. Engine oil at £ 2.34 for 2 litres, or engine oil at £ 5.80 for 5 litres

12. Chocolates at £ 1.99 for a box of 44 or chocolates at £ 1.05 for a box of 24.

MIXED EXERCISE

EXERCISE 12e

1. Copy and complete the following table which refers to the electricity meter readings in the Robinson household for a year.

Date	Meter reading	Number of units used in the specified quarter
3 January	20436	
5 April		First: 739
2 July		Second: 475
8 October	22173	Third:
5 January		Fourth: 686

In questions 2 and 3 find the numbers missing from the boxes.

2.

TARIFF	METER READING		UNITS	VAT RATE %	£
	PRESENT	PREVIOUS			
DOMESTIC	16291	15843	☐		
☐ @ 8.2p				0	☐
QUARTERLY CHARGE				0	12.60
TOTAL AMOUNT NOW DUE					☐

3.

DATE OF READING	METER READING		GAS SUPPLIED		VAT %	CHARGES
	PRESENT	PREVIOUS	CUBIC FEET (HUNDREDS)	kWh		
14 JUNE	4261	☐	143	4294	0	
STANDING CHARGE 15.5 p per day (92 days)						
TARIFF DOMESTIC 4294 kWh at 1.55 p per kWh						☐
TOTAL AMOUNT DUE						☐

4. Mrs Wells' gas bill was £112.95 including a standing charge of £11.83. If one kWh of gas costs 1.5 p how many kWh were used during the quarter?

13 TRANSFORMATIONS AND CONGRUENCE

LINE SYMMETRY

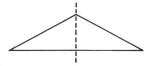

When a drawing can be folded along a line so that one half of the drawing lies exactly over the other half, we say that the drawing is symmetrical about the line. The line is called an axis of symmetry.

REFLECTIONS

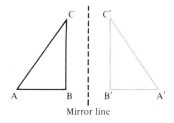

Mirror line

The object, △ABC, is reflected in the mirror line to give the image, △A′B′C′.

The object and its image are symmetrical, with the mirror line as the line of symmetry.

EXERCISE 13a

Copy the diagram on squared paper and draw the line of symmetry. Use a coloured pen or a broken line.

1. 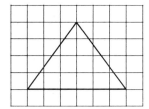   **2.**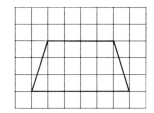

3.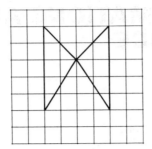

5.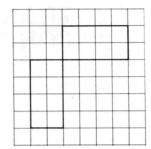

4.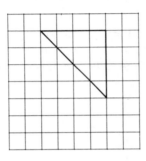

6.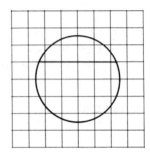

The black figure is the object and the grey figure is the image. Copy the diagram on squared paper and draw the mirror line.

7.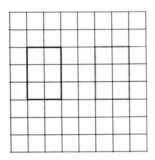

9.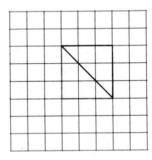

8.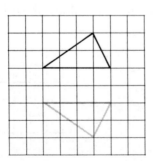

10.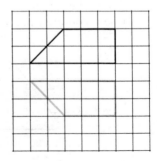

11.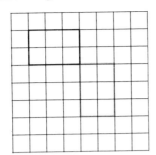

12.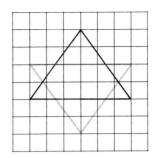

Copy the figure on squared paper and draw the reflection of the object in the mirror line.

13.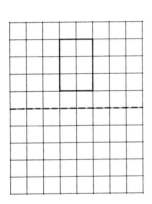

15.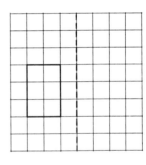

14.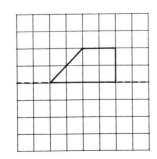

16.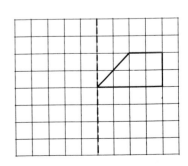

17. 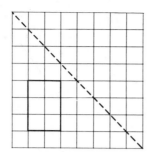   **18.**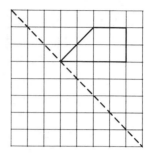

EXERCISE 13b

Copy the diagram and draw the image of the object A after reflection in
a) the x-axis and label it B   b) the y-axis and label it C.

1. 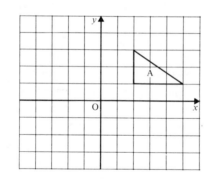   **3.**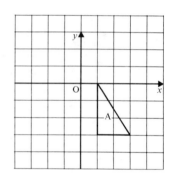

2. 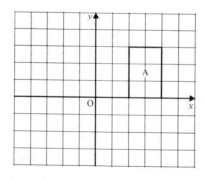   **4.**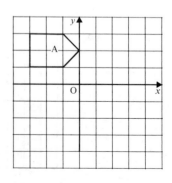

In each question from 5 to 8, copy the diagram. Draw the image of the object A after reflection in

a) the x-axis and label it B   b) the line $y = x$ and label it C.

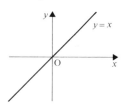

5.

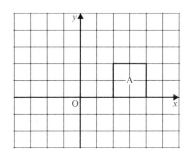

7.

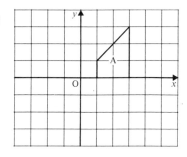

6.

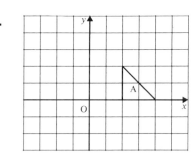

8.

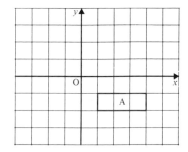

In each question from 9 to 12, the object, rectangle ABCD, is reflected in a line to give the image, A'B'C'D'. Name the line.

9.

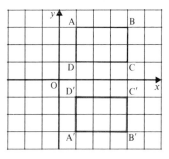

10.

11.

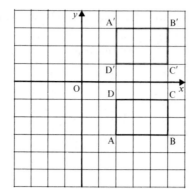

12.

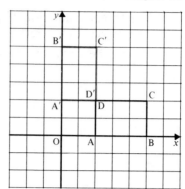

In each question from 13 to 20, the grey rectangle is the image produced by reflecting the object ABCD in a line. Copy the diagram. Label the vertices of the image A′, B′, C′, D′, so that A′ is the image of A, B′ is the image of B, etc, and draw the mirror line.

13.

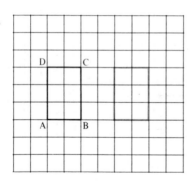

15.

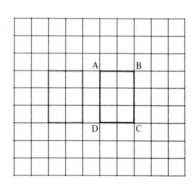

14.

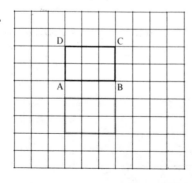

16.

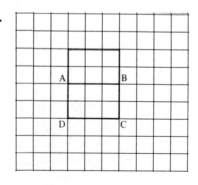

17.

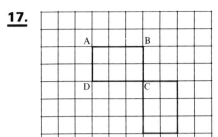

18.

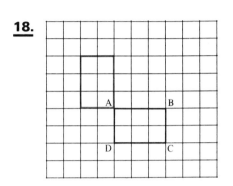

19.

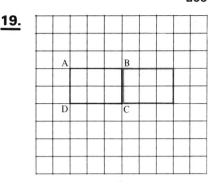

20.

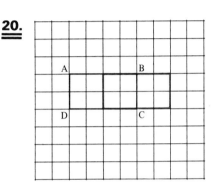

ROTATIONS

We can change the position of an object by rotating it about a point.

(i)

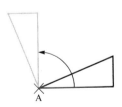

(ii)

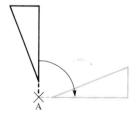

The amount of rotation is called the angle of rotation. This angle must be given by size *and* sense of turning. In Fig (i) the angle of rotation is 90° anticlockwise and in Fig (ii) the angle of rotation is 90° clockwise.

The point about which the object is rotated is called the point of rotation. Sometimes this point is on the object but it need not be.

EXERCISE 13c

The object is mapped to the image by a rotation about O. Give the angle of rotation.

1.

4.

2.

5.

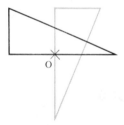

3.

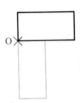

6.

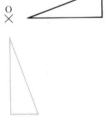

Copy the diagram. Draw the image of A after a rotation about O of
a) 90° clockwise and label it B
b) 180° and label it C.

7.

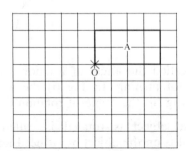

8.

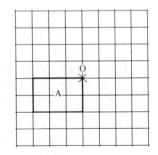

9.

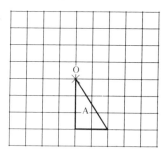

11.

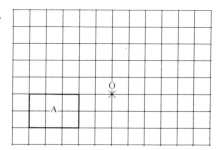

10.

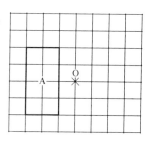

12.

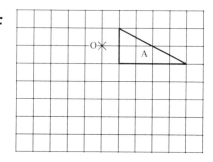

The grey image is produced by rotating the object about the point marked with a cross. Copy the diagram. Label with A′, B′, C′, etc. the vertices of the image that correspond to the vertices A, B, C, etc, of the object.

13.

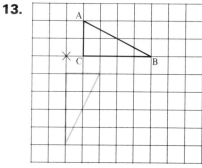

15.

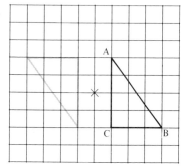

14.

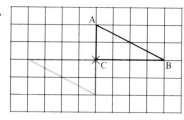

16.

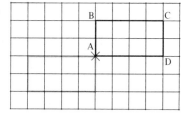

17.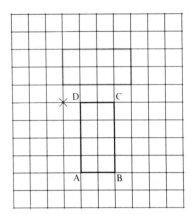

18.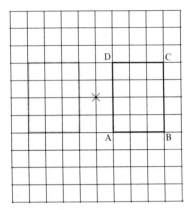

TRANSLATIONS

A translation changes the position of an object by sliding it along a straight line.

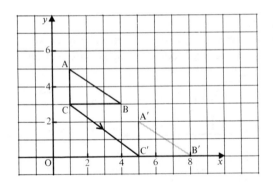

The image, A′B′C′, is produced by moving the object, ABC, 4 units to the right and 3 units down. (This movement can be seen clearly when a point on the object is joined to the corresponding point on the image.)

We use the vector $\begin{pmatrix} 4 \\ -3 \end{pmatrix}$ to describe this translation.

Notice that the top number gives horizontal movement; a positive number represents movement to the right and a negative number represents movement to the left. The bottom number gives vertical movement; a positive number represents movement up the page and a negative number represents movement down the page.

EXERCISE 13d

Write down the vectors represented by the following lines.

1.    **5.**    **9.**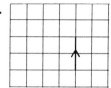

2. 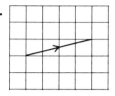   **6.**    **10.**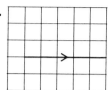

3. 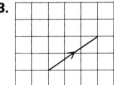   **7.**    **11.**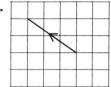

4. 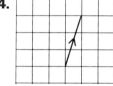   **8.** 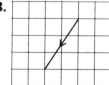   **12.**

Draw a line on squared paper to represent each of the following vectors. Don't forget to put the arrow on the line.

13. $\begin{pmatrix} 3 \\ 5 \end{pmatrix}$ **15.** $\begin{pmatrix} 5 \\ 0 \end{pmatrix}$ **17.** $\begin{pmatrix} -4 \\ 5 \end{pmatrix}$ **19.** $\begin{pmatrix} -5 \\ -5 \end{pmatrix}$

14. $\begin{pmatrix} 6 \\ 2 \end{pmatrix}$ **16.** $\begin{pmatrix} 0 \\ 3 \end{pmatrix}$ **18.** $\begin{pmatrix} 4 \\ -1 \end{pmatrix}$ **20.** $\begin{pmatrix} -3 \\ 0 \end{pmatrix}$

The grey figure is the image of the black figure. Write down the vector which describes the translation.

21.

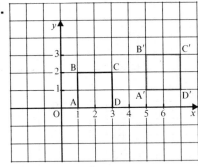

24.

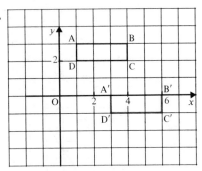

22.

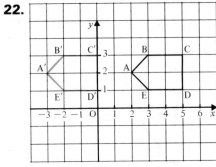

25.

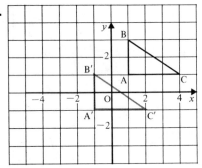

23.

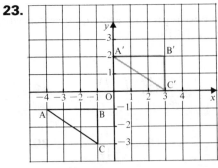

26.

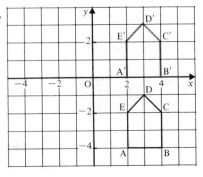

27. 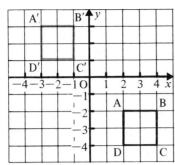   **28.**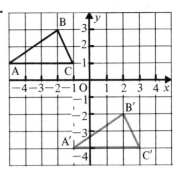

For each question from 29 to 34, copy the diagram below and use a coloured line to draw the image of the given rectangle ABCD after a translation described by the given vector. Label with A', B', etc, the vertices of the image that correspond to the vertices A, B, etc of the object.

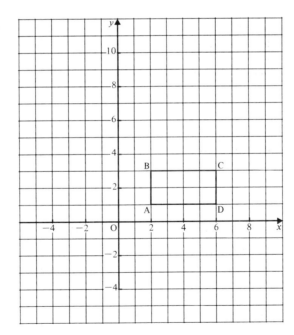

29. $\begin{pmatrix} 5 \\ 3 \end{pmatrix}$ **31.** $\begin{pmatrix} 0 \\ -4 \end{pmatrix}$ **33.** $\begin{pmatrix} -4 \\ -3 \end{pmatrix}$

30. $\begin{pmatrix} 4 \\ 6 \end{pmatrix}$ **32.** $\begin{pmatrix} -6 \\ 1 \end{pmatrix}$ **34.** $\begin{pmatrix} 2 \\ -5 \end{pmatrix}$

CONGRUENCE

Translations, rotations and reflections do not change the shape or size of an object. All they do is change the position.

We say that under these transformations the object and the image are *congruent*.

> Any two figures which are the same shape
> and size are called congruent figures.

EXERCISE 13e

State whether or not the two figures are congruent. If they are, name a transformation which maps the left-hand figure to the right-hand figure.

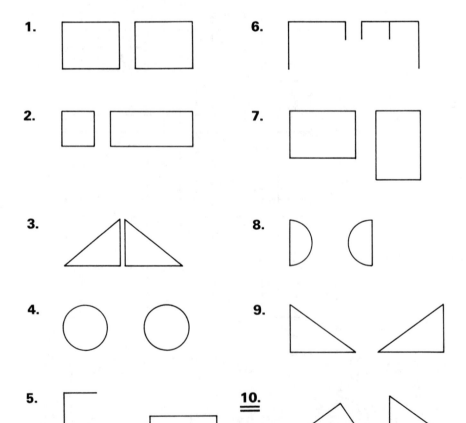

11.
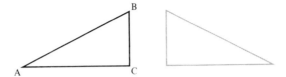

The triangles are congruent and triangle ABC is mapped to the grey triangle by a reflection. Copy the diagram. Label the vertices of the grey triangle A′, B′, C′ to correspond with the vertices of △ABC.

12.
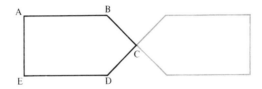

The shapes are congruent. Make two copies of the diagram. Label the vertices of the grey shape A′, B′, C′, D′, E′ to correspond with the vertices of the black shape if

a) the black shape is mapped to the grey shape by a reflection

b) the grey shape is obtained by rotating the black shape about C.

13.
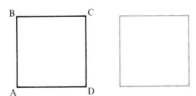

These two squares are identical. Make three copies of this diagram. Label the vertices of the grey square A′, B′, C′, D′ so that they correspond to the vertices A, B, C, D of the black square when the grey square is produced from ABCD by

a) a reflection   b) a translation   c) a rotation.

14.

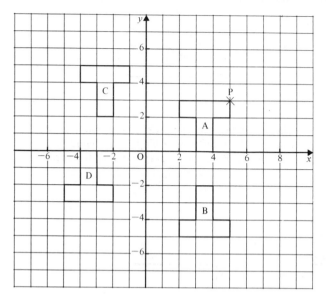

a) Name a transformation that maps A to B and write down the coordinates of the vertex of B corresponding to P.

b) Name a transformation that maps A to C and write down the coordinates of the vertex of C that corresponds to P.

c) Name a transformation that maps A to D. Give the coordinates of the vertex of D that corresponds to P.

d) Name a transformation that maps B to D.

15.

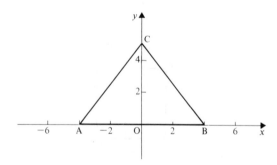

a) Name the transformation for which △ACO is the image of △BCO.

b) What type of triangle is △ACB ?

c) Write down the lengths of AB and OC.

d) Find, in square units, the area of △ABC.

14 THE TANGENT OF AN ANGLE

NAMING THE SIDES OF A RIGHT-ANGLED TRIANGLE

In Book 3B we gave the name *hypotenuse* to the side opposite to the right angle in a right-angled triangle.

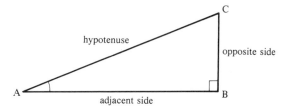

In triangle ABC, AC is the hypotenuse. It is the side opposite to the right angle.

For the angle A, we call BC the *opposite* side and AB the *adjacent*, or neighbouring, side.

EXERCISE 14a

Copy the diagrams in questions 1 to 6.

In each diagram name the hypotenuse and the side opposite and adjacent to the marked angle.

1.

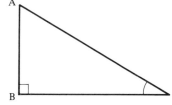

2.

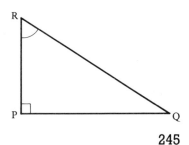

3.

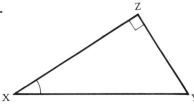

4.

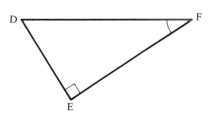

5. 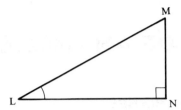   **6.**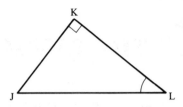

Questions 7 to 12 refer to the following diagrams.

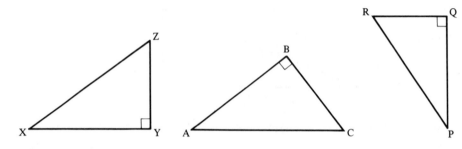

Copy and complete the following sentences.

   7. In △XYZ, for angle X, XY is the .... side.

   8. In △ABC, for angle A, AB is the .... side.

   9. In △PQR, for angle R, PQ is the .... side.

   10. In △XYZ, for angle Z, XY is the .... side.

   11. In △PQR, for angle P, the opposite side is ....

   12. In △ABC, the hypotenuse is ....

Questions 13 to 16 refer to the following diagram.

<u>**13.**</u>   In △ABC, for B$\hat{A}$C, the adjacent
      side is ......

<u>**14.**</u>   In △ACD, the hypotenuse is ......

<u>**15.**</u>   In △ABC, for B$\hat{C}$A,
      AB is the ......

<u>**16.**</u>   In △ACD, for C$\hat{A}$D,
      CD is the ......

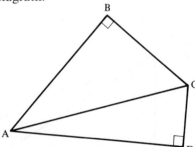

TANGENT OF AN ANGLE

Draw the diagram given below as accurately as you can, following the instructions.

You may find it convenient to use squared paper.

Draw AX of any length and let $\hat{A}$ have a value between 20° and 40°.

Mark B, C and D so that AB = 5 cm, AC = 8 cm and AD = 10 cm.

Use a protractor or set square if necessary to draw BE, CF and DG perpendicular to AX as shown.

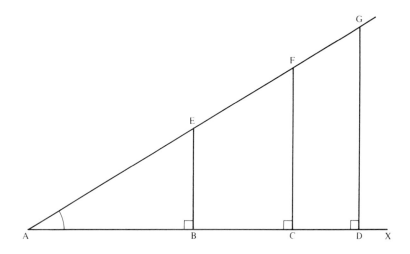

Measure BE, CF and DG.

Use these measurements to find the fractions $\dfrac{\text{BE}}{\text{AB}}$, $\dfrac{\text{CF}}{\text{AC}}$, and $\dfrac{\text{DG}}{\text{AD}}$ as decimals correct to 2 decimal places.

If we consider the angle A these fractions are given by $\dfrac{\text{the opposite side}}{\text{the adjacent side}}$ in triangles ABE, ACF and ADG.

If you have measured accurately you will find that the three fractions have the same value. This value is called the tangent of the angle A or briefly, tan A.

Its size is stored, together with the tangents of other angles, in *scientific calculators*.

Measure angle A. Using your calculator enter the size of $\hat{A}$, then press the button labelled "tan".

How does the value in the display compare with the values of the three fractions you found above ?

$$\tan A = \frac{\text{opposite side}}{\text{adjacent side}}$$

EXERCISE 14b

Use a calculator if you need one.

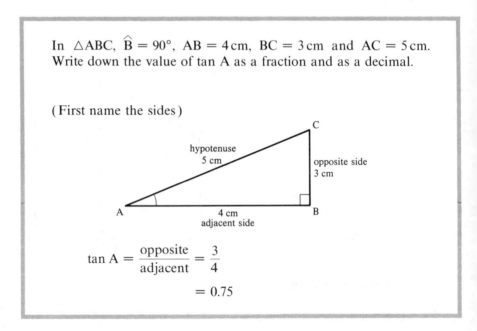

In △ABC, $\widehat{B} = 90°$, AB = 4 cm, BC = 3 cm and AC = 5 cm. Write down the value of tan A as a fraction and as a decimal.

(First name the sides)

$$\tan A = \frac{\text{opposite}}{\text{adjacent}} = \frac{3}{4}$$
$$= 0.75$$

In each of the following questions write down the tangent of the marked angle as a fraction and as a decimal (correct to 4 decimal places if necessary).

1.

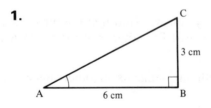

2.

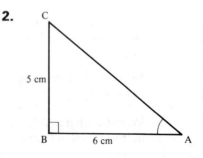

<u>3.</u>

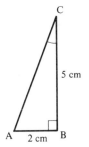

7.

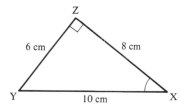

<u>4.</u>

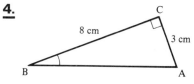

<u>8.</u>

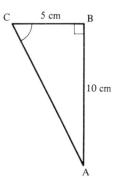

5.

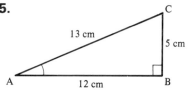

<u>9.</u>

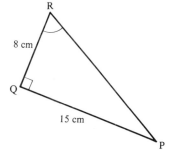

6.

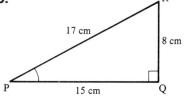

<u>10.</u>

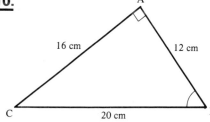

11.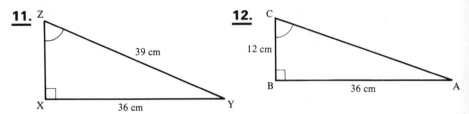

12.

For the following questions several alternative answers are given. Write down the letter that corresponds to the correct answer.

13.

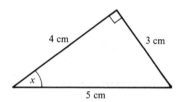

tan *x* is

A $\frac{3}{5}$ **B** $\frac{3}{4}$ **C** $\frac{4}{3}$ **D** $\frac{5}{3}$

14.

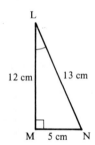

tan L is

A $\frac{5}{12}$ **B** $\frac{5}{13}$ **C** $\frac{12}{5}$ **D** $\frac{13}{5}$

15.

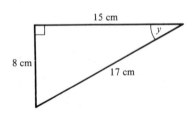

tan *y* is

A $\frac{17}{8}$ **B** $\frac{15}{17}$ **C** $\frac{8}{17}$ **D** $\frac{8}{15}$

16.

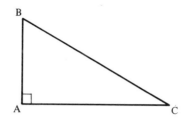

$\dfrac{AB}{AC}$ is

A   tan A   **B**   tan C   **C**   tan B   **D**   none of these

USING A CALCULATOR

To find the tangent of an angle, enter the size of the angle then press the "tan" button. Write the answer correct to 4 decimal places.

e.g.   tan 36° = 0.7265

Sometimes angles are given to the nearest tenth of a degree

e.g.   tan 42.4° = 0.9131

EXERCISE 14c

Use a calculator to find the tangents of the following angles. Give values to 4 decimal places where necessary.

1.	56°	**7.**	78°	**13.**	32.4°
2.	44°	**8.**	45°	**14.**	3°
3.	59.6°	**9.**	60°	**15.**	52.1°
4.	82.1°	**10.**	30°	**16.**	66°
5.	37°	**11.**	17.6°	**17.**	15.4°
6.	26.8°	**12.**	68.7°	**18.**	49.2°

To find an angle when its tangent is given enter the value of the tangent and then press the inverse button followed by the tangent button. Write down the size of the angle correct to 1 decimal place.

EXERCISE 14d

Find the angle whose tangent is
a) 0.75   b) 0.447

a) $\tan A = 0.75$ Press $\boxed{0}$ $\boxed{\cdot}$ $\boxed{7}$ $\boxed{5}$ $\boxed{\text{INV}}$ $\boxed{\text{TAN}}$
        $\widehat{A} = 36.9°$ The display shows 36.869 ...

b) $\tan B = 0.447$
        $\widehat{B} = 24.1°$

Find the angles whose tangents are

1.	0.5	**6.**	0.8	**11.**	0.2
2.	0.26	**7.**	0.44	**12.**	0.88
3.	0.873	**8.**	1	**13.**	0.345
4.	1.44	**9.**	1.64	**14.**	1.626
5.	1.736	**10.**	2.735	**15.**	3.668

FINDING AN ANGLE

EXERCISE 14e

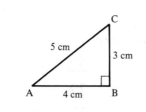

In triangle ABC, $\widehat{B} = 90°$,
AB = 4 cm, BC = 3 cm and
AC = 5 cm. Find $\widehat{A}$.

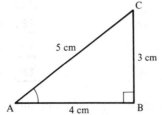

$\tan A = \dfrac{\text{opposite side}}{\text{adjacent side}} = \dfrac{3}{4}$

$= 0.75$

$\widehat{A} = 36.9°$

Use the information given in the diagrams to find $\hat{A}$. Give your answers correct to 1 decimal place.

1.

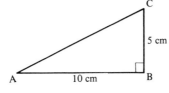

6.

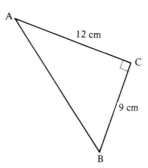

2.

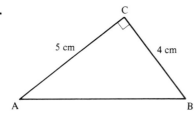

7.

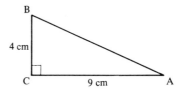

3.

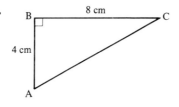

8.

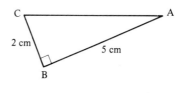

4.

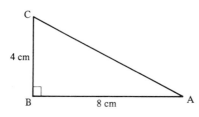

9.

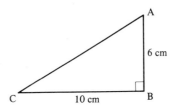

5.

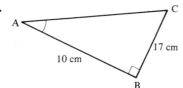

10.

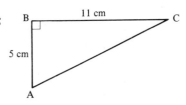

11.

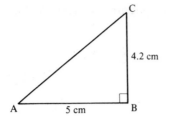

12.

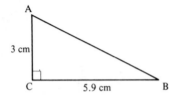

13.

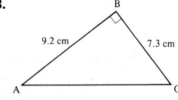

14.

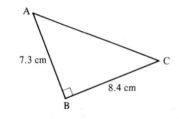

15.

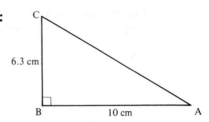

16.

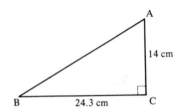

17.

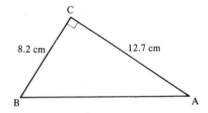

18.

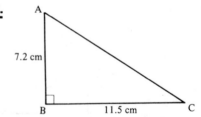

19. In triangle PQR, $\widehat{P} = 90°$, QP = 8 cm and PR = 10 cm. Find $\widehat{R}$.

20. In triangle DEF, $\widehat{D} = 90°$, DE = 18 cm and DF = 21 cm. Find $\widehat{E}$.

CALCULATIONS

When finding the tangent of an angle from a calculator write down its value correct to the fourth decimal place.

Write down all steps correct to 4 significant figures and give your final answer correct to 3 significant figures.

EXERCISE 14f

Use your calculator to find the value of

a) 12 tan 42°   b) 23 tan 62.3°

a) $12 \tan 42° = 12 \times 0.9004$

$= 10.80$

$= 10.8$ (correct to 3 s.f.)

This can be done in one step using the following sequence of buttons $\boxed{1}$ $\boxed{2}$ $\boxed{\times}$ $\boxed{42}$ $\boxed{\text{TAN}}$ $\boxed{=}$

b) $26 \tan 62.3° = 26 \times 1.9047$

$= 49.52$

$= 49.5$ (correct to 3 s.f.)

Use your calculator to find, correct to three significant figures, the value of

1.	9 tan 37°	**5.**	18 tan 53.4°	**9.**	74 tan 32.3°
2.	13 tan 46°	**6.**	8 tan 80°	**10.**	58 tan 68.4°
3.	44 tan 62.3°	**7.**	7 tan 34°	**11.**	120 tan 47.2°
4.	27 tan 22.8°	**8.**	34 tan 58.5°	**12.**	257 tan 82.8°
13.	31.7 tan 23°	**17.**	318 tan 82.1°	**21.**	59.2 tan 32.6°
14.	13.5 tan 76°	**18.**	14.8 tan 76°	**22.**	247 tan 73.9°
15.	1.36 tan 34.6°	**19.**	62.9 tan 57°	**23.**	37.6 tan 15.9°
16.	72.4 tan 47.3°	**20.**	3.49 tan 52.8°	**24.**	7.85 tan 48.16°

FINDING THE OPPOSITE SIDE TO A GIVEN ANGLE

EXERCISE 14g

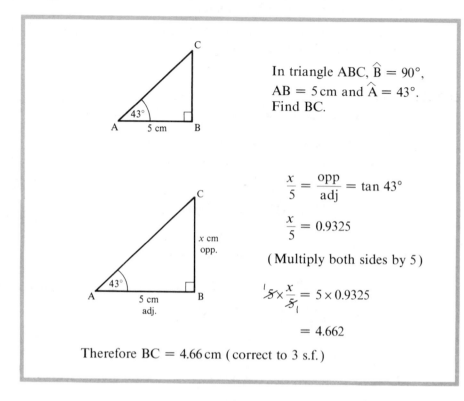

In triangle ABC, $\widehat{B} = 90°$,
AB = 5 cm and $\widehat{A} = 43°$.
Find BC.

$$\frac{x}{5} = \frac{\text{opp}}{\text{adj}} = \tan 43°$$

$$\frac{x}{5} = 0.9325$$

(Multiply both sides by 5)

$$\cancel{5} \times \frac{x}{\cancel{5}} = 5 \times 0.9325$$

$$= 4.662$$

Therefore BC = 4.66 cm (correct to 3 s.f.)

Use the information given in the diagram to find the required side correct to 3 s.f. First label the required side and the given side either "adjacent" or "opposite".

1.

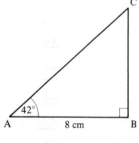

Find BC.

2.

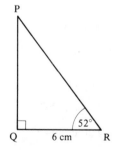

Find PQ.

3.

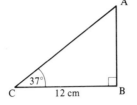

Find AB.

7.

Find PQ.

4.

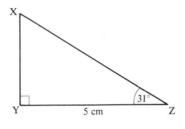

Find XY.

8.

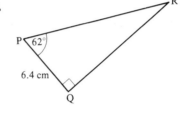

Find QR.

5.

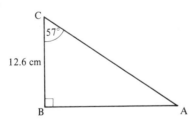

Find AB.

9.

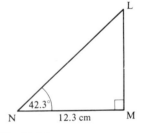

Find LM.

6.

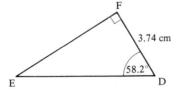

Find EF.

10.

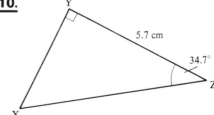

Find XY.

11. In triangle ABC, $\hat{B} = 90°$, $\hat{A} = 42°$ and AB = 8.2 cm. Find BC.

12. In triangle DEF, $\hat{D} = 90°$, $\hat{E} = 56°$ and DE = 31.4 cm. Find DF.

13. In triangle PQR, $\hat{R} = 90°$, $\hat{Q} = 12.4°$ and RQ = 28 cm. Find PR.

14. In triangle XYZ, $\hat{Z} = 90°$, $\hat{Y} = 65.4°$ and YZ = 6.3 cm. Find XZ.

15. In triangle ABC, $\hat{B} = 90°$, $\hat{C} = 37.3°$ and BC = 12.7 cm. Find AB.

FINDING THE ADJACENT SIDE FOR A GIVEN ANGLE

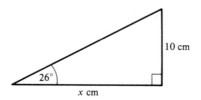

Sometimes the side whose length we are asked to find is adjacent to the given angle instead of opposite to it.

Using $\tan 26° = \dfrac{10}{x}$ gives an awkward equation so we work out the size of the other angle and use that angle instead.

In this case the other angle is 64°. (Remember that the three angles of a triangle add up to 180°.)

We now label the sides as "opposite" and "adjacent" to the angle of 64°.

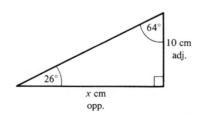

Using 64°,
$$\frac{x}{10} = \frac{\text{opp}}{\text{adj}} = \tan 64°$$

so
$$\frac{x}{10} = 2.0503 \quad \text{giving} \quad x = 20.5 \text{ to 3 s.f.}$$

EXERCISE 14h

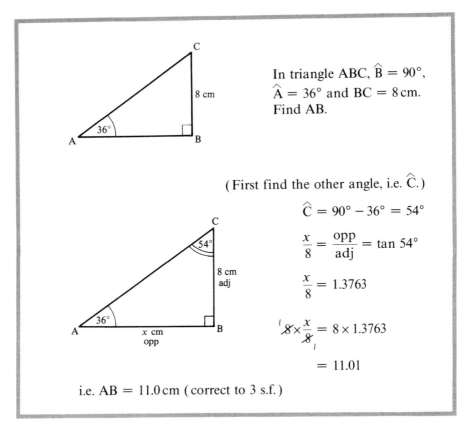

In triangle ABC, $\widehat{B} = 90°$, $\widehat{A} = 36°$ and BC = 8 cm. Find AB.

(First find the other angle, i.e. $\widehat{C}$.)

$$\widehat{C} = 90° - 36° = 54°$$

$$\frac{x}{8} = \frac{\text{opp}}{\text{adj}} = \tan 54°$$

$$\frac{x}{8} = 1.3763$$

$$\cancel{8} \times \frac{x}{\cancel{8}} = 8 \times 1.3763$$

$$= 11.01$$

i.e. AB = 11.0 cm (correct to 3 s.f.)

Use the information given in the diagram to find the required side correct to 3 s.f. It may first be necessary to find the third angle of the triangle.

1.

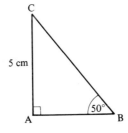

Find AB.

2.

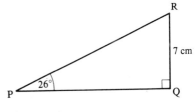

Find PQ.

3.

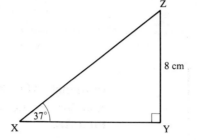

Find XY.

7.

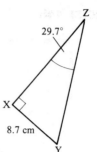

Find XZ.

4.

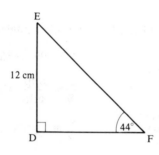

Find DF.

8.

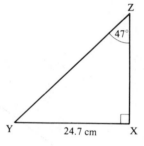

Find XZ.

5.

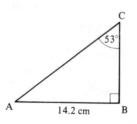

Find BC.

9.

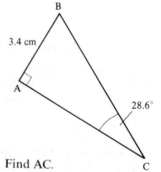

Find AC.

6.

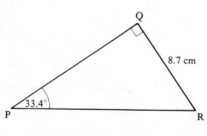

Find PQ.

10.

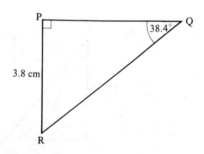

Find PQ.

ANGLES OF ELEVATION AND DEPRESSION

The *angle of elevation* is the angle through which you raise your line of view from the horizontal to look up at something.

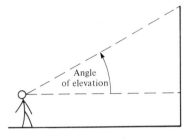

The angle of depression is the angle through which you lower your line of view from the horizontal to look down at something.

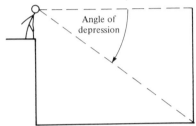

EXERCISE 14i

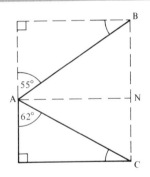

A represents a man on the top of a cliff, B represents a kite, and C a small boat directly out to sea.

Use the information given in the diagram to write down
a) the angle of elevation of (i) B from A   (ii) A from C
b) the angle of depression of (i) C from A   (ii) A from B.

a) (i) the angle of elevation of B from A is $90° - 55°$, i.e. $35°$
   (ii) the angle of elevation of A from C is $90° - 62°$, i.e. $28°$

b) (i) the angle of depression of C from A is $90° - 62°$, i.e. $28°$
   (ii) the angle of depression of A from B is $90° - 55°$, i.e. $35°$

1. In the diagram A represents the viewing platform of a lighthouse, H the position of a helicopter and B the position of a small boat.

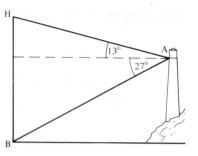

Write down

a) the angle of elevation of H from A

b) the angle of depression of B from A

c) the angle of depression of A from H

d) the angle of elevation of A from B.

2. Draw sketches to show

a) the positions of A and B if the angle of elevation of A from B is 18°

b) the positions of P and Q if the angle of depression of Q from P is 33°

c) the positions of X, Y and Z if from X the angle of elevation of Y is 60° and the angle of depression of Z is 38°.

3. A flagpole stands on level ground. From a point on the ground 30 m away from its foot, the angle of elevation of the top of the pole is 22°. Show this on a sketch and find the height of the pole.

4. From a point on level ground 40 m from the base of an oak tree, the elevation of the top of the tree is 36°. Find the height of the tree.

5. The angle of elevation of the top of a church tower from a point on level ground 500 m away, is 13°. Find the height of the tower.

6. 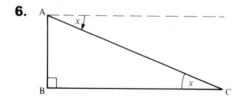 A boat C is 200 m from the foot B of a vertical cliff, which is 40 m high. What is the angle of depression of the boat from the top of the cliff?

7. The angle of depression of a milestone from the top of a castle tower is 28°. If the height of the tower is 22 m how far is the milestone from the foot of the tower?

MIXED EXERCISES

EXERCISE 14j

Questions 1 to 3 refer to the following diagram.

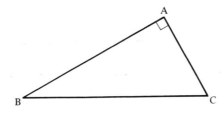

1. Name the side that is adjacent to $\hat{B}$.

2. If AB = 10 cm and AC = 8 cm write down the value of tan C.

3. If $\hat{B}$ = 42°, AC = 20 cm and AB = x cm, complete the following equation

$$\tan \ldots = \frac{x}{20}$$

4. Use your calculator to give the value of 12 tan 57° correct to three significant figures.

5. From a point A the angle of elevation of a point B is 67°. What is the angle of depression of A from B ?

6.

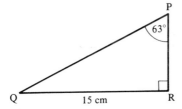

Find **PR** giving your answer correct to three significant figures.

EXERCISE 14k

1. Write down the value of tan C
   a) as a fraction
   b) as a decimal correct to 3 decimal places.

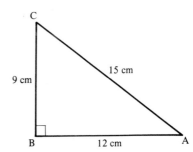

2. Use a calculator to find tan 37.7° correct to 4 decimal places.

3.

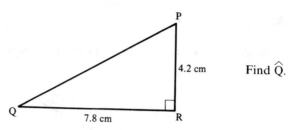

Find $\widehat{Q}$.

4. Use your calculator to find, correct to three significant figures
   a) 12 tan 72°   b) 56.2 tan 37.8°

5. Find the angle whose tangent is a) 0.7276   b) 1   c) 1.937.

6. From the top of Blackpool Tower, which is 158 m high, the angle of depression of a ship at sea is 25°. Find the distance of the ship from the base of the tower.

EXERCISE 14I

In this exercise several alternative answers are given. Write down the letter that corresponds to the correct answer.

1.

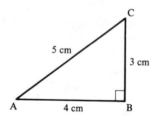

The tangent of the angle A is

A $\dfrac{4}{5}$ **B** $\dfrac{3}{5}$ **C** $\dfrac{4}{3}$ **D** $\dfrac{3}{4}$

2.

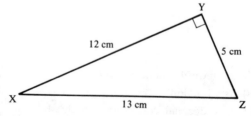

The tangent of the angle Z is

A $\dfrac{5}{13}$ **B** $\dfrac{5}{12}$ **C** $\dfrac{12}{5}$ **D** $\dfrac{12}{13}$

3.

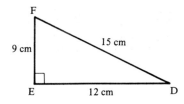

The tangent of angle D as a decimal fraction is

A 1.3333   **B** 0.75   **C** 0.8   **D** 0.6

4.

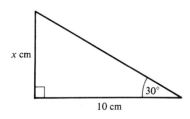

The value of x can be found from the equation

A $\dfrac{10}{x} = \tan 30°$ **B** $\dfrac{x}{10} = \tan 30°$

C $\dfrac{10}{x} = \tan 90°$ **D** $\dfrac{x}{10} = \tan 60°$

5.

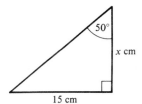

The value of x can be found from the equation

A $\dfrac{x}{15} = \tan 50°$ **B** $\dfrac{x}{15} = \tan 90°$

C $\dfrac{15}{x} = \tan 40°$ **D** $\dfrac{x}{15} = \tan 40°$

6.

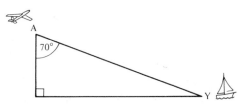

The angle of elevation of the plane A from the yacht Y is

A 70°   **B** 20°   **C** 90°   **D** 30°

15 THE SINE AND COSINE OF AN ANGLE

In Chapter 14 we considered the fraction given by $\dfrac{\text{the opposite side}}{\text{the adjacent side}}$ in any right angled triangle.

We called this fraction the tangent of the angle.

i.e. $\tan A = \dfrac{\text{opp}}{\text{adj}}$

We shall now consider the fractions we get when the hypotenuse is used.

THE SINE OF AN ANGLE

Draw the diagram given below as accurately as you can, following the instructions. You may find it convenient to use squared paper.

Draw AX of any length and let $\widehat{A}$ have a value between 20° and 40°. Mark B, C and D so that AB = 5 cm, AC = 10 cm and AD = 15 cm.

Use a protractor or set square to draw the perpendiculars from B, C and D to AX as shown.

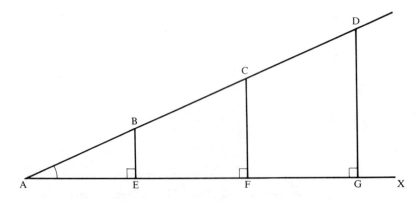

Measure BE, CF and DG.

266

Use these measurements to find the fractions $\dfrac{BE}{AB}$, $\dfrac{CF}{AC}$ and $\dfrac{DG}{AD}$ as decimals correct to two decimal places.

If we consider the angle A these fractions are given by $\dfrac{\text{the opposite side}}{\text{the hypotenuse}}$ in triangles ABE, ACF and ADG.

The three fractions have the same value. This value is called the sine of the angle A or, briefly, sin A. Its size is stored, together with the sines of other angles, in scientific calculators.

Measure angle A in your diagram, and use a calculator to find sin A. How does this value compare with the values of the three fractions found above ?

$$\sin A = \frac{\text{opposite side}}{\text{hypotenuse}}$$

All values found from the calculator should be written down correct to 4 significant figures and answers should be given correct to 3 significant figures unless stated otherwise.

The sizes of angles should be given correct to 1 decimal place.

EXERCISE 15a

Questions 1 to 4 refer to the following diagram.

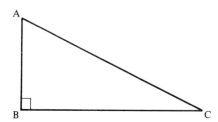

Copy the following sentences and fill in the blanks.

1. For angle C, the opposite side is ..... and the hypotenuse is .....

2. Side AB is the ..... side for angle A.

3. Side BC is the ..... side for angle C.

4. For angle A, BC is the ..... and AC is the .....

In △ABC, $\hat{B} = 90°$, AC = 20 cm, AB = 16 cm and BC = 12 cm. Write down the value of sin A as a fraction and as a decimal.

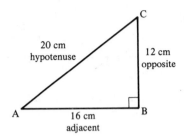

(First name the sides.)

$$\sin A = \frac{\text{opposite}}{\text{hypotenuse}} = \frac{12}{20}$$

$$= \frac{3}{5}$$

$$= 0.6$$

In each of the following questions write down the sine of the marked angle as a fraction and as a decimal (correct to 4 decimal places if necessary).

5.

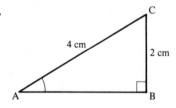

8.

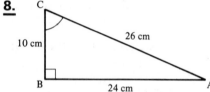

6.

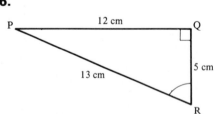

9.

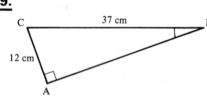

7.

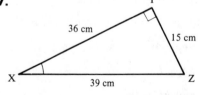

10.

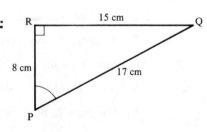

11. Use the diagram to complete the following ratios

a) $\sin A = \dfrac{}{AC}$

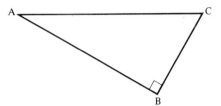

b) $\sin C = \dfrac{}{AC}$

USING A CALCULATOR

To find the sine of an angle, enter the size of the angle then press the "sin" button. Write the answer correct to 4 decimal places.

e.g. $\sin 63° = 0.8910$

and $\sin 39.3° = 0.6334$

EXERCISE 15b

Use a calculator to find the sines of the following angles. Give values correct to 4 decimal places where necessary.

1. 44°	**4.** 18.2°	**7.** 17.4°	**10.** 49°
2. 67°	**5.** 80°	**8.** 59.8°	**11.** 82.5°
3. 54.7°	**6.** 33°	**9.** 56°	**12.** 72.3°

To find the angle when the sine is given enter the value of the sine and then press the inverse button followed by the sin button. Write down the size of the angle correct to 1 decimal place.

e.g. if $\sin A = 0.7264$ Press $\boxed{0}$ $\boxed{\cdot}$ $\boxed{7}$ $\boxed{2}$ $\boxed{6}$ $\boxed{4}$ $\boxed{\text{INV}}$ $\boxed{\text{SIN}}$

$\widehat{A} = 46.6°$

EXERCISE 15c

Find the angles whose sines are

1. 0.4264	**4.** 0.5645	**7.** 0.8844	**10.** 0.3782
2. 0.1297	**5.** 0.7359	**8.** 0.5649	**11.** 0.9271
3. 0.8143	**6.** 0.2431	**9.** 0.2645	**12.** 0.6677

FINDING AN ANGLE

EXERCISE 15d

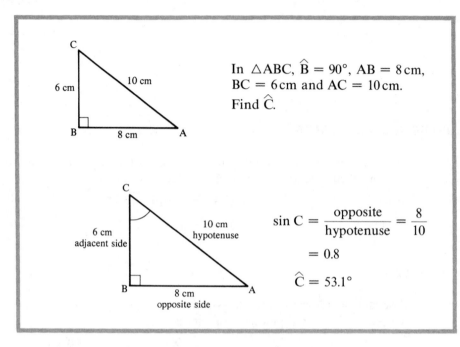

In $\triangle ABC$, $\widehat{B} = 90°$, $AB = 8\,cm$,
$BC = 6\,cm$ and $AC = 10\,cm$.
Find $\widehat{C}$.

$$\sin C = \frac{\text{opposite}}{\text{hypotenuse}} = \frac{8}{10}$$

$$= 0.8$$

$$\widehat{C} = 53.1°$$

Use the information given in the diagram to find $\widehat{A}$.

1.

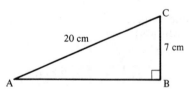

3.

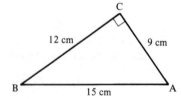

2.

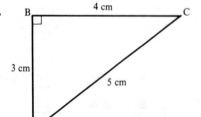

4.

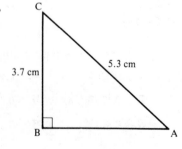

5.

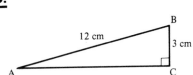

7.

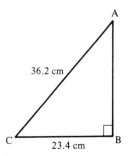

6.

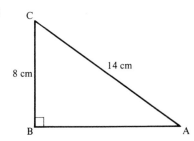

8.

CALCULATIONS

EXERCISE 15e

Find 54.7 sin 48.8°

$$54.7 \sin 48.8° = 54.7 \times 0.7524$$
$$= 41.15$$
$$= 41.2 \text{ correct to 3 s.f.}$$

To do this in one step press

⌐5⌐ ⌐4⌐ ⌐·⌐ ⌐7⌐ ⌐×⌐ ⌐4⌐ ⌐8⌐ ⌐·⌐ ⌐8⌐ ⌐SIN⌐ ⌐=⌐

Use your calculator to find, correct to 3 significant figures, the value of

1.	10 sin 34°	**5.**	15 sin 62°	**9.**	20 sin 85°
2.	36 sin 59°	**6.**	82 sin 16°	**10.**	59 sin 72°
3.	88 sin 48.5°	**7.**	57 sin 70.9°	**11.**	18 sin 62.6°
4.	4.2 sin 61.3°	**8.**	5.9 sin 32.5°	**12.**	15.6 sin 50.7°

FINDING THE OPPOSITE SIDE FOR A GIVEN ANGLE ──────

EXERCISE 15f

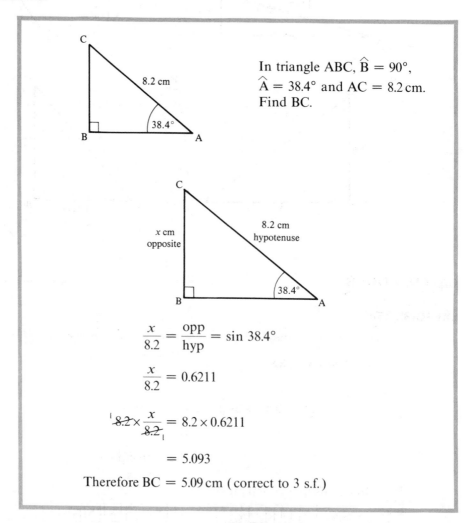

In triangle ABC, $\hat{B} = 90°$, $\hat{A} = 38.4°$ and AC = 8.2 cm. Find BC.

$$\frac{x}{8.2} = \frac{\text{opp}}{\text{hyp}} = \sin 38.4°$$

$$\frac{x}{8.2} = 0.6211$$

$$8.2 \times \frac{x}{8.2} = 8.2 \times 0.6211$$

$$= 5.093$$

Therefore BC = 5.09 cm (correct to 3 s.f.)

Use the information given in the diagram to find the required side.

1.

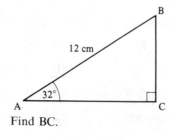

Find BC.

2.

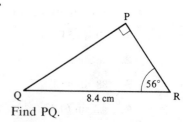

Find PQ.

3.

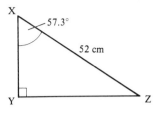

Find YZ.

5.

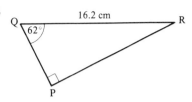

Find PR.

4.

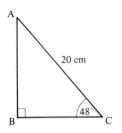

Find AB.

6.

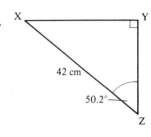

Find XY.

7. In $\triangle ABC$, $\widehat{B} = 90°$, $\widehat{C} = 37.4°$ and $AC = 16.4\,cm$. Find AB.

8. In $\triangle PQR$, $\widehat{Q} = 90°$, $\widehat{R} = 61.8°$ and $PR = 37.9\,cm$. Find PQ.

THE COSINE OF AN ANGLE

Use the diagram you drew from the instructions given on page 266.

Measure AE, AF and AG.

Find the fractions $\dfrac{AE}{AB}$, $\dfrac{AF}{AC}$ and $\dfrac{AG}{AD}$.

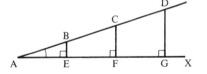

If we consider the angle A in triangles ABE, ACF and ADG, these ratios are the ratios of the adjacent side to the hypotenuse.

The three fractions have the same value. This value is called the cosine of the angle A or briefly cos A. Its size is stored, together with the cosines of other angles, in scientific calculators.

Measure angle A in your diagram, and use a calculator to find cos A. How does this value compare with the three fractions you found above ?

$$\cos A = \frac{\text{adjacent side}}{\text{hypotenuse}}$$

EXERCISE 15g

Questions 1 to 4 refer to the following diagram.

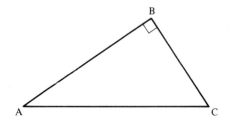

Copy the following sentences and fill in the blanks.

1. For angle A the adjacent side is ..... and the hypotenuse is .....

2. Side BC is the ..... side for angle C.

3. Side AC is the .....

4. For angle C, BC is the ..... and AC is the .....

In each of the following questions write down the cosine of the marked angle as a fraction and as a decimal (correct to 4 d.p. if necessary).

5.

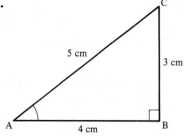

7.

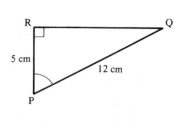

6.

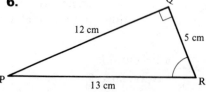

8.

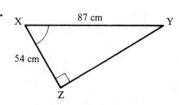

9.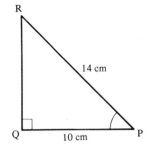

11.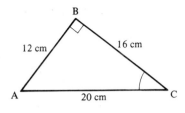

10.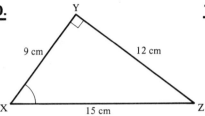

12.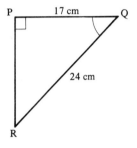

13. Use a calculator to find the cosines of the following angles.

a) 68° d) 49° g) 27°

b) 23.9° e) 59.2° h) 17.6°

c) 42.7° f) 18.4° i) 73.6°

14. Use a calculator to find the angles whose cosines are

a) 0.7464 d) 0.8283 g) 0.1479

b) 0.2668 e) 0.5492 h) 0.1696

c) 0.5374 f) 0.9106 i) 0.7009

In △ABC, $\hat{B} = 90°$, BC = 7 cm and AC = 12 cm. Find $\hat{C}$.

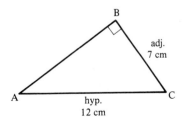

$$\cos C = \frac{\text{adj}}{\text{hyp}} = \frac{BC}{AC}$$

$$= \frac{7}{12}$$

$$= 0.5833$$

$$\hat{C} = 54.3°$$

Use the information given in the diagram to find Â.

15.
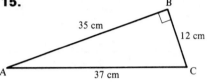

18.
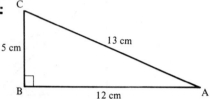

16.
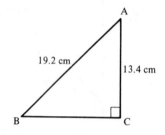

19.
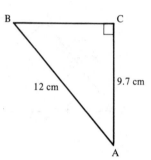

17.
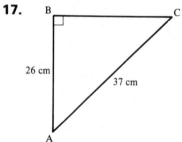

20.
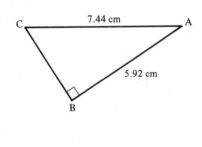

CALCULATIONS

EXERCISE 15h

Use your calculator to find, correct to 3 significant figures, the value of:

1. 20 cos 42°   **4.** 73 cos 60°   **7.** 59 cos 49°

2. 6.71 cos 63.4°   **5.** 34.2 cos 82.8°   **8.** 80.2 cos 58.4°

3. 4.97 cos 14.7°   **6.** 15.3 cos 15.7°   **9.** 57.9 cos 32.5°

10. Write down the sequence of keys you used for
a) question 1   b) question 9.

FINDING THE ADJACENT SIDE FOR A GIVEN ANGLE

EXERCISE 15i

In triangle ABC, $\widehat{B} = 90°$, AC = 24 cm and $\widehat{A} = 33°$
Find AB.

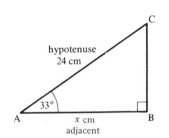

$$\frac{x}{24} = \frac{adj}{hyp} = \cos 33°$$

Therefore $\dfrac{x}{24} = 0.8387$

$$\cancel{24} \times \frac{x}{\cancel{24}} = 24 \times 0.8387$$

$$= 20.13$$

Therefore AB = 20.1 cm (correct to 3 s.f.)

Use the information given in the diagram to find the required side.

1.

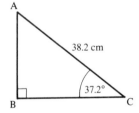

Find BC.

3.

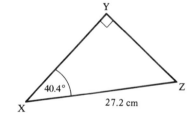

Find XY.

2.

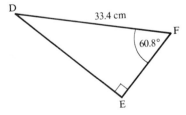

Find EF.

4.

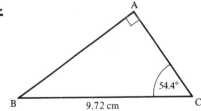

Find AC.

5.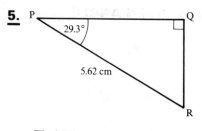

Find PQ.

6.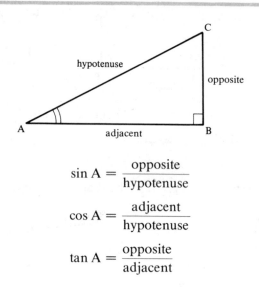

Find RT.

SUMMARY

$$\sin A = \frac{\text{opposite}}{\text{hypotenuse}}$$

$$\cos A = \frac{\text{adjacent}}{\text{hypotenuse}}$$

$$\tan A = \frac{\text{opposite}}{\text{adjacent}}$$

MIXED QUESTIONS

EXERCISE 15j

This exercise uses all three ratios: sine, cosine and tangent.
To decide which ratio to use, label the sides.

1. Find AB.

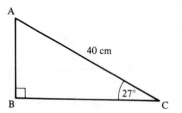

2. Find $\widehat{A}$.

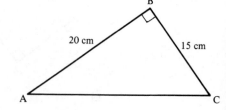

3. Find PQ.

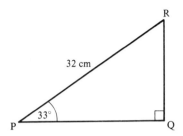

7. Find $\widehat{A}$.

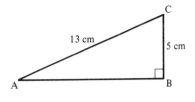

4. Find XZ.

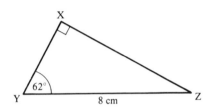

8. Find $\widehat{R}$.

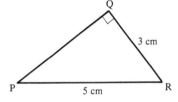

5. Find BC.

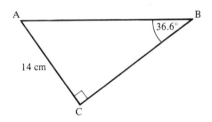

9. Find AB.

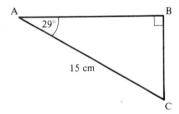

6. Find LM.

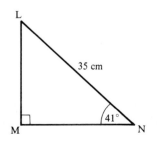

10. Find $\widehat{Q}$.

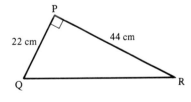

11.

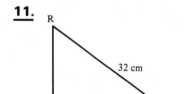

Find RS.

14.

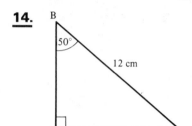

Find AB.

12.

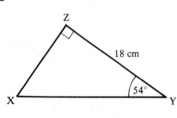

Find XZ.

15.

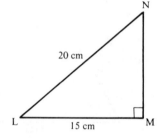

Find N.

13.

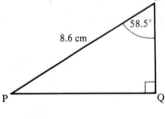

Find RQ.

16.

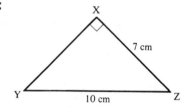

Find $\widehat{Z}$.

17.

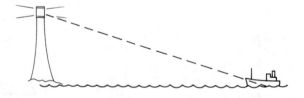

An observer at the top of the lighthouse measures the angle of depression of a ship as 15°. The lighthouse is 50 m high. How far is the ship from the base of the lighthouse ?

18.

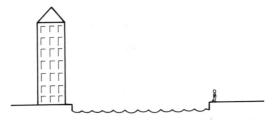

The diagram shows an office tower which is 100 m tall (to the top of the roof). The tower is on one bank of a river. Peter is standing on the opposite bank, 150 m away from the base of the tower. What is the angle of elevation of the top of the tower from Peter?

EXERCISE 15k

In this exercise several alternative answers are given.
Write down the letter that corresponds to the correct answer.

1.

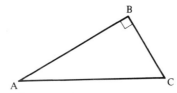

The cosine of $\widehat{A}$ is

A $\dfrac{AC}{AB}$ **B** $\dfrac{BC}{AC}$ **C** $\dfrac{AB}{AC}$ **C** $\dfrac{AB}{BC}$

2.

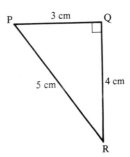

The sine of $\widehat{R}$ is

A $\dfrac{4}{5}$ **B** $\dfrac{3}{5}$ **C** $\dfrac{3}{4}$ **D** $\dfrac{5}{3}$

3.

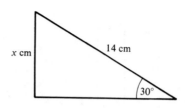

The value of *x* can be found from the equation

A $\dfrac{x}{14} = \tan 30°$ **B** $\dfrac{14}{x} = \cos 30°$

C $\dfrac{x}{14} = \sin 60°$ **D** $\dfrac{x}{14} = \sin 30°$

4.

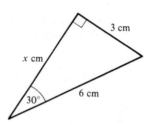

The value of *x* can be found from the equation

A $\dfrac{6}{x} = \cos 30°$ **B** $\dfrac{x}{3} = \tan 30°$

C $\dfrac{x}{6} = \cos 60°$ **D** $\dfrac{x}{6} = \cos 30°$

5.

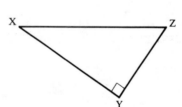

The tangent of $\widehat{Z}$ is

A $\dfrac{XY}{XZ}$ **B** $\dfrac{YZ}{XY}$ **C** $\dfrac{XY}{YZ}$ **D** $\dfrac{YZ}{XY}$

6.

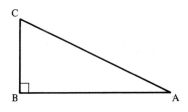

In the diagram $\dfrac{BC}{CA}$ is equal to

A   tan A   **B**   sin C   **C**   cos A   **D**   none of these

16 STATISTICS

MEAN, MODE AND MEDIAN

> The *mean*, or arithmetic average, of a set of say twelve numbers is found by adding them up and dividing by 12.

To give a meaning to the calculated value for a mean, suppose that the numbers of goals scored by a football team in the eight matches it played one monthe were 0, 1, 1, 2, 2, 2, 3 and 5. If it were possible to even out the scores for the matches to give the same total, then this equal score would be the mean, which in this case is $\frac{16}{2}$, i.e. 2.

The mean does not have to be an integer, or one of the given values, or indeed a possible value. Suppose that the numbers 1, 2, 2, 3, 5, 6, 8, 8, 8 are the scores obtained from 9 balls on a pin-ball machine. If it were possible to even out the score in this case, the score would have to be $\frac{43}{9}$, i.e. $4\frac{7}{9}$. This is impossible to score, but the mean value is correctly given as $4\frac{7}{9}$.

> The *mode* is the value that occurs most often.

Sometimes there are two or more numbers that occur equally often. When the numbers are all different there is no mode.

The mode of the set of numbers 1, 2, 2, 3, 5, 6, 8, 8, 8 is 8, whereas there is no mode for the set of numbers 1, 3, 5, 9, 12, 13. There are two modes for the set of numbers 1, 1, 2, 3, 3, 4.

> The *median* of a set of numbers is the middle number when the numbers are arranged in order of size.

If there is no middle number, the median is the mean of the two middle numbers. The median of 1, 2, 2, 3, 5, 6, 8, 8, 8 is 5 and the median of 1, 3, 5, 9, 12, 13 is $\dfrac{5+9}{2}$, i.e. 7

EXERCISE 16a

Find the mean, mode and median of the set of numbers
3, 3, 4, 4, 4, 8, 8, 9, 9, 9.

$$\text{Mean} = \frac{(2 \times 3) + (3 \times 4) + (2 \times 8) + (3 \times 9)}{10}$$

$$= \frac{61}{10}$$

$$= 6.1$$

There are two modes, 4 and 9

The median is the mean of 4 and 8, i.e. 6

1. Find the mean, mode and median of each of the following sets of data. Give answers that are not exact correct to three significant figures. Remember to put the numbers in order of size before finding the median.

   a) 3, 2, 4, 7, 3, 2, 6, 5
   b) 1.2, 1.5, 1.5, 1.8
   c) 1, $1\frac{1}{2}$, 2, 4, 5, 6, $8\frac{1}{2}$
   d) 10, 7, 4, 1, −2, −5, −8
   e) 4, 3, 4, 5, 2, 5, 4, 3
   f) 0.8, 0.7, 0.6, 0.7, 0.8, 0.8, 0.9, 0.5

2. When Sean calculated his mean mark for eight tests that he sat in geography he found it to be 83. How many marks did he score altogether?

3. Four pupils sat ten tests. Their mean marks were 50, 55, 60 and 75. Find the total number of marks scored by each student.

4. In a rugby team the mean weight for the 8 forwards is 95 kg and the mean weight for the 7 backs is 76 kg. Find
   a) the total weight of the forwards
   b) the total weight of the backs
   c) the total weight of the team
   d) the mean weight of the team.
      Give your answer to (d) correct to the nearest kg.

In five consecutive frames a snooker player scored 73, 0, 18, 121 and 48. Find his average score per frame. How many would he have to score in the next frame to raise his average to 60 ?

$$\text{Average score for 5 frames} = \frac{73 + 0 + 18 + 121 + 48}{5}$$

$$= \frac{260}{5}$$

$$= 52$$

If the average score after 6 frames is 60

$$\text{total scored in 6 frames} = 60 \times 6 = 360$$

But total scored in 5 frames = 260

$\therefore$ score in sixth frame

$$= \text{total score for 6 frames} - \text{total score for 5 frames}$$

$$= 360 - 260$$

$$= 100$$

Therefore the sixth frame score would have to be 100.

5. In a boat race the mean weight of the eight oarsmen was 75.3 kg and the mean weight of the crew (i.e. 8 oarsman plus the cox) was 73.2 kg. How heavy was the cox ?

6. A small firm employs nine people. The annual salaries of these employees are £8K (ie £8000), £9K, £10K, £10K, £10K, £12K, £20K, £25K and £60K. Find the mean, modal and median salary.
Which of these three figures would you be most interested in if you were involved in negotiating salary increases and were
a) the employer
b) a union official ?
Give brief reasons for your answer.

7. The ages of five girls are: 14y 7m, 14y 2m, 15y 1m, 15y 5m, 16y 7m.
Find   a) the mean age
        b) the median age
        c) the modal age.

BAR CHARTS AND HISTOGRAMS

Consider the following frequency table, which was compiled from the weights (in kilograms) of 100 people

Weights (kg)	50–	60–	70–	80–	90–	100–	
Frequency	15	30	35	15	3	2	Total = 100

A frequency table tells us the number of items in each group. In this example, there are 15 people with weights 50 kg or more but less than 60 kg, 30 people with 60 kg or more but less than 70 kg and so on. The bar chart below illustrates this frequency table.

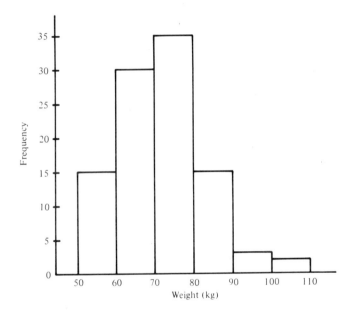

It is often the *area* of a bar that gives the impression of the number of items in a group.

In the above example each group covers the same span so each bar has the same width. Hence the *area* of each bar is proportional to its *height*. In this case, therefore, the area of each bar is proportional to the number of items in the group.

When a bar chart is constructed so that the *area* of each bar is proportional to the number of items in each group it is called a *histogram*.

So the bar chart above is a histogram.

Most bar charts showing frequencies are histograms but some are not. Consider the bar chart below. It shows the number of cans of fizzy drink sold by a manufacturer for each of the years 1989, 1990 and 1991.

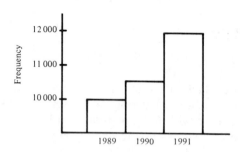

The bars are all the same width, but because the frequency scale does not start at zero the heights, and therefore the areas, of the bars are not proportional to the frequencies of sales each year.

Hence this bar chart is *not* a histogram.

The bar for 1991 looks twice the height of the bar for 1990. The bar chart is visually misleading.

EXERCISE 16b

Draw a histogram to represent the frequency table in questions 1 to 3.

1. The table shows the distribution of ages of 100 people attending a school concert.

Age (years)	0–19	20–39	40–59	60–79	80–99
Frequency	43	24	17	10	6

2. The table shows the results of a survey on the weekly earnings, rounded up to the nearest £, of 100 sixteen-year-olds.

Weekly earnings (£)	0–9	10–19	20–29	30–39	40–49	50–59
Frequency	45	10	11	21	10	3

3. The table shows the distribution of the average marks of 40 children in the end-of-year examinations.

Average mark	1–20	21–40	41–60	61–80	81–100
Frequency	2	4	19	12	3

4. The histogram shows the distribution of the times taken by 50 children to get to school.

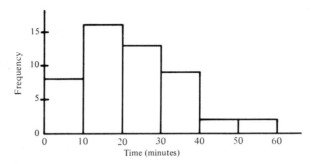

Construct a frequency table from this histogram.

5. The histogram is based on the number of hours that 30 children spent watching television on a particular Saturday.

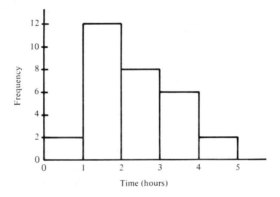

Construct a frequency table from this histogram.

6. The bar chart shows the distribution of the scores obtained when an ordinary dice was thrown 50 times.

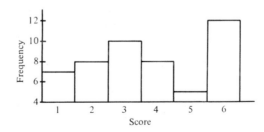

Use this bar chart to construct
a) a frequency table
b) a histogram.

FREQUENCY POLYGONS

This table gives the marks obtained by children in an examination:

Mark	1-10	11-20	21-30	31-40	41-50	51-60	61-70	71-80	81-90	91-100
Frequency	1	3	6	13	14	12	7	5	4	1

The histogram representing the data is given below.

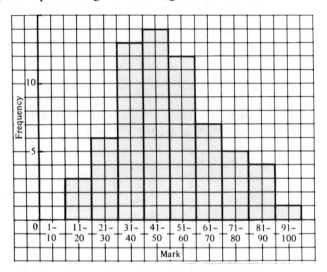

If, on a separate diagram, we plot the middle point at the top of each column of the histogram, and join these points in order, we have a *frequency polygon*. The frequency polygon for our histogram is given below.

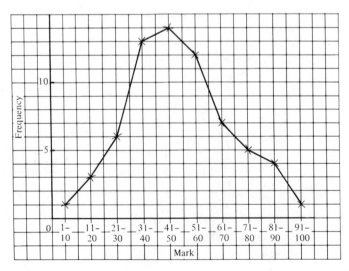

Sometimes the frequency polygon is superimposed on the histogram to give two different representations of the data in a single diagram.

The combined histogram and frequency polygon is shown below.

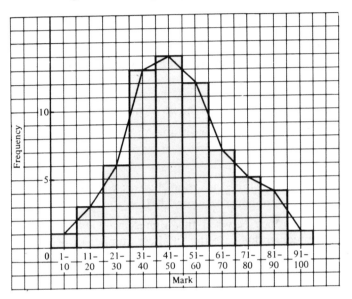

EXERCISE 16c

In questions 1 and 2 represent the data given in the table by

a) a histogram   b) a frequency polygon

1. The table shows the results of a survey on the pocket money received by 100 ten-year-olds.

Weekly pocket money (p)	0–19	20–39	40–59	60–79	80–99	100–119
Frequency	5	15	27	33	16	4

2. The table shows the distribution of goals scored in the 46 football league matches played on Saturday.

Total number of goals scored	0	1	2	3	4	5	6	7
Frequency	7	10	9	3	9	4	1	3

3. Draw, on the same diagram, the histogram and frequency polygon for the data given in the following table which shows the distribution of goals scored by the twenty-six teams in a hockey league.

Number of goals scored	50–54	55–59	60–64	65–69	70–74	75–79	80–84
Frequency	3	9	4	6	0	2	2

4. Draw, on the same diagram, the histogram and frequency polygon for the data given in the following table, which shows the distribution of shoe sizes for the sixty teachers on a school staff.

Shoe size	3	4	5	6	7	8	9	10	11
Frequency	2	5	8	9	11	13	8	3	1

FINDING THE MODE AND RANGE FROM A FREQUENCY TABLE

The frequency table shows the numbers of houses in a village that are occupied by different numbers of people.

Number of people living in one house	1	2	3	4	5	6
Frequency	10	8	15	25	12	4

It is clear that there are more houses with four people living in them than any other number, i.e. the mode is 4.

The difference between the highest and lowest number in a set is called the range. In this case the smallest number of people living in any house is 1 and the largest number is 6 so the range of the number of occupants is 6 − 1, i.e. 5

EXERCISE 16d

Write down the mode and range for each of the following frequency tables or bar charts.

1. The number of newspapers bought in one week by the occupants of each house in a particular road was recorded. The results are shown in this frequency table.

No. of newspapers/week	2	3	4	5	6	7	8	9
Frequency	9	3	2	10	12	15	6	3

2.

Number of tickets bought per person for a football match	1	2	3	4	5	6	7
Frequency	250	200	100	50	10	3	1

3.

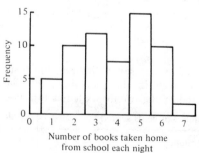

Number of books taken home
from school each night

FINDING THE MEAN FROM A FREQUENCY TABLE

The pupils in class 9 were asked to state the number of children in their own family and the following frequency table was made.

Number of children per family	1	2	3	4	5
Frequency	7	15	5	2	1

Total number of families = 30

This information has not been grouped: all the numbers are here so we can total this set. We have seven families with one child giving seven children, fifteen with two children giving thirty children and so on, giving the total number of children as

$$(7 \times 1) + (15 \times 2) + (5 \times 3) + (2 \times 4) + (1 \times 5) = 65$$

There are 30 numbers in the set, so the mean is

$$\frac{65}{30} = 2.2 \text{ to 1 d.p.}$$

i.e. there are, on average, 2.2 children per family.

To avoid unnecessary errors, this kind of calculation needs to be done systematically and it helps if the frequency table is written vertically. We can then add a column for the number of children in each group and sum the numbers in this column for the total number of children.

Number of children per family x	Frequency f	Number of children in group fx
1	7	7
2	15	30
3	5	15
4	2	8
5	1	5
	No. of families: 30	No. of children: 65

$\therefore$ the mean is $\dfrac{65}{30} = 2.2$ to 1 d.p.

EXERCISE 16e

1. This table shows the results of counting the number of prickles per leaf on some holly leaves.

Number of prickles	1	2	3	4	5	6
Frequency	4	2	8	7	20	9

a) Draw up a frequency table similar to the example given on the previous page.

b) Find the total number of leaves.

c) Find the total number of prickles.

d) Find the mean number of prickles per leaf.

2. A six-sided dice was thrown 50 times. The table gives the number of times each score was obtained.

Score	1	2	3	4	5	6
Frequency	7	8	10	8	5	12

Find the mean score per throw.

3. Three coins were tossed together 30 times and the number of heads per throw was recorded.

Number of heads	0	1	2	3
Frequency	3	12	10	5

Find the mean number of heads per throw.

FINDING THE MEDIAN FROM A FREQUENCY TABLE

To find the median of a set of *items* we need to arrange them in order of size and pick out the one in the middle. This can easily be done if there are not many items and they can all be written down in order.

Now consider this frequency table which shows the distribution of the types of house currently on the list of a local estate agent.

Number of bedrooms	1	2	3	4	5	6
Frequency	6	7	16	12	3	1

The total number of houses is 45

If we want the median we must find the number of bedrooms in the 23rd house when they are arranged in order of size.

By beginning to add the frequencies we see that

There are 6 houses in the first column   – not as many as 23
There are $6 + 7 = 13$ houses in the first two columns
                                                          – not as many as 23
There are $6 + 7 + 16 = 29$ houses in the first three columns
                                                          – more than 23

So the 23rd house is in the third column of the table,
i.e. the median number of bedrooms is 3.

Remember that if the total number of items is even, two of them are equally "in the middle" and we take the mean of their values.

EXERCISE 16f

1. Six sweet pea seeds were planted in each of twenty-five plant pots. After germination the number of seedlings in each pot was counted and the results are given in this table

Number of seedlings	1	2	3	4	5	6
Frequency	1	1	4	6	7	6

Find the median number of seedlings per pot.

2. Use Exercise 16e to find the median of the data given in
a) question 1   b) question 2   c) question 3.

FINDING THE MODE AND RANGE FROM A GROUPED FREQUENCY TABLE

This frequency table was made from information about the weights (in kg) of 90 eleven-year-olds.

Weight (w kg)	$35 \leqslant w < 40$	$40 \leqslant w < 45$	$45 \leqslant w < 50$	$50 \leqslant w < 55$	$55 \leqslant w < 60$	$60 \leqslant w < 65$
Frequency	4	10	30	28	10	8

Because the weights have been placed in groups, we have lost some of the detail; we do not know how many children have a weight of 46 kg or any other particular weight. It is possible that more children have a weight of 52 kg than any other weight, but, as we just do not know, we cannot give the mode as a single figure.

However, we *can* say that more children have a weight in the group $45 \leqslant w < 50$ than in any other group. We call this the *modal group*.

To find the range we need the difference between the least weight and the greatest weight. We do not know exactly what the least weight is but it cannot be less than 35 kg and the greatest weight can be any value right up to 65 kg (although it cannot actually *be* 65 kg).

Therefore we *estimate* the range as

$$65\,\text{kg} - 35\,\text{kg} = 30\,\text{kg}$$

EXERCISE 16g

Write down the modal group and estimate the range for each of the following frequency tables.

This table shows the duration of all telephone calls made from an office one morning.

1.

Duration of a phone call (t minutes)	$0 \leqslant t < 5$	$5 \leqslant t < 10$	$10 \leqslant t < 15$	$15 \leqslant t < 20$
Frequency	20	30	10	5

2. This table shows the age groups of the employees at a small factory.

Age of employee (n years)	$18 \leqslant n < 28$	$28 \leqslant n < 38$	$38 \leqslant n < 48$	$48 \leqslant n < 58$	$58 \leqslant n < 68$
Frequency	46	59	41	37	17

3. This table shows the distribution of the number of morning customers at the Village Post Office in six months.

Number of customers	26–30	31–35	36–40	41–45	46–50
Frequency	20	31	54	35	16

FINDING THE MEAN FROM A GROUPED FREQUENCY TABLE

The pupils in one class were asked to count the number of items in their pockets and the following frequency table was drawn up.

Number of items	0–4	5–9	10–14	15–19	20–24
Frequency	6	11	6	4	3

We can see that eleven pupils had from 5 to 9 items in their pockets but we do not know the exact number that each individual pupil had. Therefore we cannot find exactly how many items the eleven pupils had altogether.

However, if we *assume* that the average number of items in that group is halfway between 5 and 9, i.e. $\frac{5+9}{2} = 7$, then we can estimate the total number of items in the group as $11 \times 7 = 77$.

Using the halfway value in the same way for the other groups we can find (approximately) the total number of items in the pockets of all 30 pupils.

(Note that a "halfway" value found in this way is not always a whole number.)

Number of items	Frequency f	Halfway value x	Number of items in group fx
0–4	6	2	12
5–9	11	7	77
10–14	6	12	72
15–19	4	17	68
20–24	3	22	66
	Total: 30		Total: 295

Therefore, the mean number of items is $\frac{295}{30} = 9.8$ to 1 d.p.

Remember that this calculation is based on the assumption that the average of each group is the "halfway" value in that group, so what we have found is an *estimate* of the mean value.

EXERCISE 16h

1. Fifty boxes of peaches were examined and the number of bad peaches in each box was recorded, with the following result

No. of bad peaches per box	0–4	5–9	10–14	15–19
Frequency	34	11	4	1

Estimate the mean number of bad peaches per box.

2. Twenty tomato seeds were planted in a seed tray. Four weeks later the heights of the resulting plants were measured and the following frequency table was made.

Height (h cm)	$1 \leqslant h < 4$	$4 \leqslant h < 7$	$7 \leqslant h < 10$	$10 \leqslant h < 13$
Frequency	2	5	10	3

Estimate the mean height of the seedlings. (To estimate the average height of the seedlings in the first group we use $\frac{1}{2}(1+4)$, i.e. 2.5).

3. The histogram shows the result of an examination of 20 boxes of screws.

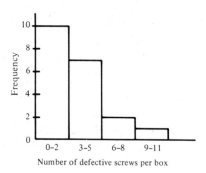

Number of defective screws per box

Make a frequency table and estimate the mean number of defective screws per box.

4. The table shows the distribution of heights of 50 adult females, measured to the nearest cm.

Height (h cm)	$145 \leqslant h < 150$	$150 \leqslant h < 155$	$155 \leqslant h < 160$	$160 \leqslant h < 165$	$165 \leqslant h < 170$	$170 \leqslant h < 175$
Frequency	1	3	21	18	5	2

Find the mean height.

FINDING THE MEDIAN FROM A GROUPED FREQUENCY TABLE

The frequency table below shows the distribution of the weights, in kilograms, of one hundred eleven-year-old children.

Weight (w)	$35 \leqslant w < 40$	$40 \leqslant w < 45$	$45 \leqslant w < 50$	$50 \leqslant w < 55$	$55 \leqslant w < 60$	$60 \leqslant w < 65$
Frequency	7	15	32	25	13	8

The total number of children is 100, so to find the median we must consider the weights of the 50th and 51st children when the weights are arranged in order. We add the frequencies in the columns until we find the column in which these two pupils are located.

$$7 + 15 = 22 \qquad \text{less than 50}$$
$$7 + 15 + 32 = 54 \qquad \text{more than 51}$$

The median weight occurs in the third column of the table so it lies in the range $45 \leqslant w < 50$.

We could give an estimate of the median by taking the value at the middle of this range, i.e. $\frac{1}{2}(45 + 50)$, giving the median weight as $47\frac{1}{2}$ kg.

EXERCISE 16i

Estimate the median value of the data given in questions 1 to 3 of Exercise 16h.

4. The table shows the result of a survey amongst 100 pupils on the amount of money each of them spent in the school tuck shop on one particular day.

Amount (pence)	0–24	25–49	50–74	75–99
Frequency	26	15	38	21

Find an estimate for the median amount of money spent.

COMPARING THE MEAN AND THE MEDIAN

If the median is bigger than the mean then more than half of the values are bigger than the mean. Conversely, if the median is smaller than the mean then more than half of the values are less than the mean.

A consumer organisation tested a batch of light bulbs from one manufacturer to determine the life of each. The results were analysed and yielded the following histogram, mean and median.

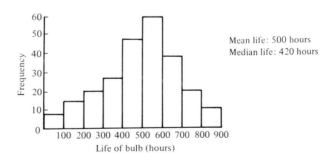

Mean life: 500 hours
Median life: 420 hours

The median is less than the mean so more than half the bulbs had a life less than the mean life. This means that if you buy one of these bulbs it is more likely than not to fail in less than 500 hours.

EXERCISE 16j

1. The histogram shows the distribution of the marks scored by a group of students sitting a science test.

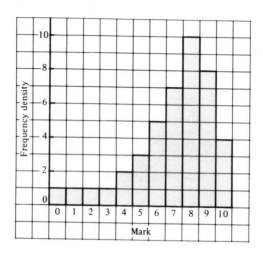

a) Construct a frequency table.

b) Find (i) the mean mark (ii) the median mark.

c) Which of the following statements are true ?
    (i) Half the students did better than average (i.e. got more than the mean mark).
    (ii) More than half the students did better than average.
    (iii) Less than half the students did better than average.

2. At a Mediterranean resort the mean number of hours of sunshine per day during June is 10.2 hours while the median number of hours of sunshine is 9.6 hours. If you visit the resort for one day are you likely to have more than 10.2 hours sunshine ?

3. One hundred AA batteries were tested to find out how long they lasted. The mean life was 36.5 hours and the median life was 40.2 hours. If you bought one of this brand of batteries, is the probability that it will fail under 37 hours more or less than 0.5 ? Give brief reasons for your answer.

4. Framley and Allington both compete in Barchester Football League. Last season, for home matches, Framley's mean score was 2.8 and their median score was 3.1. For Allington the comparable figures were 3.3 and 3.1. Next Saturday both teams are playing at home. Ted Blackstone cannot decide which match to go to. His main interest is to see the home side score as many goals as possible. Which home ground would you suggest he visits ? Justify your answer.

COMPARING DISTRIBUTIONS

Consider these two histograms: they show the scores obtained by two school groups in an English test.

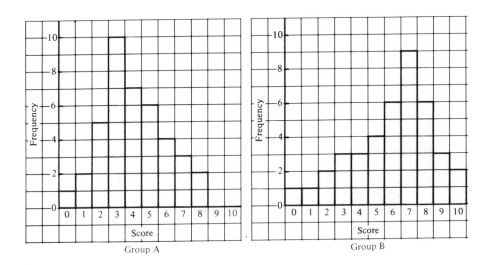

Group A

Group B

The mean, mode, median and range for each group are given in the table.

	Mean	Mode	Median	Range
Group A	4.025	3	4	8
Group B	5.875	7	6	10

Using the information on the histograms and in the table we can conclude that

a) there are 40 pupils in each group

b) there is a greater spread of scores in group B than group A

c) the mean, mode and median of group B are all larger than the corresponding values for group A

d) more pupils score less than the mean value in group A than above it, whereas in group B far more have a score above the mean value than below it.

EXERCISE 16k

1. Two manufacturers produce electric light bulbs. When 500 bulbs from each manufacturer were tested to see how long they would last before they burnt out, the following results were obtained

	Life of bulb in hours		
	Mean	Mode	Median
Manufacturer A	630	650	600
Manufacturer B	530	550	600

a) If you choose a bulb from manufacturer A is it more likely than not to last more than 600 hours ?

b) Repeat part (a) for manufacturer B.

c) From which manufacturer would you be tempted to buy ?

2.
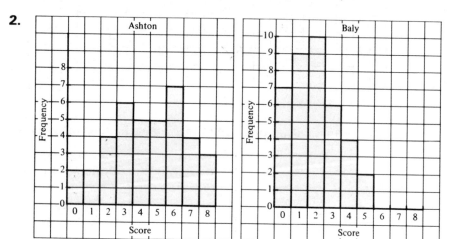

The histograms show the distributions of the goals scored by Ashton and Baly football clubs in the league matches they played last season. Each team played all the other teams in the league twice.

a) How many league matches did each team play ?

b) How many teams were there in the league ?

c) For each team find
   (i) the mean, modal and median number of goals scored
   (ii) the range.

d) Which team has the higher mean score ?

e) For each team compare the median score with the mean score.

f) On how many occasions did Ashton score 5 or more goals ?

g) For any given match what is the probability that Ashton score 5 or more goals ?

h) What is the probability that Baly score 5 or more goals in a match ?

3. Two groups of pupils sat a geography test that was marked out of 10. From their marks the following information was obtained.

	Mean	Mode	Median	Range
Group P	6.6	9	7.5	8
Group Q	2	5	4	6

a) Which group has the better results ?

b) What is similar about these distributions ?

c) What is different ?

4. The heights, in cm, of the people in two different African tribes were measured. The results are given in the table

	Mean	Median	Range
Tribe A	180	181	18
Tribe B	166	164	10

Say whether or not each of the following conclusions is true.

a) On average people in Tribe A are taller than those in Tribe B.

b) In tribe B more than half the people are more than 166 cm tall.

c) There are some people in tribe B taller than some people in tribe A.

d) There is more variation in the heights of those belonging to tribe B than to tribe A.

MIXED QUESTIONS

EXERCISE 16I

1. Find the mean, mode and median of the numbers 5, 9, 2, 3, 9, 3, 4, 12, 7

2. A rugby team has 8 forwards and 7 backs. The total mass of the forwards is 608 kg and the average mass of the backs is 64 kg. Find

a) the mean mass for the forwards

b) the total mass of the backs

c) the mean mass for the team.

3. The mean age of a family of six is 27 years 1 month. If the mean age of the parents is 46 years 3 months, find the mean age of the children. If the mother's age is 43 years 10 months, how old is the father ?

Use the data given in each question from 4 to 7 to

(a) draw a histogram and superimpose a frequency polygon

(b) find the modal group

(c) state the maximum possible range

(d) find the group in which the median lies.

4. This table shows the distribution of the ages of the people attending a Pop Festival.

Age (n years)	$15 \leqslant n < 19$	$19 \leqslant n < 23$	$23 \leqslant n < 27$	$27 \leqslant n < 31$
Frequency	1900	2700	1600	3000

5. The distribution of the marks obtained by pupils sitting a test are given in the following table.

Mark	0–9	10–19	20–29	30–39	40–49	50–59
Frequency	9	13	27	43	28	20

6. A school organises a Grand Prize Draw to raise money to buy a minibus. Tickets are sold at 50 p per book and pupils are encouraged to sell as many as possible. The table below shows the distribution of the numbers of books sold by pupils in the school.

Number of books sold	0–5	6–10	11–15	16–20	21–25	26–30
Frequency	33	124	173	144	95	31

7. This table is based on a cricketer's scores in one season.

Score	0–19	20–39	40–59	60–79	80–99	100–119	120–139
Frequency	8	14	33	6	5	3	1

8. Ninety pupils in one year sat a mathematics examination and the following frequency table was drawn up from the results.

Mark	0–14	15–29	30–44	45–59	60–74	75–89	90–100
Frequency	7	5	6	34	22	12	4

a) Find the modal group and estimate the range and the median.

b) Find the likely mean mark.

9. This table shows the results of a survey among 70 pupils on the amount of money each of them brought to school on a particular morning:

Amount (pence)	0–49	50–99	100–149	150–199
Frequency	11	35	15	9

a) Estimate the mode and the median amount of money.

b) Find the likely mean amount of money.

In questions 10 and 11 find a value for the mean of the frequency distribution.

10. This table shows the distribution of the ages of the people in the audience at a school concert.

Age (n years)	$0 \leqslant n < 20$	$20 \leqslant n < 40$	$40 \leqslant n < 60$	$60 \leqslant n < 80$	$80 \leqslant n < 100$
Frequency	73	34	27	10	6

11. The table gives the distribution of marks of 30 children in a test:

Mark	0–39	40–59	60–79	80–99
Frequency	8	8	10	4

12. Use the information gathered from a project of your own to find the mean
a) from the raw data
b) from a grouped frequency distribution made from the raw data.

PROJECTS

EXERCISE 16m

From a chosen project, collect the information (raw data), decide on the groups it can be divided into and make a frequency table. Illustrate your results with a frequency polygon and find the mean value from the frequency table. Find also the mode or modal group and range of the data.

Suggestions for Class Projects

1. Heights of pupils in the class.

2. Weights of pupils in the class.

3. Costs of journeys to school this morning.

4. Times of journeys to school (in minutes).

5. Numbers of brothers and sisters per pupil.

6. If you have done projects 1 and 2 draw a scatter diagram to see if there is any connection between a pupil's height and a pupil's weight.

7. Draw a scatter diagram which shows your results for projects 3 and 4. Are the two quantities connected?

Suggestions for Individual Projects

For these projects also find the median.

8. Choose a page of text from a book and record the number of letters per word (about 100 words is enough).

9. Use the same page of text and record the number of words per sentence.

10. Choose a completely different type of book from that used in question 6 and repeat questions 6 and 7. Use your answers for questions 6, 7 and 8 to compare the distributions of the number of letters per word, and the number of words per sentence, for the two books.

11. Count the number of people per car passing a particular place in the evening rush hour.

12. Repeat question 9 at a different time of day and compare your results with those you obtained in question 9.

17 RATIO AND PROPORTION

Ratio is a form of *comparison*. 'The ratio 5 cm to 15 cm' means '5 cm compared with 15 cm' and can be simplified to '1 compared with 3'.

In symbols we write

$$5\,\text{cm} : 15\,\text{cm} = 1 : 3$$

SIMPLIFYING RATIOS

EXERCISE 17a

> Write the following sentence using the symbol :
> 9 cm compared with 12 cm is the same as 3 compared with 4.
>
> $$9\,\text{cm} : 12\,\text{cm} = 3 : 4$$

Write the following sentences using symbols.

1. 10 km compared with 4 km is the same as 5 compared with 2.

2. 27 p compared with £1 is the same as 27 compared with 100.

3. 6 cm compared with 15 cm is the same as 2 compared with 5.

4. 240 compared with 180 is the same as 4 compared with 3.

> Simplify the ratio 45 cm : 75 cm
>
> $$45\,\text{cm} : 75\,\text{cm} = 45 : 75$$
> $$= 9 : 15 \qquad (\text{dividing by } 5)$$
> $$= 3 : 5 \qquad (\text{dividing by } 3)$$

Simplify the following ratios.

5. 36 p : 24 p

6. 20 cm : 25 cm

7. 150 : 72

8. 30 km : 48 km

9. 144 : 90

10. 32 m : 24 m

11. £ 16 : £ 12

12. 40 hours : 16 hours

13. 18 p : 14 p

14. 35 mm : 63 mm

Simplify the ratio 4 kg : 300 g

(Since the units are different we must change one of them so that both are in the same unit. We will change the larger unit to the smaller unit, noting that 1 kg = 1000 g.)

$$4 \text{ kg} : 300 \text{ g} = 4000 \text{ g} : 300 \text{ g} \quad \text{(changing to the smaller unit)}$$
$$= 4000 : 300$$
$$= 40 : 3 \quad \text{(dividing by 100)}$$

Simplify the following ratios. If the units are not the same, change the larger unit to the smaller one.

15. £ 1 : 80 p

16. £ 1.25 : 85 p

17. 4 m : 360 cm

18. 35 cm : 175 mm

19. 2 hours : 150 minutes

20. 2.4 m^2 : 6000 cm^2

21. 1 km : 100 m

22. 32 mm : 1.6 cm

23. 2 kg : 450 g

24. 1 litre : 250 cm^3

25. 2.5 cm : 175 cm

26. 550 mm^2 : 2.5 cm^2

Write the ratio $4:7$ in the form $1:n$

$$4:7 = 1:\frac{7}{4} \quad (\text{dividing by } 4)$$

$$= 1:1\frac{3}{4} \quad \text{or} \quad 1:1.75$$

Write the following ratios in the form $1:n$ where n is a decimal.

25. $5:8$ **27.** $8:9$ **29.** $4:7$

26. $2:3$ **28.** $10:7$ **30.** $5:9$

Write the following ratios in the form $1:n$ where n is a fraction.

31. $6:7$ **33.** $3:10$ **35.** $9:13$

32. $7:11$ **34.** $11:3$ **36.** $4:5$

If $x:4 = 6:5$, find x

$$x:4 = 6:5$$

$$\frac{x}{4} = \frac{6}{5}$$

Multiply both sides by 4 $4 \times \dfrac{x}{4} = 4 \times \dfrac{6}{5}$

$$x = \frac{24}{5}$$

So $\quad x = 4\frac{4}{5}$

Find x in the following ratios.

37. $x:3 = 4:5$ **40.** $x:10 = 3:4$

38. $x:2 = 6:7$ **41.** $4:9 = x:6$

39. $3:4 = x:5$ **42.** $x:12 = 7:3$

PROBLEMS ──

EXERCISE 17b

Give the ratios in this exercise in their simplest form. Make sure the numbers are in the correct order.

In a school, 864 pupils are right-handed and 96 are left-handed. What is the ratio of the number of right-handed pupils to the number of left-handed pupils ?

Number of right-handed pupils : number of left-handed pupils

$$= 864 : 96 \qquad (96 : 864 \text{ is wrong})$$
$$= 72 : 8$$
$$= 9 : 1$$

---

1. A flower bed contains 20 red rose bushes and 24 white ones. Find the ratio of the number of red rose bushes to the number of white ones.

2. In a school there are 512 boys and 484 girls. Find the ratio of the number of boys to the number of girls.

3. In a class, 12 pupils have an old version of a mathematics book and 15 pupils have a new version. Find the ratio of the number of old versions to the number of new versions.

4. In a pile of bath towels in a sale, 21 are pink and 28 are yellow. Find the ratio of the number of pink towels to the number of yellow towels.

5. The normal cost of the table is £36 but in a sale its cost is reduced to £30. Find the ratio of the sale cost to normal cost.

6. In a car park there are 32 British cars and 108 foreign cars. Find the ratio of the number of British cars to the total number of cars.

DIVISION IN A GIVEN RATIO

EXERCISE 17c

> Divide 36 p into two parts in the ratio 4 : 5.
>
> (One part is made up of 4 portions, the other of 5 portions)
>
> There are 9 portions altogether
>
> $$1 \text{ portion} = \frac{36}{9} \text{p}$$
>
> $$= 4 \text{p}$$
>
> $\therefore$ First part $= 4 \times 4 \text{p}$
>
> $$= 16 \text{p}$$
>
> Second part $= 5 \times 4 \text{p}$
>
> $$= 20 \text{p}$$
>
> (Check $16 \text{p} + 20 \text{p} = 36 \text{p}$)

1. Divide 80 cm into two parts in the ratio 3 : 5

2. Divide 24 p into two parts in the ratio 1 : 7

3. Divide 48 m into two parts in the ratio 2 : 1

4. Divide 18 mm into two parts in the ratio 4 : 5

5. Divide £25 into two parts in the ratio 2 : 3

6. A school collected £168 in aid of charity. The money was divided between Oxfam and the RSPCA in the ratio 3 : 5. How much did each charity receive ?

7. Mr Brown watched 105 minutes of television one evening. The time was divided between advertising and programmes in the ratio 1 : 6. How much time was given to advertising and how much to programmes ?

8. Bill and Joanna played one game on a fruit machine. Bill contributed 6 p and Joanna contributed 4 p for the 10 p needed. They won the jackpot which came to £25 and divided it so that the ratio of their shares was equal to the ratio of their contributions. How much did each one get ?

9. A school canteen sells two kinds of soft drink and finds that 5 cans of cola are sold for every 2 cans of lemonade. If 280 cans of drink were sold one lunchtime, how many of these were cans of cola ?

10. In his will, a man leaves £6000 to be divided between his two sons in the ratio of their ages. They are now 13 and 17 years old.
   a) If the money is divided between them now how much does each receive ?
   b) If the money is divided between them in five years' time how much will each of them receive ?

11. Annie Cooper makes a gift of £350 to her two grandchildren, Alex and Beryl. The money is to be divided between Alex and Beryl in the ratio 2 : 3. If Beryl is to get the larger share what percentage does Alex get ?

DIRECT PROPORTION

Reminder 'Proportion' is another word used for comparison. When one quantity is proportional to another then if, say, one is doubled, the other will also be doubled.

For example, if we buy oranges at a certain price each, then if we double the number of oranges bought, the total cost will double.

The total cost is proportional to the number of oranges.

This type of proportion is called *direct* proportion.

EXERCISE 17d

The total cost of 9 oranges is £1.35.

Find   a) the cost of 1 orange   b) the cost of 5 oranges.

$$9 \text{ oranges cost } 135\,\text{p}$$

a) $1 \text{ orange costs } \dfrac{135}{9}\,\text{p}$

$$= 15\,\text{p}$$

b) $5 \text{ oranges cost } 5 \times 15\,\text{p}$

$$= 75\,\text{p}$$

1. It costs 36 p to keep an electric fire on for four hours. Find how much it will cost to have the fire on for

a) 1 hour   b) 3 hours.

2. At a children's party three bottles of orange squash are needed for 24 children. Find the number of children who could be served from

a) one bottle   b) five bottles.

3. To make 8 pancakes, 128 g of flour are needed. Find the number of grams of flour needed to make

a) one pancake   b) 9 pancakes.

4. To bind the edges of 9 aprons, 36 m of bias binding are needed. Find the length of binding needed for

a) one apron   b) 5 aprons.

In the following questions you may need to find out about 1 item, as you did in questions 1 to 4, before completing your answer.

5. Twelve tins of Kitfood will feed Sara's cats for four days. How many tins would she need to feed the cats for seven days?

6. An office is packing parcels of papers to be posted. All the parcels are the same size and tied in the same way. On the first day 8 parcels are packed and 12 m of string is used.

a) On the second day, 10 parcels are packed. How much string is used?

b) On the third day, 18 m of string are used. How many parcels are packed?

7. A typist charges £ 18 for 4 hours work.

a) What would be the charge for 9 hours work?

b) How many hours of work would cost £ 27?

8. A ream of paper (500 sheets) is 7 cm thick. How thick a pile would 400 sheets make?

9. A gardener takes 56 minutes to dig a flower bed area 8 m². At the same rate, how long would he take to dig a bed of area 11 m²?

10. It costs £ 5.50 to feed a cat for 10 days.

a) How much would it cost to feed the cat for 9 days?

b) For how many days could the cat be fed for the cost of £ 7.70?

11. Carpet to cover a floor of area 12 m² costs £ 108.

a) How much would a similar carpet of area 14 m² cost?

b) How big a carpet could be bought for £ 144?

INVERSE PROPORTION

So far all the questions have involved *direct* proportion, i.e. if one quantity increases, so does the other one. Sometimes however, when one quantity increases the other decreases.

For example, if when flying from London to New York, the average speed is *increased,* the time taken *decreases*. The two quantities, speed and time, are in *inverse proportion.*

The product of two inversely proportional quantities is constant.

In this case the distance flown (speed × time) is constant.

EXERCISE 17e

A plate contains enough sandwiches for 5 people to have 8 sandwiches each. How many can each have if only 4 people arrive ?

5 people eat 8 sandwiches each

∴ there are 40 sandwiches

∴ 4 people eat $\frac{40}{4}$ sandwiches each

i.e. 10 each

1. In an examination room each row contains eight desks, and there are 14 rows.

a) How many desks are there ?

b) If the layout is changed so that each row contains seven desks, how many rows would there have to be ?

2. An agricultural supplier delivers a quantity of pignuts to a pigfarm. This quantity lasts for 9 days when there are 200 pigs.

a) How many helpings of pignuts are there ?

b) If the farm had 180 pigs, for how many days would this same quantity of pignuts last ?

3. If a school buys textbooks which cost £4.50 each it can afford to get 56 of them.

    a) How much money is there to spend on the textbooks ?

    b) If instead the textbooks cost £3.50, how many could be bought with the same amount of money ?

In the following questions it may be necessary to find a total quantity first, as in questions 1 to 3, before completing your answer.

4. Alan bought a number of stamps which were arranged in 12 columns of 18 stamps each. If this same number of stamps were arranged in 9 columns, how many rows would there be ?

5. A plane does a journey in 3 hours at 720 m.p.h. How long would the journey take at 600 m.p.h. ?

6. In a factory, tins of baked beans are packed in cartons so that there are six rows of six tins in each carton. If the same number of tins are to be packed in a carton with nine to the row, how many rows will there be ?

7. A woodwork teacher estimates that he can allow twelve nails per pupil from his available stock. There are twelve pupils. If, instead, there are eight pupils, how many nails can he give each pupil ?

8. The length of a newspaper article is 98 lines with an average of 12 words per line. If it is reset with an average of 14 words per line, how many lines will be needed ?

9. If there is enough food in an emergency pack to last 8 climbers for 3 days, how long would the food last if there were 4 climbers ?

10. A farmer employs 9 men to harvest her potato crop. They take 8 days to do the job. If she had employed just 6 men, how long would it have taken them ?

MIXED PROPORTION QUESTIONS

EXERCISE 17f

1. Mary's hair grows at the rate of 6 cm in 3 months.

    a) How long does it take to grow 16 cm ?

    b) How much does it grow in 5 months ?

2. A class of 19 uses exercise books at the rate of 76 a term. If there were 21 in the class how many books would you expect the class to use in a term ?

3. A plate of cakes contains enough for 12 people if each has 4 cakes. If, instead, there were 16 people how many cakes could each of them have ?

4. A carpet of area $12\,m^2$ costs £84. What would be the cost of a similar carpet of area $20\,m^2$?

5. Fifteen metres of material will make six summer skirts. How much material should a manufacturer allow for making 14 similar skirts ?

6. If the pupils of a middle school were divided into classes of 24 they would need 18 rooms. How many rooms would they need if they were divided into classes of 27 ?

7. 4 oz of flour are needed for 10 Yorkshire puddings. How many puddings can be made with 10 oz of flour ?

8. Martin takes 36 minutes to walk 3 km. How long would it take him to walk 7 km at the same speed ?

9. Mr Brown has set aside a sum of money with which to buy fencing. If he buys fencing at £2 per metre he can buy 7.8 m. How many metres would he get if he bought fencing at £3 a metre ?

10. For planting 24 seedlings, $216\,cm^2$ of space are needed.

a) How much space would be needed for 32 seedlings ?

b) How many seedlings could be planted in $81\,cm^2$ of space ?

11. A book of 500 pages is 40 mm thick (not counting the covers).

a) How thick is a book of 320 pages ?

b) How many pages are there in a book 50 mm thick ?

MAP SCALES

Scales are a form of comparison or ratio. First we will look at their use in maps and scale drawings.

EXERCISE 17g

On a scale drawing 1 cm represents 5 cm. What actual length is represented by
a) 9 cm   b) 4.2 cm ?

a) 1 cm represents 5 cm

9 cm represents 9×5 cm

$= 45$ cm

b) 4.2 cm represents 4.2×5 cm

$= 21$ cm

1. In a scale drawing 1 cm represents 10 cm. Find the actual lengths represented by
a) 8 cm   b) 3.2 cm   c) 42 cm.

2. On a map 1 cm represents 5 km. Find the actual lengths represented by
a) 6 cm   b) 11 cm   c) 7.2 cm.

3. The scale of a map is 1 cm to 100 m. What actual length is represented by   a) 6 cm   b) 20 cm. (Give the answer to (b) in km.)

On a map, 1 cm represents 100 m. What length on the map represents an actual length of 900 m ?

100 m is represented by 1 cm

900 m is represented by $\dfrac{900}{100}$ cm

$= 9$ cm

4. On a scale drawing, 1 cm represents 2 m. Give the length on the drawing that represents an actual length of
a) 10 m   b) 9 m   c) 32 m.

5. The scale of a map is 1 cm to 100 m. Give the length on the map that represents an actual length of

a) 200 m   b) 1200 m   c) 240 m.

6. A map scale is 1 cm to 5 km. Give the length on the map that represents an actual length of

a) 30 km   b) 100 km   c) 28 km.

MAP SCALES AND RATIOS

A map scale can be given as a ratio, say 1 : 10 000,
or in the form   1 to 10 000.

This means that the ratio of a length on the map to the actual length is 1 : 10 000, so 1 cm represents 10 000 cm.

i.e. 1 cm represents 100 m (dividing by 100).

EXERCISE 17h

A map scale is given as 1 : 2 000 000. What actual length in km is represented by

a) 1 cm   b) 9 cm.

a) The map ratio is 1 : 2 000 000

so 1 cm represents 2 000 000 cm

$$= \frac{2\,000\,000}{100} \text{ m} \qquad (100\,\text{cm} = 1\,\text{m})$$

$$= 20\,000 \text{ m}$$

$$= \frac{20\,000}{1000} \text{ km} \qquad (1000\,\text{m} = 1\,\text{km})$$

$$= 20 \text{ km}$$

b) 9 cm represents 9×20 km

$$= 180 \text{ km}$$

1. A map scale is 1 : 10 000.

   a) Find the actual distance in m represented by 1 cm.

   b) Find the actual distance represented by 4 cm.

2. A map scale is 1 : 500 000.

   a) Find the distance in km represented by 1 cm.

   b) Find the actual distance represented by 5 cm.

3. The scale of a model of a plane is 1 to 600. The length of the model is 12 cm. What is the length of the plane ?

4. A map scale is given as 1 : 1 000 000. On the map, Bristol and Gloucester are 5.3 cm apart. What is the real distance between Bristol and Gloucester ?

5. On an Ordnance Survey map the map scale is 1 : 50 000 and Eastbourne and Bexhill are 31 cm apart. How far is Eastbourne from Bexhill ?

On a map, 1 cm represents 2 km. What is the scale of the map in the form of a ratio ?

(First express both quantities in cm so that we can compare them.)

   1 cm represents 2 km

$$= 2 \times 1000 \, m \qquad (1000 \, m = 1 \, km)$$

$$= 2000 \times 100 \, cm \qquad (100 \, cm = 1 \, m)$$

$$= 200 000 \, cm$$

   $\therefore$ the map ratio is 1 : 200 000

---

6. On a map, 1 cm represents 400 m. What is the scale expressed as a ratio ?

7. On a map, the scale is 1 cm to 5 km. What is the scale expressed as a ratio ?

8. The scale of a drawing is 1 cm to 2 km. What is the scale expressed as a ratio ?

A map scale is 1 : 100 000. What real length is represented by a length of 5 cm on the map ?

(First find the scale using units.)

    1 cm represents 100 000 cm

                   = 1000 m   (100 cm = 1 m)

                   = 1 km   (1000 m = 1 km)

∴   5 cm represents 5 km

9. A map scale is 1 : 1000. What real length is represented by a length of 8 cm on the map ?

10. A map scale is 1 : 10 000 000. On the map the two points representing Trieste and Zagreb are 1.5 cm apart. How far apart are these two towns ?

11. The scale of an Ordnance Survey Landranger map is 1 : 50 000. On the map the length of Lake Bala is 11.5 cm. What is the real length of Lake Bala ?

A map scale is 1 : 10 000. What length on the map represents 600 m ?

(First find the scale using units.)

    The map scale is 1 : 10 000

    i.e. 1 cm represents 10 000 cm

                  = 100 m

∴   600 m is represented by 6 cm

12. A map scale is 1 : 1 000 000. What length on the map represents 80 km ?

13. A map scale is 1 : 500 000. What length on the map represents 300 km ?

14. Canberra is 930 km from Brisbane. If a map scale is 1 : 10 000 000 how far apart are the points representing the two cities ?

15.

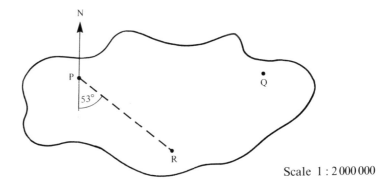

Scale 1 : 2 000 000

The diagram is the map of a county. P, Q and R represent the towns of Pressley, Queensgate and Ropton.

a) Measure PQ and PR.

b) How far is Pressley from Queensgate ?

c) How far is Pressley from Ropton ?

d) How far is Ropton from Queensgate ?

16.

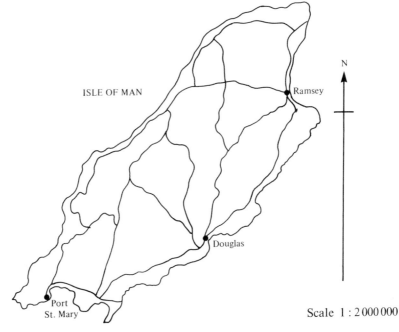

ISLE OF MAN

Scale 1 : 2 000 000

Find the distance, as the crow flies, between

a) Douglas and Ramsay

b) Douglas and Port St Mary.

c) Trace this map, showing clearly the positions of the towns.

d) Use your copy to find the bearing of Port St Mary from Ramsey.

17. Scale 1 : 50 000

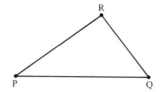

The diagram is a sketch of a map showing the position of three villages, Pickswell, Quinton and Ruffield. On the map, PQ = 8 cm and QR = 5 cm.

a) How far is Pickswell from Quinton ?

b) How far is Quinton from Ruffield ?

c) Ruffield is 4.5 km from Pickswell. What is the length of RQ on the map ?

d) Make a scale drawing showing triangle PQR.

18. Scale 1 cm to 20 m

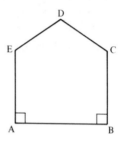

The diagram is a sketch for a scale drawing. On the scale drawing, AB = 8 cm and BC = 5.5 cm.

a) What is the real length of AB ?

b) What is the real length of BC ?

c) The real length of DC is 90 m. What is the length of CD on the scale drawing ?

d) Make the scale drawing.

MIXED EXERCISES

EXERCISE 17i

1. Simplify the ratio 108 : 72

2. Divide 39 m into two parts in the ratio 4 : 9

3. Simplify the ratio £1.25 : 65 p

4. Give the ratio 4 : 13 in the form 1 : n

5. Eight cows eat a quantity of silage in six days. Assuming that the cows all eat at the same rate, how long would the same amount of silage last if there were twelve cows ?

6. If the scale of a map is 1 cm to 25 km, how many kilometres are represented by 3.5 cm ?

7. If the scale of a map is 1 cm to 40 m, what length on the map represents a real length of 100 m ?

8. Eight equal shelves together hold 328 textbooks. How many textbooks will eleven similar shelves hold ?

EXERCISE 17j

1. Divide £72 into two parts in the ratio 5 : 19

2. Simplify the ratio 256 : 108

3. Find x if $x : 8 = 5 : 6$

4. Simplify the ratio 3.2 m : 240 cm

5. A map scale is 1 : 100 000. What length on the map represents a real length of 12 km ?

6. If the scale of a map is 1 cm to 40 m, how many metres are represented by 7.8 cm ?

7. To pot 3 amaryllis bulbs, 840 g of compost are needed. How many grams of compost would be needed to pot 5 bulbs ?

8. I have enough rug wool to cover 2400 cm² of canvas if I set the tufts in at 8 tufts per cm². If instead I decide to set 6 tufts per cm² how many square centimetres of canvas can I cover ?

EXERCISE 17k

In this exercise several alternative answers are given. Write down the letter that corresponds to the correct answer.

1. The ratio 9 : 15 is equal to

  A 1 : 7   **B** 5 : 3   **C** 3 : 5   **D** 1 : 3

2. £3 is divided into two parts in the ratio 1 : 5 . The two parts are

  A £3 and £15   **B** £1 and £2   **C** 10 p and 50 p   **D** 50 p and £2.50

3. The scale of a map is 1 cm to 50 km. A distance on the map is 5.5 cm. The real distance is

    A 275 km   **B** 250 km   **C** 1.1 km   **D** 2750 km

4. Four men can paint 240 m^2 of the Forth Bridge in a day. In the same time, five men working at the same rate could paint

    A 60 m^2 **B** 300 m^2 **C** 1200 m^2 **D** 192 m^2

5. The scale of a drawing of a coffee-table top is 1 cm to 5 cm. The real length of the table is 66 cm. On the drawing the length of the table is

    A 330 cm   **B** 1.32 cm   **C** 132 cm   **D** 13.2 cm

18 ENLARGEMENT AND SIMILARITY

ENLARGEMENT

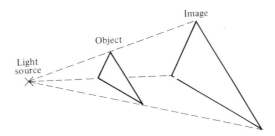

When a projector throws an image on to a screen, the image is the same shape as the object but larger. The same idea can be used to enlarge any shape. Suppose that we want to enlarge a shape so that the lengths of the enlarged version are twice those of the original.

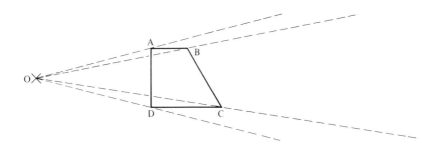

First the 'light source' is marked. This point, O, is called the *centre of enlargement.*

Then lines are drawn from O through the vertices of the object and extended. These lines are called *guide lines.*

The amount by which we extend the guide lines depends on the size of image required. In this case we want the lines on the image to be twice as long as the corresponding lines on the object,
i.e. the enlargement has a *scale factor* of 2.

The vertex on the image that will correspond to A is A′. To find A′ we draw the guide line from O through A and extend it until its length is twice that of OA, then OA′ = 2OA.

Similarly, we mark B′ on the guide line through B so that OB′ = 2OB.

Then C′ and D′ are marked on their guide lines so that OC′ = 2OC and OD′ = 2OD.

Notice that we measure all the lengths from O.

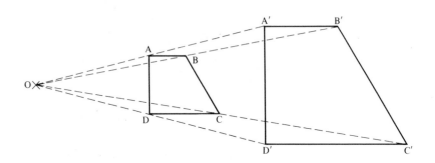

EXERCISE 18a

1.

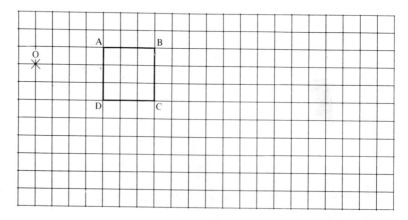

Copy the diagram on squared paper. Using O as the centre of enlargement and a scale factor of 2, draw the enlargement of ABCD. Label the vertices A′B′C′D′. Check that the enlarged square has sides twice as long as the original.

2. Repeat question 1 using a scale factor 3 (i.e. OA′ is 3 times as long as OA, etc.). Check that the enlarged square has sides three times as long as the original.

3.

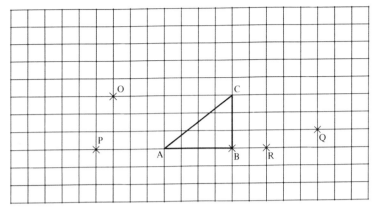

Using squared paper make a copy of △ABC. (You will need a separate copy for each part of this question.) Draw an enlargement of △ABC with a scale factor of 2 when the centre of enlargement is

a) O   b) P   c) Q   d) R   e) B.

In each case label the vertices of the image A′, B′, C′ to correspond with the vertices A, B, C of the subject. What is the effect on the image of changing the centre of enlargement ?

In questions 4 to 7, use squared paper and copy the diagram. Enlarge the figure using the given scale factor and the given centre of enlargement. In each case measure AB and the corresponding side on the enlargement. Check that the second measurement is the scale factor times the first measurement.

4.

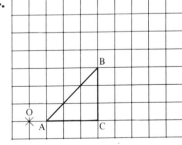

Scale factor 2

5.

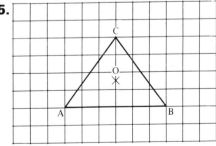

Scale factor 2

6.

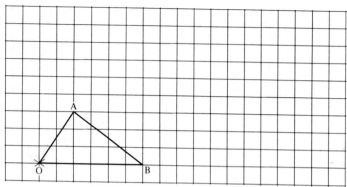

Scale factor 3

7.

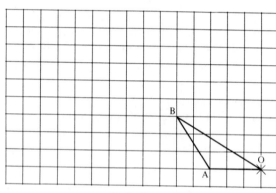

Scale factor 3

8. Copy the figure on squared paper. Use O as the centre of enlargement and, on the same diagram, draw an enlarged figure using scale factor
a) $1\frac{1}{2}$ b) 3.

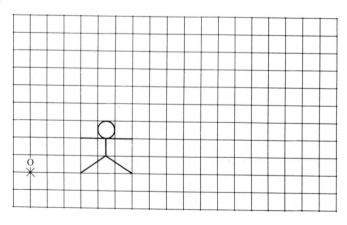

In questions 9 to 14, the grey figure is an enlargement of the black figure. Label the vertices of the grey figure A′, B′,... to correspond with the vertices A, B,... of the object.

9.

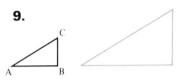

12.

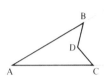

10.

13.

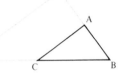

11.

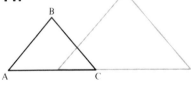

14.

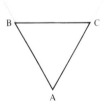

15. Triangle ADE is an enlargement of triangle ABC. Write down the vertex of △ADE that corresponds to

a) B in △ABC   b) C in △ABC   c) A in △ABC.

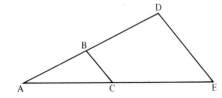

16.

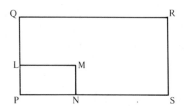

Rectangle PQRS is an enlargement of rectangle PLMN.

a) Write down the vertex in PQRS that corresponds to   (i) L   (ii) M.

b) Write down the side in PQRS that corresponds to LM in PLMN.

c) Write down the side in PLMN that corresponds to RS in PQRS.

17.

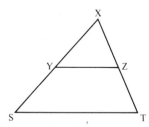

△XST is an enlargement of △XYZ.

a) Which angle of △XYZ corresponds to $S\widehat{X}T$ of △XST ?

b) Which side of △XST corresponds to the side XZ of △XYZ ?

c) Which vertex of △XYZ corresponds to the vertex S of △XST ?

18.

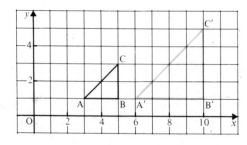

△A′B′C′ is an enlargement of △ABC. Draw the guidelines through the corresponding vertices of the two triangles and give the coordinates of the point where they meet. What special point is this?

19.

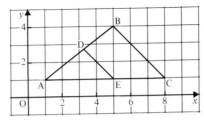

△ABC is an enlargement of △ADE. Where do the guidelines for the enlargement meet ?

20.

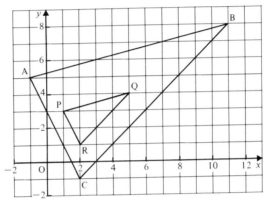

△ABC is an enlargement of △PQR. Where do the guidelines for the enlargement meet ?

FRACTIONAL SCALE FACTOR

If the scale factor is less than 1 it is unnecessary to extend the guidelines beyond the vertices of the original figure. For example, if triangle ABC is enlarged using a scale of $\frac{1}{3}$ then A' is the point on OA such that OA' = $\frac{1}{3}$OA. Similarly OB' = $\frac{1}{3}$OB and OC' = $\frac{1}{3}$OC.

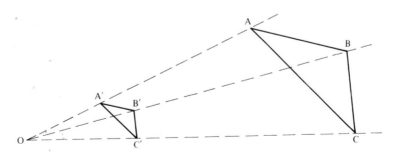

Notice that if the scale factor is less than 1, the image is smaller than the object, but the word enlargement is still often used to describe the transformation.

EXERCISE 18b

1.

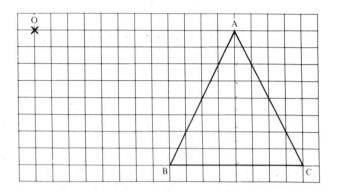

Copy the diagram on squared paper. Using O as the centre of enlargement and a scale factor of $\frac{1}{2}$, draw the enlargement of ABC. Label the vertices A'B'C'. Check that the image triangle has sides half as long as the original.

In questions 2 to 5 use squared paper and copy the diagram. Enlarge the figure using the given scale factor and the given centre of enlargement. In each case measure AB and the corresponding side on the image. Check that the second measurement is the scale factor multiplied by the first measurement.

2.

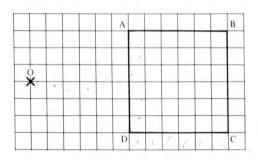

Scale factor $\frac{1}{3}$

3. Repeat question 2 using a scale factor of $\frac{2}{3}$.

4.

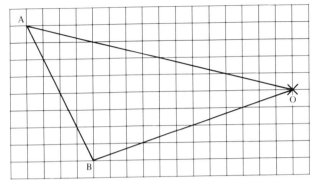

Scale factor $\frac{1}{4}$

5. Repeat question 3 using a scale factor of $\frac{3}{4}$.

FINDING THE CENTRE OF ENLARGEMENT

EXERCISE 18c

In this exercise, the grey figure is an enlargement of the black figure. Copy the diagram on squared paper. Draw the guide lines for the enlargement. The point where these lines meet is the centre of enlargement. Give the coordinates of this point, and the scale factor of the enlargement.

1.

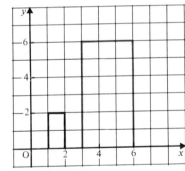

3.

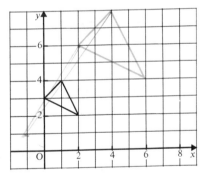

2.

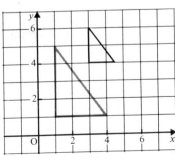

4.

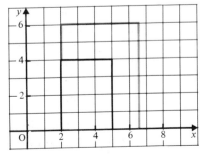

5.

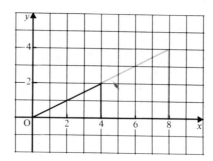

6.

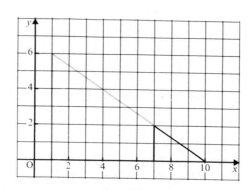

SIMILAR FIGURES

When an object is enlarged, the shape does not alter but the size does. Even if the enlarged figure is turned round or turned over, it still remains an enlargement of the object.

Two figures are called *similar figures* when one of them is an enlargement of the other.

Notice that the mathematical use of the word 'similar' is very precise: it is used only to describe figures when one is an enlargement of another.

There are other words that are used to describe similar objects. The word 'model' for example can be used to mean a smaller replica, so a car can be considered as an enlargement of a model of the car, i.e. the model and the car are similar.

Scale drawings of objects are similar to the object they represent. Again the actual object can be considered as an enlargement of the scale drawing.

Remember that similar figures are the same shape, i.e. corresponding *angles* in the two figures are *equal*.

EXERCISE 18d

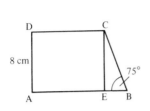
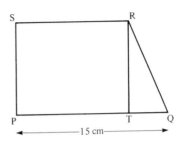

Two scale drawings are made of the same plot of land. The scale factor to enlarge ABCD to PQRS is $1\frac{1}{2}$.

a) If AD = 8 cm, find the length of PS.

b) If $\widehat{CBE}$ = 75°, find $\widehat{RQT}$.

c) If PQ = 15 cm, find AB.

(The scale factor is $1\frac{1}{2}$, so the lengths in PQRS are $1\frac{1}{2}$ times the corresponding lengths in ABCD.)

a) If AD = 8 cm   then   PS $= 1\frac{1}{2} \times 8$ cm

$$= \frac{3}{2} \times \frac{8}{1} \text{ cm}$$

$$= 12 \text{ cm}$$

b) Enlargement does not alter angles,

∴ if $\widehat{CBE}$ = 75°,   then $\widehat{RQT}$ = 75°

c) If PQ = 15 cm,   then   15 cm $= 1\frac{1}{2} \times AB$

$$= \frac{3}{2} \times AB$$

Multiply both sides by 2:   30 cm $= 3 \times AB$

Divide both sides by 3:   10 cm = AB

i.e.   AB = 10 cm

1.

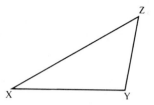

$\triangle XYZ$ is an enlargement of $\triangle ABC$, scale factor 2.

a) If $AB = 3$ cm, find XY.

b) If $AC = 6$ cm, find XZ.

c) If $YZ = 8$ cm, find BC.

2.

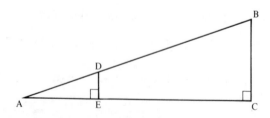

A car designer makes a model of his design for a new car. The model is $\frac{1}{10}$th the length of the proposed car (i.e. the scale factor for enlarging the model to the actual car is 10).

a) The diameter of the wheels on the model is 6 cm. What will be the diameter of the wheels on the actual car?

b) The length of the model is 52 cm. How long will the actual car be?

c) The windscreen of the model slopes at 45° to the vertical. At what angle to the vertical will the actual windscreen slope?

d) The model has six windows. How many windows will the actual car have?

3.

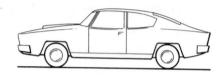

$\triangle ABC$ is an enlargement of $\triangle ADE$, scale factor 3.

a) If $AD = 3$ cm, find AB.

b) If $AE = 2$ cm, find AC.

c) If $BC = 3$ cm, find DE.

d) If $A\widehat{D}E = 60°$, find $A\widehat{B}C$ and $D\widehat{A}E$.

4.

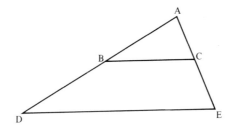

△ABC and △ADE are similar. AB = 4 cm and BD = 4 cm.

a) Write down the length of AD.

b) What is the scale factor for enlarging △ABC to △ADE ?

c) If DE = 7 cm, find BC.

5.

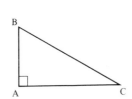 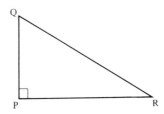

△ABC and △PQR are similar right-angled triangle not drawn to scale. The scale factor is 2.

a) (i) If AB = 5 cm, find PQ   (ii) If PR = 12 cm, find AC.

b) Calculate the area of   (i) △ABC   (ii) △PQR.

c) By what factor has the area of the object increased ?

6.

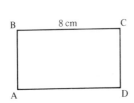 

Rectangles ABCD and PQRS are similar, and the scale factor for enlarging ABCD to PQRS is 2.5. BC = 8 cm and PQ = 15 cm.

a) Find   (i) QR   (ii) CD.

b) Find the area of ABCD and the area of PQRS.

c) By what factor has the area of ABCD increased ?

7.

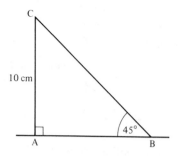

The diagram is a scale drawing. AC represents a tree, C being the top of the tree, and A the base of the tree. B is a point on level ground some distance from the base of the tree.

a) Find $A\widehat{C}B$.

b) Describe $\triangle ABC$ and write down the length of AB.

c) If the scale factor for enlarging the drawing to the real situation is 100, find the height of the actual tree and the angle of elevation of the top of the tree from B.

8.

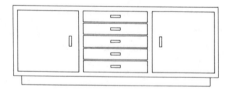

The diagram shows part of a technical drawing made by a furniture designer. The drawing is made $\frac{1}{20}$ th of the actual size and shows the front of a storage unit which stands on a plinth.

a) How many drawers does the actual unit have ?

b) Use your ruler to measure the diagram, finding
   (i) its overall width   (ii) its overall height

c) Find, in centimetres, the overall width and the overall height of the actual unit.

d) By making further measurements from the diagram, find the height and the length of the actual plinth.

9.

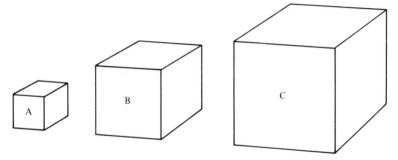

A, B and C are cubes. Each edge of A is 2 cm long. The scale factor for enlarging A to B is 2 and the scale factor for enlarging A to C is 3.

a) Find the lengths of the edges of B.

b) Find the lengths of the edges of C.

c) Find the volumes of A, B and C.

d) A fourth cube D. not shown, is such that the scale factor for enlarging A to D is 6. Find the lengths of the edges of D.

10.

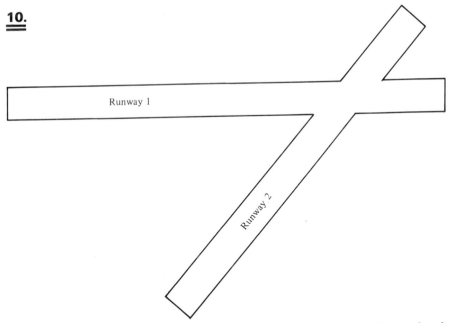

The diagram is a scale drawing of the main runways at an international airport. The scale is 1 to 20 000. By taking measurements from the diagram find

a) the length of Runway 1

b) the length of Runway 2

c) the angle between the runways.

FINDING THE SCALE FACTOR

If we know that two figures are similar, and we know the measurements of two corresponding lines, then we can work out the scale factor.

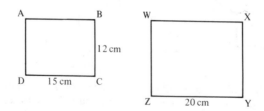

ABCD and WXYZ are similar.

YZ and CD are corresponding lengths.

To find the scale factor we divide the longer length by the shorter length. This may sometimes give a fraction rather than a whole number.

$$\frac{YZ}{CD} = \frac{20}{15} = \frac{4}{3}$$

i.e. YZ is $\frac{4}{3}$ times CD.

So the scale factor is $\frac{4}{3}$ or $1\frac{1}{3}$.

Then, as BC = 12 cm, XY = $\frac{4}{3} \times 12$ cm

$$= 16 \text{ cm}$$

EXERCISE 18e

In questions 1 to 6, which are *not* drawn to scale, the grey figure is similar to the black figure. Find the scale factor in each case.

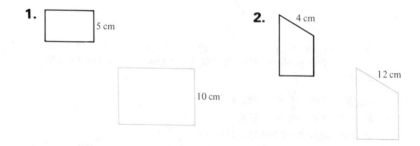

1. 5 cm

10 cm

2. 4 cm

12 cm

3.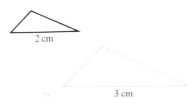

2 cm

3 cm

5.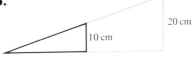

20 cm

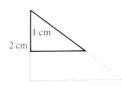

10 cm

4.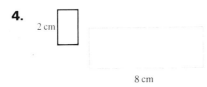

2 cm

8 cm

6.

1 cm

2 cm

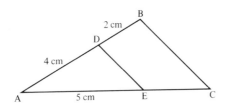

2 cm

B

D

4 cm

A   5 cm   E   C

△ABC and △ADE are similar. AD = 4 cm, DB = 2 cm and AE = 5 cm. Find the length of AC.

(First find the scale factor. AD and AB are corresponding sides, so we use them.)

$$AB = 6\,cm \qquad AD = 4\,cm$$

$$\frac{AB}{AD} = \frac{6^{\,3}}{4_{\,2}}$$

$$= \frac{3}{2}$$

The scale factor is $\frac{3}{2}$ so $AC = \frac{3}{2} \times AE$

$$= \frac{3}{2} \times 5\,cm$$

$$= 7\frac{1}{2}\,cm$$

7.

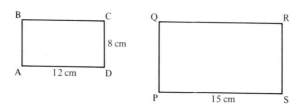

ABCD and PQRS are similar rectangles. Find the length of PQ.

8.

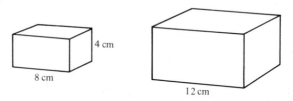

The diagram shows a pair of similar cuboids. Find the height of the larger cuboid.

9.

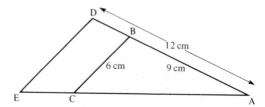

△ABC and △ADE are similar. Find the length of DE.

10.

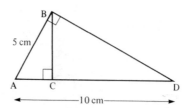

△ABC is similar to △ADB.

a) Which side of △ABD corresponds to AB in △ABC ?

b) Draw △ABD and △ABC separately so that they are the same way round, both with the right angle at the top.

c) On the diagrams drawn for (b), mark the lengths of as many sides as are given above.

d) Find the length of AC.

11.

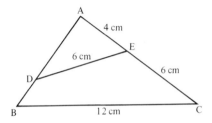

△ABC is similar to △AED.

a) Which angle of △AED corresponds to angle ABC in △ABC ?

b) Draw △ABC and △ADE separately so that they are the same way round, both with the vertex A at the top.

c) On the diagrams drawn for (b), mark the lengths of as many sides as you can.

d) Find any remaining lengths.

12.

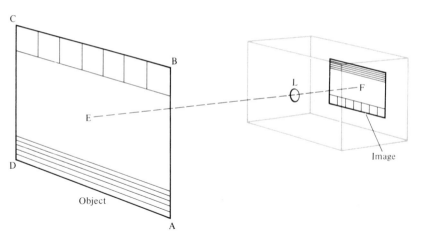

The diagram shows a rectangular card, ABCD, with a pattern printed on it, and the image of ABCD produced at the back of a camera.

L is the lens of the camera.

The centre, E, of ABCD is 8 cm from L and the centre, F, of the image is 4 cm from L.

The length, AD, of rectangle ABCD is 6 cm and the height, AB, is 4 cm.

a) Write down the dimensions of the image.

b) Explain why the image of ABCD is upside down.

c) Make a *sketch* of the image and label its vertices A', B', C' and D' to correspond with the vertices A, B, C and D of the object.

19 BRACKETS AND FACTORS

SIMPLIFYING ALGEBRAIC EXPRESSIONS

Remember that terms containing the same letter can usually be collected, e.g. $x + 2x = 3x$, but that terms that are different cannot be collected, e.g. $a + b$ or $x^2 + x$.

Remember also that subtracting a negative number has the same effect as adding a positive number e.g. $-(-2) = +2$.

EXERCISE 19a

> Simplify where possible
> a) $3x + 4x + 5x$ b) $a + b + c$ c) $2a - (-3a) + 7$
>
>   a) $3x + 4x + 5x = 12x$
>
>   b) $a + b + c$ cannot be simplified
>
>   c) $2a - (-3a) + 7 = 2a + 3a + 7$
> $$= 5a + 7$$

Simplify where possible:

1. $5a + 2b + 3c$	**6.** $4 + 3x + 5 + 6x$	**11.** $a^2 + a + 1$
2. $3y + 4y + y$	**7.** $5x + 6y + 5y$	**12.** $5t - (-4t) - 3t$
3. $5x - 2x$	**8.** $7x + 2y - 4x$	**13.** $x + 4y - 3x$
4. $3p - 4q$	**9.** $4a - (-2a) + b$	**14.** $5a + 4a - 6a$
5. $3p - (-p)$	**10.** $9y - 10y + 5$	**15.** $3b - 7b + 4b$

344

Remember that a) $x \times y$ can be written as xy

b) $x \times x$ can be written as x^2

c) multiplication or division by like signs gives a positive answer

d) multiplication or division by unlike signs gives a negative answer.

EXERCISE 19b

Simplify

a) $5x \times y$ b) $4a \times (-3a)$ c) $(-3a) \times (-5a)$

a) $5x \times y = 5xy$

b) $4a \times (-3a) = 4 \times (-3) \times a \times a$
$$= -12a^2$$

c) $(-3a) \times (-5a) = (-3) \times (-5) \times a \times a$
$$= 15a^2$$

Simplify:

1.	$3b \times 6$	**6.**	$(-4) \times 5r$	**11.**	$6p \times 3p$
2.	$3a \times b$	**7.**	$(-3a) \times (2a)$	**12.**	$5 \times (-5y) \times 2$
3.	$5a \times 3b$	**8.**	$(-x) \times (-2x)$	**13.**	$(-2) \times (8y)$
4.	$5a \times (-3)$	**9.**	$(-8x) \times (-3y)$	**14.**	$4r \times (-5r)$
5.	$4p \times (-8)$	**10.**	$3x \times (-2)$	**15.**	$(-5s) \times (-2t)$

REMOVING BRACKETS

Reminder. Each term inside the bracket is multiplied by the term outside

e.g. $4(2x + 3) = 4 \times 2x + 4 \times 3$
$$= 8x + 12$$

and $7x(3 - 5x) = 7x \times 3 + 7x \times (-5x)$
$$= 21x - 35x^2$$

EXERCISE 19c

Remove the brackets.

1. $8(5x-2)$

2. $5(3-2x)$

3. $2x(4x+3)$

4. $5(2x+7)$

5. $3(5-4a)$

6. $4x(5-x)$

7. $3(4x-3)$

8. $6(2-7a)$

9. $5x(3x-2)$

10. $7(2-3x)$

Remove the brackets and simplify

a) $5(3x-2) + 3(2x+3)$ b) $7(x+2) - 2(x-4)$

a) $5(3x-2) + 3(2x+3) = 15x - 10 + 6x + 9$
$$= 21x - 1$$

b) $7(x+2) - 2(x-4) = 7x + 14 - 2x + 8$
$$= 5x + 22$$

Remove the brackets and simplify:

11. $5(x+2) + 3(x+1)$

12. $4(x-3) + 2(x+2)$

13. $2(x+2) - 3(x+5)$

14. $4(a+2) - 2(a-5)$

15. $7(1+x) - 5(2-x)$

16. $6(x-1) + 4(x+3)$

17. $3(x+3) + 5(x+2)$

18. $3(x+1) - 6(x+2)$

19. $2(3+x) - 5(x-3)$

20. $8(x+4) - 3(2-x)$

21. $6(3x+4) + 3(x+2)$

22. $5(4x-3) + 2(2x+1)$

23. $3(2x-3) + 3(2x-1)$

24. $2(7x+2) + 5(x-4)$

25. $4(2x-7) - 7(3x-2)$

26. $7(3x+5) - 4(4x-1)$

FINDING FACTORS

In the previous exercises we removed brackets and expanded expressions. Often we need to do the reverse, that is to find the factors of an expression. This is called *factorising*.

COMMON FACTORS

In the expression $4x + 8$ we could write the first term as $4 \times x$ and the second term as 4×2

i.e. $$4x + 8 = 4 \times x + 4 \times 2$$

The 4 is a common factor.

However, we already know that $4(x + 2) = 4 \times x + 4 \times 2$

$\therefore$ $$4x + 8 = 4 \times x + 4 \times 2 = 4(x + 2)$$

EXERCISE 19d

Factorise $2x - 6$

$$2x - 6 = 2(x - 3)$$

Factorise:

1. $3x + 6$	**5.** $12x + 8$	**9.** $3a - 9$
2. $4a + 12$	**6.** $15 - 10x$	**10.** $8 - 12x$
3. $25t - 5$	**7.** $10x - 5$	**11.** $7 + 14t$
4. $12x - 9$	**8.** $6b + 9$	**12.** $21x + 9$

Factorise $4a + 2b$

$$4a + 2b = 2(2a + b)$$

Factorise:

13. $5x + 10y$	**17.** $10x - 5y$	**21.** $12x + 8y$
14. $24x - 18y$	**18.** $3a + 6b$	**22.** $15a - 10b$
15. $12x - 4y$	**19.** $25s + 5t$	**23.** $6a + 9b$
16. $8a + 24b$	**20.** $9x - 12y$	**24.** $14x - 21y$

Factorise $2x^2 + 8x$

$$2x^2 + 8x = 2x \times x + 2x \times 4$$
$$= 2x(x + 4)$$

Factorise

25. $x^2 + 5x$	**28.** $x^2 - 9x$	**31.** $x^2 + 8x$
26. $a^2 - 3a$	**29.** $t^2 + 10t$	**32.** $b^2 - 9b$
27. $7x - x^2$	**30.** $5x - x^2$	**33.** $8a - a^2$

34. $4x^2 + 2x$	**38.** $9x^2 - 6x$	**42.** $5x^2 + 10x$
35. $10a^2 - 15a$	**39.** $2t^2 + 4t$	**43.** $9a - 3a^2$
36. $12x^2 + 8x$	**40.** $9y^2 - 15y$	**44.** $12z^2 - 4z$
37. $7x - 14x^2$	**41.** $4p + 12p^2$	**45.** $25q - 10q^2$

MIXED EXERCISES

EXERCISE 19e

In this exercise several alternative answers are given. Write down the letter that corresponds to the correct answer.

1. $8x - (-3x)$ can be written as

   A $24x$ **B** $24x^2$ **C** $11x$ **D** $5x$

2. $5p \times (-2q)$ can be written as

   A $-10pq$ **B** $3pq$ **C** $-7pq$ **D** $-3pq$

3. $4x + 3y - 5x + 2y$ can be written as

   A $-x + 6y$ **B** $4xy$ **C** $-5xy$ **D** $5y - x$

4. $(-8p) \times (-4p)$ can be written as

   A $32p$ **B** $-12p$ **C** $12p$ **D** $32p^2$

5. $8(3 - 4x)$ simplifies to

   A $-8x$ **B** $24 - 8x$ **C** $24 - 32x$ **D** $-56x$

6. $5(x + 2) - 3(x - 7)$ simplifies to

   A $2x - 11$ **B** $2x + 31$ **C** $2x - 3$ **D** $15x + 14$

7. $2(2 - x) - 3(5x + 2)$ simplifies to

   A $10 - 17x$ **B** $-17x - 2$ **C** $-13x - 2$ **D** $10 - 13x$

8. $-3(3x - 2) + 4(5 - 2x)$ simplifies to

   A $26 - x$ **B** $11x - 2$ **C** $9x$ **D** $26 - 17x$

EXERCISE 19f

1. Simplify

   a) $7x \times 3x$ b) $y \times (-4y)$

2. Remove the brackets and simplify:

   a) $7(7x + 2)$ b) $-3(2x - 4)$ c) $-5(2 - 3x)$

3. Remove the brackets and simplify

   a) $4(5x - 2) + 2(3x + 7)$
   b) $3(9x - 2) - 4(4x - 2)$
   c) $5(4 + 3x) - 3(3 - 4x)$

4. Factorise   a) $7a - 14b$ b) $x^2 - 3x$

5. Factorise   a) $8b - 12c$ b) $2x^2 - 6x$

implify

a) $(-8a) \times (4a)$ b) $(-7x) \times (-5x)$

Remove the brackets and simplify

a) $-2(9+2x)$ b) $3(7-4x)$ c) $-5x(x+3)$

3. Remove the brackets and simplify

a) $2(9x+1) + 5(x+3)$

b) $4(4+3x) - 6(2-x)$

c) $-3(2x-4) + 5(x-3)$

4. Factorise   a) $5y - 15x$ b) $3a - 2a^2$

5.

1	3
2	8
3	15
4	24
.	.
.	.
.	.
n	

In this table the rule for getting the second number in each row is 'double the first number and then add the square of the first number'.

a) Write down the 5th and 6th rows in the table.

b) Find an expression for the number on the right of n.

c) Factorise the expression obtained in part (b).

20 LOCI

THE PATH OF A MOVING OBJECT

If you were to look at the many still pictures that go to make up a cine or video film of Seve Ballesteros playing a shot to the green, you would see a large number of different positions of the golf ball as it sailed through the air. While the path traced out by such a golf ball would be difficult to describe precisely, there are many paths that can be described in fairly simple mathematical terms. For example, the tip of the minute hand of Big Ben at Westminster moves in a circle as time passes, and a lorry creeping slowly up a hill in the inside lane of a straight section of motorway, travels in a straight line.

EXERCISE 20a

In this exercise, describe, and illustrate with a sketch, the path traced out in each of the given situations. There is no precise answer to most of these questions. Any reasonable sketch is acceptable.

1. A cricket ball is bowled at the wicket.

2. A cricket ball is hit along the ground for four.

3. A cricket ball is hit for six.

4. A rugby player takes a conversion and scores two points.

5. A soccer player takes a corner which results in a goal without any other player touching the ball.

6. A tennis player serves the ball and the ball is returned.

7. A car moves from the centre lane to the fast lane to overtake another car.

8. A hubcap of a car that is travelling in a straight line.

9. My hand as I push the form-room door open.

10. A pupil gets up from a desk in one room and walks to a desk in the room next door.

11. My wrist as I brush my front teeth in the morning.

12. A point on the equator of a globe as it spins on its axis.

13. The head of a swimmer as he swims 50 metres using the butterfly stroke.

14. The path of the cue ball as a snooker player pots a black from the spot.

351

15. The tip of my pen as I write the word 'one'.

16. The path of the sun in the sky from dawn to dusk, as seen from your home   a) in midwinter   b) in midsummer.

17. The tip of the pendulum in a grandfather clock.

18. The path of a jet airliner   a) on take off   b) on landing.

19. The figure that an ice skater might generate in a few seconds of skating.

20. You need a Mercator map of the world for this question.
What is the path traced out if you follow on the map

a) the equator

b) the tropic of Cancer

c) the tropic of Capricorn

d) a line of longitude from the north pole to the south pole

e) the line of longitude through Greenwich ?

21. You need a world globe for this question.

Repeat question 20 using a globe instead of the map.
Why are the paths of the same thing (e.g. the equator) different in the two questions ?

22.

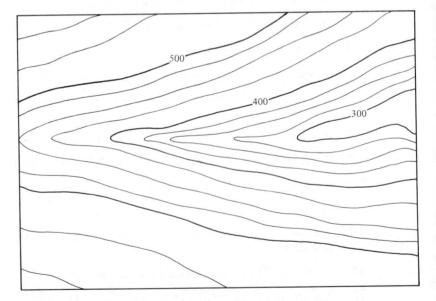

Beginning at the right-hand side of the map, follow the locus of a walker who

a) follows the 400 m contour   b) follows the 325 m contour.

23.

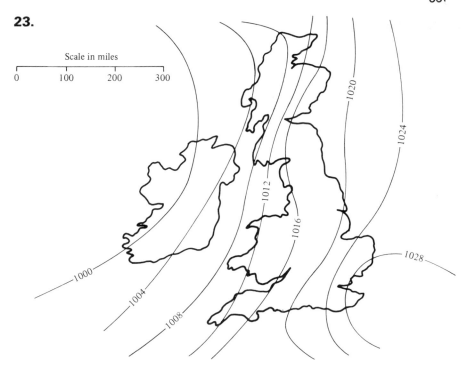

The diagram shows the air pressure, in millibars, over the British Isles on a particular day.

a) Sketch the locus of an aeroplane which flies along the 1016 millibar isobar.

b) Shade the area where the pressure is above 1020 millibars.

LOCUS

The mathematical name given to the path traced out by the set of points where positions satisfy a given rule is the *locus*. The plural of locus is *loci*.

When the locus is a straight or curved line it is convenient to think of it as the path that is traced out by a single moving point.

Remember that every point on a locus must obey the given conditions or law, and that every point that obeys the law must lie on that locus.

EXERCISE 20b

Describe the locus, between 2 p.m. and 2.45 p.m. of

a) the tip of the hour hand of a clock

b) the tip of the minute hand of a clock.

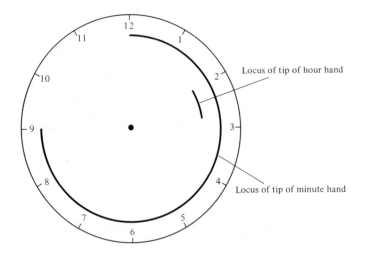

a) The tip of the hour hand traces out $\frac{1}{16}$th of a circle in three-quarters of an hour, since the hand takes 12 hours to turn through a complete circle.

b) The tip of the minute hand traces out three-quarters of a circle, since this hand takes one hour for one complete turn.

1. Describe the locus of a point on this page which moves so that it is always

a) 5 cm from the bottom edge

b) 3 cm from the right hand edge.

2. Draw a straight line AB across the width of a page of your exercise book. Describe the locus of a point C on the page that moves so that it is always 5 cm away from AB.

3.

C is the middle point of a 30 cm ruler AB.

a) Describe the locus of A if the ruler is rotated about C

b) Describe the locus of C if the ruler is rotated about A

c) Describe the locus of B if the ruler is rotated about C

d) Describe the locus of B if the ruler is rotated about A.

Is there a close relationship between any two of the loci ?

4.

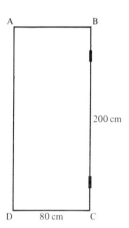

ABCD represents a door, measuring 200 cm by 80 cm, which is hinged along BC.

Describe the locus of points on the door that are

a) the same distance from AD as they are from BC

b) 80 cm from C.

Describe the locus, as the door shuts, of

c) A   d) the midpoint of AB   e) B

5.

X and Y represent two farms 1 km apart. Describe the locus of a hiker who walks so that he is always the same distance from X as he is from Y.

6.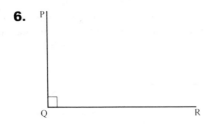

PQ and QR represent two streets of houses that intersect at right angles. Describe the locus of a drop of water which flows towards Q if it is always the same distance from PQ as it is from QR.

SPECIAL LOCI

The three most important loci in two dimensional work are:

1. The locus of a point that moves in such a way that it is always at a fixed distance from a fixed point, is called a circle. The fixed point is the centre of the circle, and the fixed distance is its radius.

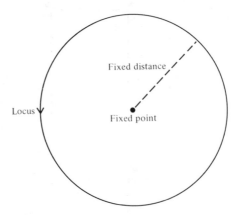

2. The locus of a point that moves in such a way that it is at a constant distance d from a line through two fixed points A and B, is the pair of straight lines drawn parallel to AB and distance d from it.

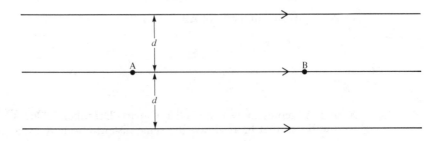

3. For points that are equidistant from two fixed points A and B, the locus is the perpendicular bisector of AB.

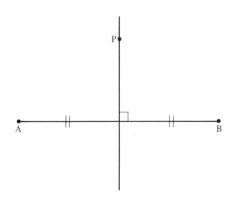

EXERCISE 20c

1. A straight line AB is 10 cm long. Describe the locus of points which are
a) 4 cm from A   b) 4 cm from B   c) equidistant from A and B.

Does any point lie on all three loci ?

2. A straight line PQ is 12 cm long and R is its midpoint. Describe the locus of points which are

a) equidistant from P and R   b) 10 cm from Q.

Do any points lie on both loci ?

3.

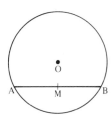

AB is a chord in a circle centre O, and M is its midpoint.

a) Describe the locus of M as the chord moves around the circle.

b) Describe the locus of the midpoints of the set of chords parallel to AB.

4. AB is a straight line of length 8 cm. Draw the locus of the point that is

a) 6 cm from A   b) 6 cm from B.

Mark as X and Y the two points that are 6 cm from both A and B. Join the points A, X, B and Y in order. Describe the figure AXBY.

5. X, Y and Z are three points such that $X\hat{Y}Z = 90°$, YX = 5 cm and YZ = 5 cm. Draw the locus of a point that is

a) 5 cm from X   b) 5 cm from Z.

Let W be the point, other than Y, that is 5 cm from both X and Z. What kind of quadrilateral is WXYZ?

(Draw a rough sketch before you attempt the accurate drawing.)

6. A and B are two fixed points such that AB = 8 cm. C is a third point such that the area of triangle ABC is 24 cm². Remembering the fact that the area of a triangle is equal to half the product of its base and its height, draw AB and mark any suitable position for C.

Next mark another position for C which satisfies the given condition. Describe the locus of all points C that satisfy the given condition.

A rectangular field measures 60 m by 100 m. A goat is tethered to the midpoint of one of the long sides of the field by a rope of length 30 m. Shade the region that the goat can graze.

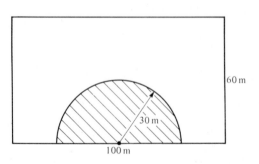

7. A donkey is tethered to the corner of a square field of side 100 m by a rope of length 25 m. Shade the region that the donkey can graze.

8. A cowboy sits astride his horse at the centre of a square corral of side 50 m. He can lasso any animal within 20 m. Shade the 'safe' area for a young calf.

9. A horse trainer sits on the fence of a circular corral of radius 25 m. He can lasso any pony within 25 m. Draw a diagram to show the region of the corral where a pony may stand without being caught.

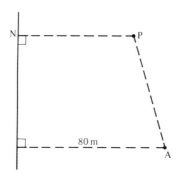

A house, A, is 80 m from the main road. A farmer wishes to erect a fence so that each post, P, is the same distance from the house (PA) as it is from the main road (PN). Plot several different positions for P such that PA = PN. Hence show the line of the fence when the farmer has completed the job. Do you know what the shape is called ?

11.

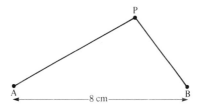

Fix two pins into a board at two points A and B, 8 cm apart. Tie a piece of string or cotton about 11 cm long between the two pins. Put a pencil inside the string, in a position such as P, so that the string becomes taut. Keeping the string taut move the pencil to all possible positions. Remove the pencil and repeat the procedure with P on the lower side of AB. What shape have you drawn ?

12.

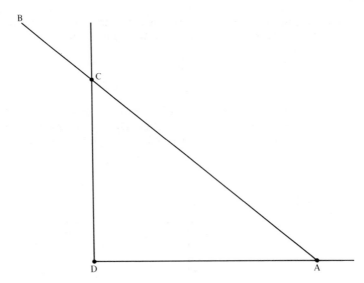

The diagram shows the stay AB of a kitchen cabinet, which moves through a slot C as the front of the cabinet turns, about the hinge at D, from the horizontal position to the vertical position. If AB = 30 cm, AD = 12 cm and CD = 24 cm, draw the diagram accurately with the door horizontal as shown. Then plot the different positions of B as the door closes 10° at a time.

Estimate the maximum distance of B from the front of the cabinet.

13.

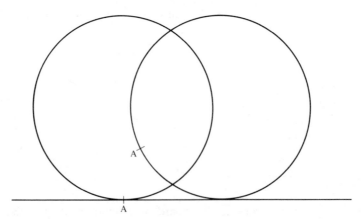

Draw a line across your exercise book. Take a 2p or 10p coin, and mark a point, A, on its circumference using chalk or plasticine or felt pen. Roll the coin along a ruler placed on your line and mark several positions of A. (Mark about ten positions for one complete revolution of the coin.)

EXERCISE 20d

1.

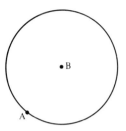

A is a fixed point and B is the centre of a 2p coin which has a radius of 1.3 cm. Describe the locus of B if the edge of the coin must always pass through A.

2. ABCD is a square of side 8 cm. The square is rotated through 90° about A, in the plane of the paper. Describe

a) the locus of D   b) the locus of C.

Does this rotation cause C and D to travel equal distances ?

3.

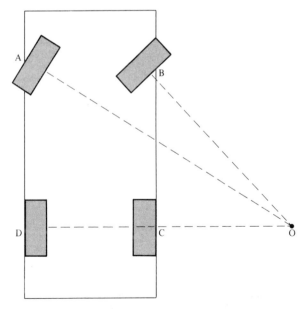

The diagram shows the wheels of a car turned so that the car can take a bend in the form of a quarter of a circle, centre O. Draw, on the same diagram, the locus of each wheel. Compare the distances travelled by the centre of each wheel.

4.

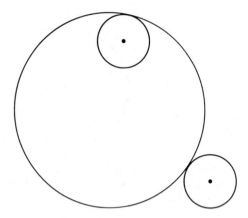

The large circle represents a circular ring of radius 4 cm. Describe the locus of the centre of a coin of diameter 2 cm if it

a) rolls around the inside of the ring

b) rolls around the outside of the ring.

5.

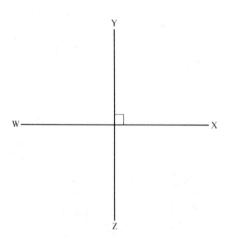

A house is to be built 100 m from the road WX and 50 m from the road YZ. Mark on a sketch the possible positions for the house, lettering each position in alphabetical order.

What shape do you get by joining up all the possible positions of the house in clockwise order ?

6.

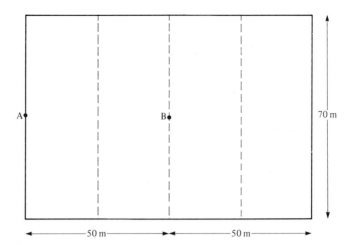

A and B represent two rugby players 50 m apart. Sketch the loci that will enable you to shade the area of the field that is both nearer to A than to B and also within 40 m of B.

21 GRAPHS

MISLEADING GRAPHS

Graphs are used to give a visual picture of information about two related varying quantities.

You can see graphs in many newspapers. The best of them give a clear picture of the way in which the two quantities vary. Many however are misleading, often because the axes are incorrectly labelled or because the scales are distorted.

Here is an example of a correctly drawn graph, showing how the cost of 1 tonne of coffee beans varied over several months.

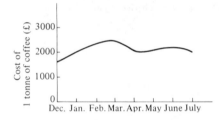

Notice that the vertical axis starts at zero, and that the graduations are equal for each £1000.

This graph gives a clear picture of the way that coffee prices varied from December to July.

Also we can see that the price of coffee in March was £2500 per tonne, and in July it was £2000 per tonne.

Here is the same graph, with the vertical axis starting at £1500.

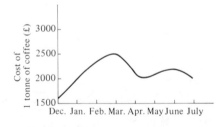

We can get the same information from this graph, but its appearance this time suggests that the variation in price was greater than it really was.

EXERCISE 21a

1.

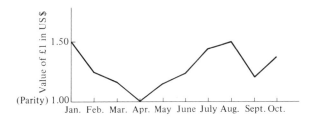

This graph shows the value of £1 in US$ at different times of one year.

a) What was the value in $ of £1 in   (i) February   (ii) April ?

b) Why could this graph be misleading ?

2.

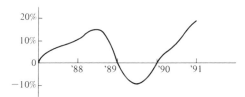

This graph was used to illustrate a comparison between the performances of two motor cycles.

a) Can you say how long it took either motor cycle to reach a speed of 60 m.p.h. ?

b) Can you get any information from this graph ?

c) What kind of impression do you think this graph is intended to give ?

3.

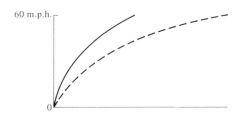

This graph illustrates the percentage change in the number of people using a particular bus service over a period of four years.

a) Can you tell how many people were using the bus service in 1987 ?

b) Can you say what happened between '89 and '90 ?

c) What kind of information do you think this graph is intended to convey ?

4.

This graph was used in the sales literature of a company selling slimming products. It illustrates the weights of two different people over a period of 21 days, one of them using the company's product 'B' plan and one of them using an ordinary diet.

a) What visual impact is this graph supposed to have ?

b) Why did they draw it like this ?

c) Why is it misleading ?

5.

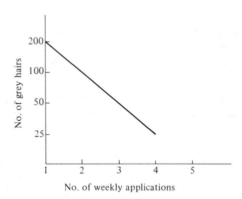

No. of weekly applications

An advertisement for a hair treatment lotion contained this graph. The advertisement claimed that if the lotion was applied weekly it would halve the number of grey hairs each time it was applied.

a) What do you think this graph is intended to infer about the number of grey hairs left after five applications ?

b) How many grey hairs are left after five applications ?

c) What do you notice about the vertical scale ?

d) How many applications are needed to get rid of all grey hairs ?

GRAPHS FROM TABLES

Before we can draw a graph we need to know how the quantities vary. Sometimes this information is given in a table as in the following case.

A horticultural fertilizer manufacturer did a trial on a particular type of fertilizer. The results are given in the table below.

Quantity used in grams per sq metre	0	5	10	15	20	25
Weight (kg) of tomatoes cropped per sq metre	5	6	8	11	12	11

To draw a graph representing this information we

a) draw axes at right angles, intersecting towards the bottom left-hand corner of the graph paper

b) mark scales on the axes and label them
   (The quantity in the top row of a table is usually on the horizontal axis.)

c) carefully plot the points representing the information given in the table

d) draw a smooth curve through the points

e) give the graph a title.

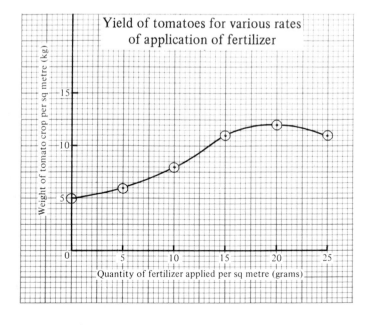

EXERCISE 21b

1. The table shows the value in £s of a motor cycle during the first five years of its life.

Age (in years)	0	1	2	3	4	5
Value in £	850	650	550	500	460	420

Draw a graph showing this information using a scale of 2 cm for 1 year on the horizontal axis and 1 cm for £100 on the vertical axis.
Use your graph to find

a) the value of the motorcycle when it is $2\frac{1}{2}$ years old

b) how much it depreciates during its first year

c) how much it depreciates during its fourth year.

2. When Amanda was born, her grandparents invested £100 for her in a building society account. The table shows the amount in the account after a given number of years.

Number of years	0	1	2	3	4	5	6
Amount (£)	100	109	119	130	141	154	168

Using a scale of 2 cm for 1 year on the horizontal axis and 1 cm for £10 on the vertical axis, draw the graph illustrating this information.
Use your graph to find

a) the value of the investment after $3\frac{1}{2}$ years

b) when the investment is worth £150

c) the percentage rate of interest during the first year.

3. A manufacturer of insecticides conducted the following experiment. Five hundred fruit flies were placed in a glass box. Insecticide was sprayed into the box and the number of dead flies was counted at one second intervals after administration of the insecticide. The table shows the number of live insects.

Time after spraying (seconds)	0	1	2	3	4	5	6
Number of insects alive	500	360	260	185	160	150	150

Use a scale of 2 cm for 1 second on the horizontal axis and a scale of 2 cm for 50 insects on the vertical scale, and draw the graph illustrating this result. Use your graph to find

a) the number of insects alive $3\frac{1}{2}$ seconds after spraying

b) the time taken to destroy half the insects.

c) Will all the insects be killed eventually?

The makers want to use these results in the sales literature. How can they draw the graph to give an impression of mass slaughter?

4. A metal spring was tested to determine how much it would stretch when various loads were hung on it. The table shows the results.

Load (kg)	0	1	2	3	4	5	6	7
Length of spring (cm)	20	22	24	26	28	30	34	44

Using a scale of 2 cm for 1 kg on the horizontal axis and 4 cm for 10 cm on the vertical axis, draw the graph illustrating these results.

a) What is the unloaded length of the spring?

b) Can you use this graph to estimate what the length of the spring would be if a load of 8 kg were hung on it?

c) What do you think happened to the spring when a load greater than 5 kg was hung on it?

CONSTRUCTING A TABLE FROM A FORMULA

Sometimes the relationship between two quantities is given by a formula and we have to make a table of values before we can draw the graph.

Suppose that a car, starting from rest, travels s metres in t seconds and, for the first 6 seconds,
$$s = 4t^2$$

Taking whole number values of t from 0 to 6, we can calculate the corresponding value of s.

When $t = 0$, $s = 4 \times (0)^2 = 0$

When $t = 1$, $s = 4 \times (1)^2 = 4$

When $t = 2$, $s = 4 \times (2)^2 = 16$

When $t = 3$, $s = 4 \times (3)^2 = 36$

When $t = 4$, $s = 4 \times (4)^2 = 64$

When $t = 5$, $s = 4 \times (5)^2 = 100$

When $t = 6$, $s = 4 \times (6)^2 = 144$

These related values of s and t can be set out in a table.

t	0	1	2	3	4	5	6
s	0	4	16	36	64	100	144

Now we can draw the graph illustrating the relationship.

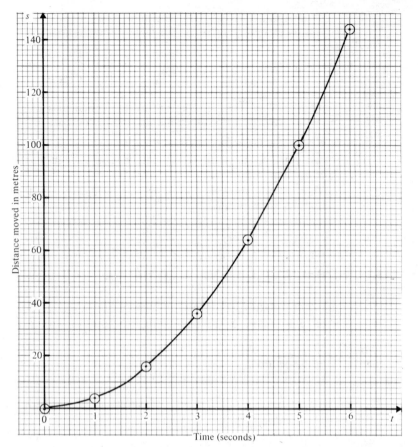

We can use this graph to find s for any given value of t within the range 0 to 6. When $t = 4.5$, $s = 81$

We can also find t for any given value of s within the range 0 to 142. When $s = 120$, $t = 5.5$

Sometimes when we are given a formula, we do not know what the symbols represent.

For example, if we are given the relationship $y = x^2$ we can make a table of values without knowing what x or y represents,

$$\text{when} \quad x = 1, \quad y = (1)^2 = 1$$
$$\text{when} \quad x = 2, \quad y = (2)^2 = 4$$
$$\text{when} \quad x = 3, \quad y = (3)^2 = 9$$

i.e.

x	1	2	3
y	1	4	9

EXERCISE 21c

1. Copy and complete the following table giving values of y for values of x from 1 to 5 where $y = 3x^2$

x	1	2	3	4	5
y	3	12			75

    Using a scale of 2 cm for 1 unit on the horizontal x-axis and a scale of 2 cm for 10 units on the vertical y-axis, draw the graph of $y = 3x^2$ for values of x from 1 to 5.

    Use your graph to find the value of y when $x = 2.5$ and the value of x when $y = 8$.

2. The area, $A \, cm^2$, covered by mould growing on a culture dish is measured daily and for the first six days it is found that $A = \frac{1}{2}d^2$ where d is the number of days that have passed since the culture was seeded.

    Copy and complete the following table.

d	0	1	2	3	4	5	6
A	0	$\frac{1}{2}$	2			12.5	

    Using a scale of 2 cm for 1 unit on the horizontal axis for d and a scale of 1 cm for 1 unit on the vertical axis for A, draw the graph of $A = \frac{1}{2}d^2$ and use it to find d when $A = 4$.

    If 1 day is 24 hours, in how many hours does the area of mould increase from $2 \, cm^2$ to $4 \, cm^2$?

3. Copy and complete the following table which gives values of s for values of t from -3 to 3 where $s = 5t^2$

t	-3	-2	-1	-0.5	0	0.5	1	2	3
s	45			1.25		1.25		20	

    Using a scale of 2 cm for 1 unit on the horizontal axis for t and 2 cm for 5 units on the vertical axis for s, draw the graph of $s = 5t^2$.

    a) Use the graph to find the value of s when $t = 1.5$ and the value of s when $t = -2.5$.

    b) What are the values of t when $s = 10$?

4. A rectangular plot of land is offered for sale. The advertisement gives the area as $3600\,\text{m}^2$ but does not give the length and breadth of the plot. The relationship between the length, l metres, and breadth, b metres, is given by $l = \dfrac{3600}{b}$

a) Copy the following table and complete the middle row.

b	20	30	40	50	60	70	80	90	100	110
l	180	120				51				33
P	400	300								

b) The third row of the table gives the perimeter, P metres, of the plot. Write down a formula relating P, l and b.

c) Complete the third row of the table.

d) Using a scale of 1 cm for 10 units on the horizontal axis for b and a scale of 2 cm for 50 units on the vertical axis for P, draw the graph illustrating how P varies for different values of b.

e) Use your graph to find the value of b which gives the shortest perimeter. What is the corresponding value of l?

GRAPHS OF ALGEBRAIC RELATIONSHIPS

Equations relating x and y can be put into categories: for example

$y = x - 1$, $y = 2x$, $y = 3$ are all of the form $y = mx + c$

$y = x^2$, $5x^2$, $y = \frac{1}{2}x^2$ are all of the form $y = ax^2$

$y = \dfrac{1}{x}$, $y = \dfrac{10}{x}$, $y = \dfrac{1}{2x}$ are all of the form $y = \dfrac{a}{x}$

Each of these categories gives a characteristically shaped graph, and we will look at each one in turn.

STRAIGHT LINE GRAPHS

In Book 3B, Chapter 24, we saw how to draw the graph of a straight line from its equation by plotting any three convenient points that satisfy the given equation. We begin this chapter by revising the earlier work.

EXERCISE 21d

The equation of a straight line is $y = 2x + 1$.
Copy and complete the table to give the coordinates of three points on the line.

x	-2	0	2
y			

Draw x and y axes in the ranges $-3 \leqslant x \leqslant 3$ and $-4 \leqslant y \leqslant 6$ using a scale of 1 cm for 1 unit on each axis. Plot the three points and draw a straight line through them.

When $x = -2$
$$y = 2(-2) + 1$$
$$= -4 - 1$$
$$= -3$$

When $x = 0$
$$y = 2(0) + 1$$
$$= 1$$

When $x = 2$
$$y = 2(2) + 1$$
$$= 4 + 1$$
$$= 5$$

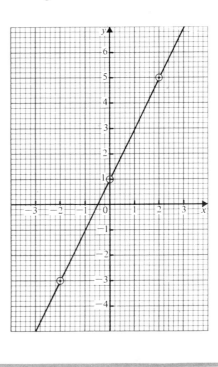

x	-2	0	2
y	-3	1	5

1. The equation of a line is $y = 3x$. Copy and complete the following table to give the coordinates of three points on the line.

x	-2	0	3
y			

Draw x and y axes for the ranges $-3 \leqslant x \leqslant 4$ and $-8 \leqslant y \leqslant 10$. Plot the three points. If they are in a straight line, draw that line. If they are not in a straight line, check your working.

2. Repeat question 1 for the line with equation $y = 2 - 3x$.

x	-1	0	3
y			

Make your own choice for the ranges for x and y.

3. You are given the graph of $y = -\frac{1}{2}x$. Use the graph to find

a) y when $x = 2$

b) y when $x = -4$

c) x when $y = 1$

d) x when $y = -2$.

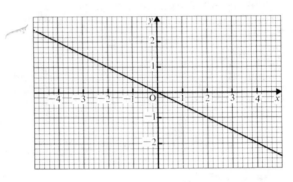

4. The equation of a line is $y = \frac{1}{2}x + 3$. Copy and complete the table to give the coordinates of three points on the line

x	-1	0	2
y			

Draw x and y axes for the ranges $-3 \leqslant x \leqslant 5$ and $-2 \leqslant y \leqslant 10$. Plot the three points, and draw the straight line through them. Draw, on the same axes, the graphs of $x = 3$ and $y = 1$.

If $y = \frac{1}{2}x + 3$ intersects $x = 3$ at A and $y = -1$ at B write down the coordinates of A and B. What type of triangle these three lines enclose ?

FINDING WHETHER A GIVEN POINT IS ON A LINE

Suppose that we want to find out if the point A$(5, 2)$ is on the line with equation $y = 2x$.

The line with equation $y = 2x$ is the set of points for which the y-coordinate is twice the x-coordinate.

For A, the y-coordinate is 2 and the x-coordinate is 5.

2 is not equal to 2×5.

Therefore A is not on the line.

EXERCISE 21e

Do the points $(2, 8)$ and $(-4, 20)$ lie on the line whose equation is $y = -5x$?

For $(2, 8)$, $x = 2$ and $y = 8$

On $y = -5x$, when $x = 2$, $y = (-5) \times 2 = -10$

Therefore $(2, 8)$ is not on the line $y = -5x$

For $(-4, 20)$, $x = -4$ and $y = 20$

On $y = -5x$, when $x = -4$, $y = (-5) \times (-4) = 20$

Therefore $(-4, 20)$ is on the line.

1. Is $(2, 3)$ a point on the line whose equation is $y = x$?

2. Is $(-1, -1)$ a point on the line whose equation is $y = x$?

3. Is $(2, -2)$ a point on the line whose equation is $y = x$?

4. Is $(4, 8)$ a point on the line whose equation is $y = \frac{1}{2}x$?

5. Is $(3, 1\frac{1}{2})$ a point on the line whose equation is $y = \frac{1}{2}x$?

6. Is $(-10, -5)$ a point on the line whose equation is $y = \frac{1}{2}x$?

7. Is $(3, 6)$ a point on the line whose equation is $y = 2x$?

8. Is $(2, 2)$ a point on the line whose equation is $y = -x$?

9. Is $(2, -4)$ a point on the line whose equation is $y = -2x$?

10. Is $(8, 2)$ a point on the line whose equation is $y = \frac{1}{4}x$?

GRADIENTS

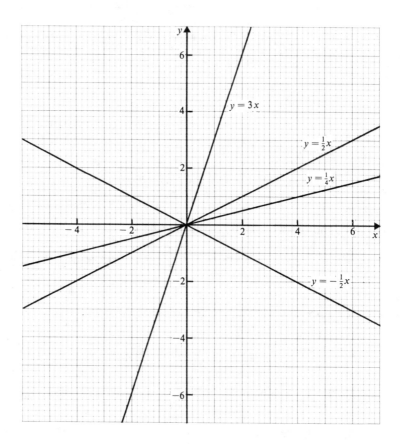

The lines in the diagram all have different slopes. We use the word *gradient* to describe slope.

If you start at a point on a line and move along the line to the right, you will find that, for the three lines with equations $y = \frac{1}{4}x$, $y = \frac{1}{2}x$ and $y = 3x$, you are moving uphill.

We say that these lines have *positive gradients*.

However, for the line with equation $y = -\frac{1}{2}x$, you will find that as you move to the right you are moving downhill.

We say that the line $y = -\frac{1}{2}x$, has a *negative gradient*.

A horizontal line has a *zero gradient*.

EXERCISE 21f

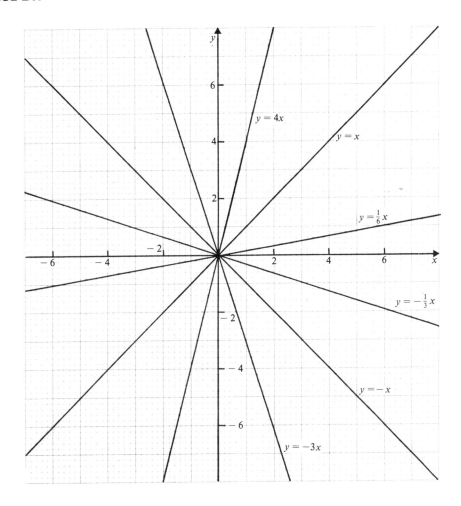

1. Use the diagram to write down

  a) the equations of the lines with positive gradients

  b) the equations of the lines with negative gradients.

2. Is there any connection between the equation of a line and the fact that it has a positive or a negative gradient ?

3. State whether each of the following lines has a positive or a negative gradient. Do not draw the lines.

  a) $y = 10x$ c) $y = -7x$

  b) $y = \frac{1}{5}x$ d) $y = \frac{1}{4}x$

CALCULATING THE GRADIENT

To work out the gradient of a line we first draw a diagram and mark two points, A and B, on the line. We next write on the diagram the change in x values and the change in y values as we move *right* across the page from A to B.

Then we work out the fraction

$$\frac{\text{change in } y \text{ values}}{\text{change in } x \text{ values}}$$

If we go *up* from A to B, the change in y values is positive.

If we go *down* from A to B, the change in y values is negative.

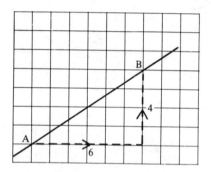

In this case the gradient is $\frac{4}{6}$ which simplifies to $\frac{2}{3}$

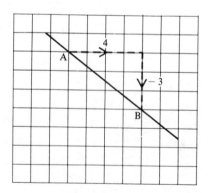

This time we have to move *down* to get from A to B, so the change in y values is negative.

$$\text{gradient} = \frac{-3}{4} = -\frac{3}{4}$$

EXERCISE 21g

Find the gradient of the line joining the points

a) A(4, 2) and B(6, 7)

b) C(2, 3) and D(4, −3)

a)

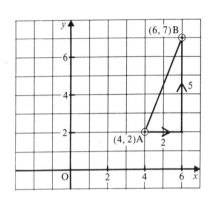

The gradient of AB is $\frac{5}{2}$

(We go *up* from A to B)

b)

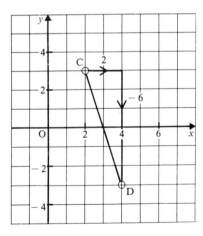

The gradient of CD is $\frac{-6}{2} = -3$

(We go *down* from C to D)

Use squared paper in this exercise and draw x and y axes for $-7 \leqslant x \leqslant 7$ and $-7 \leqslant y \leqslant 7$ using one square for 1 unit on each axis.

Plot both points and then find the gradient of the line joining them.

1. A$(2,3)$ and B$(4,5)$ **6.** A$(1,3)$ and B$(4,6)$

2. C$(1,1)$ and D$(4,6)$ **7.** C$(1,6)$ and D$(3,1)$

3. A$(2,2)$ and B$(4,-5)$ **8.** E$(2,-3)$ and F$(5,3)$

4. A$(5,2)$ and B$(7,-4)$ **9.** A$(-5,2)$ and B$(-1,5)$

5. C$(-2,3)$ and D$(1,5)$ **10.** M$(-5,-1)$ and N$(-1,-7)$

The diagram shows the graph of the line whose equation is $y = 5x$. Points A and B are marked on the graph.
Use these points to find the gradient of the line.

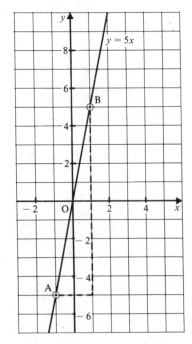

From A to B we go 2 units to the right and 10 units up.

Gradient of AB $= \dfrac{10}{2}$

$= 5$

In each of the following questions you are given the equation of a line and its graph. Two points are marked on the line. Use these points to find the gradient of the line.

11.

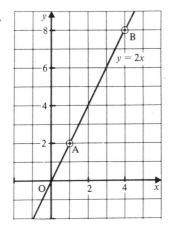

13.

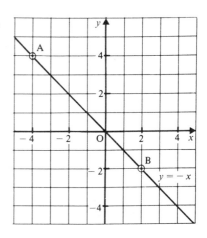

12.

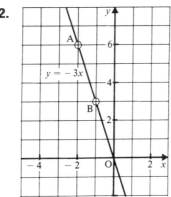

14.

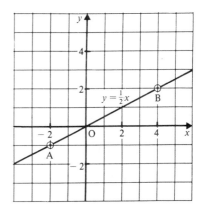

15.

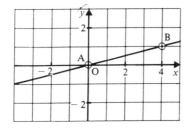

16.

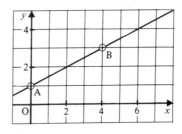

17. For questions 11 to 16 look at the value that you found for the gradient and then look at the number of xs in the equation of the line. What do you notice ?

18. How does the size of the gradient affect how steep the line is ?

In questions 19 to 24 you are given the equation of a line.
Do not draw the line, just write down its gradient.

19. $y = 10x$

20. $y = \frac{7}{4}x$

21. $y = 8x$

22. $y = -\frac{1}{2}x$

23. $y = -20x$

24. $y = \frac{9}{2}x$

25. Draw the line joining the points $(4, 3)$ and $(7, 3)$.
Which axis is the line parallel to ?
What is the equation of the line ?
What is its gradient ?

26. Plot the points $(4, 3)$ and $(4, 6)$ and draw the line joining them.
Which axis is this line parallel to ?
What happens when you try to work out its gradient ?

CONCLUSIONS SO FAR

From the last exercise we see that we can "read" the gradient of a line through the origin, from its equation.

For example

the line with equation $y = -\frac{7}{5}x$ has a gradient of $-\frac{7}{5}$.

In general

for a line with equation $y = mx$, the gradient is m.

We also conclude that

the larger the gradient, the steeper is the line.

If the gradient is 1, the line goes "uphill" at 45°.

If the gradient is −1, the line goes "downhill" at 45°.

EXERCISE 21h

Sketch the line with equation $y = -\frac{3}{2}x$,

("Sketch" means give a rough idea of the slope and position of the line.)

(In this example $y = -\frac{3}{2}x$, therefore the gradient is negative and we see that the line slopes downhill. We see that the line slopes fairly steeply because the gradient is $-1\frac{1}{2}$.)

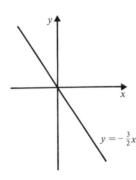

$y = -\frac{3}{2}x$

Sketch the lines whose equations are

1. $y = x$ **6.** $y = -x$

2. $y = -\frac{1}{2}x$ **7.** $y = \frac{1}{2}x$

3. $y = 2x$ **8.** $y = -2x$

4. $y = -\frac{1}{4}x$ **9.** $y = \frac{1}{4}x$

5. $y = 3x$ **10.** $y = -3x$

11. $y = 4x$ **16.** $y = -\frac{1}{3}x$

12. $y = -4x$ **17.** $y = 5x$

13. $y = \frac{3}{2}x$ **18.** $y = -5x$

14. $y = -\frac{3}{2}x$ **19.** $y = \frac{5}{2}x$

15. $y = \frac{1}{3}x$ **20.** $y = -\frac{5}{2}x$

THE EQUATION $y = mx + c$

EXERCISE 21i

For each of the following equations, copy and complete the table to give the coordinates of three points on the line.

a) $y = x$

x	-4	0	5
y			

b) $y = x + 3$

x	-4	0	5
y			

c) $y = x - 2$

x	-4	0	5
y			

d) On the same set of axes, plot the points and draw the lines.

e) What do you notice about the three lines ?

f) Where does the line with equation $y = x + 3$ cut the y-axis ?

g) Where does the line with equation $y = x - 2$ cut the y-axis ?

a) $y = x$

x	-4	0	5
y	-4	0	5

b) $y = x + 3$

x	-4	0	5
y	-1	3	8

$$\left\{ \begin{array}{l} \text{When } x = -4, \; y = -4 + 3 = -1 \\ \text{When } x = 0, \; y = 0 + 3 = 3 \\ \text{When } x = 5, \; y = 5 + 3 = 8 \end{array} \right\}$$

c) $y = x - 2$

x	-4	0	5
y	-6	-2	3

d)

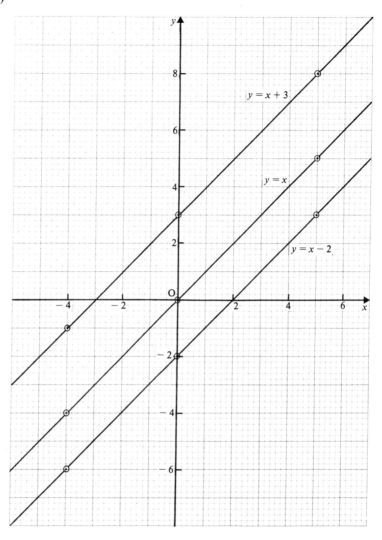

e) All three lines are parallel.

f) The line with equation $y = x + 3$ cuts the y-axis 3 units above the origin.

g) The line with equation $y = x - 2$ cuts the y-axis 2 units below the origin.

1. On graph paper draw the x and y axes for $-8 \leqslant x \leqslant 8$, $-8 \leqslant y \leqslant 8$ using 1 cm for 1 unit on each axis.

Copy and complete the table to give the coordinates of three points on the line whose equation is given.

a) $y = 2x$

x	-2	0	3
y			

b) $y = 2x + 2$

x	-2	0	3
y			

c) $y = 2x - 3$

x	-2	0	3
y			

d) For the line given in (a), plot the points and draw the line. Using the same set of axes, do the same for the lines given in (b) and (c).

e) What do you notice about the three lines ?

f) Where does the line whose equation is given in (a) cut the y-axis ?

g) Where does the line whose equation is given in (b) cut the y-axis ?

2. Repeat question 1 for the following lines.

a) $y = -x$

x	-4	0	4
y			

b) $y = -x + 4$

x	-4	0	4
y			

c) $y = -x - 1$

x	-4	0	4
y			

3.

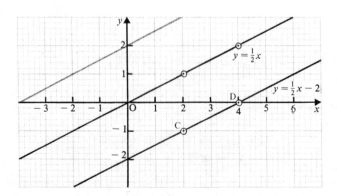

The diagram on the opposite page shows the graphs of the lines $y = \frac{1}{2}x$ and $y = \frac{1}{2}x - 2$.

a) Write down the gradient of the line whose equation is $y = \frac{1}{2}x$. Where does this line cut the y-axis ?

b) What do you think is the gradient of the line with equation $y = \frac{1}{2}x - 2$. Use the points C and D to calculate the gradient of this line. Does your answer agree with your guess ?

c) Where does the line with equation $y = \frac{1}{2}x - 2$ cut the y-axis ? Is there any connection between your answer and the equation of the line ?

d) Try to write down the equation of the grey line.

4.

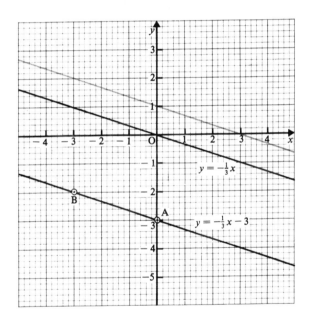

The diagram shows the graphs of the lines $y = -\frac{1}{3}x$ and $y = -\frac{1}{3}x - 3$.

a) Write down the gradient of the line $y = -\frac{1}{3}x$. Where does this line cut the y-axis ?

b) Write down what you think is the gradient of $y = -\frac{1}{3}x - 3$. Use the points A and B to calculate the gradient of this line. Do your two answers agree ?

c) Where does the line with equation $y = -\frac{1}{3}x - 3$ cut the y-axis ? Is there a connection between your answer and the equation of the line ?

d) Try to write down the equation of the grey line.

FINDING THE GRADIENT AND y INTERCEPT FROM AN EQUATION

From the last exercise we conclude that, given the equation of a line, we can "read" the gradient and the distance from O of the point where the line cuts the y-axis (called the y intercept).

For example, if the equation of a line is $y = 5x + 3$ we know that it is parallel to the line $y = 5x$, so its gradient is 5. We also know that it cuts the y-axis 3 units above the origin.

In general

> the line with equation $y = mx + c$ has gradient m
> and cuts the y-axis at a point c units from the origin.
> If c is positive, the point is above the origin.
> If c is negative, the point is below the origin.

EXERCISE 21j

Sketch the line whose equation is $y = \frac{1}{3}x - 4$

$y = \frac{1}{3}x - 4$

The gradient is $\frac{1}{3}$ and the y intercept is -4

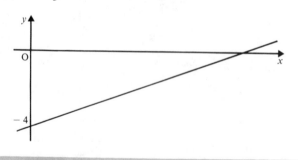

Sketch the lines whose equations are given.

1. $y = x + 2$

2. $y = -x + 3$

3. $y = 2x$

4. $y = \frac{1}{2}x + 5$

5. $y = -3x + 2$

6. $y = \frac{1}{4}x - 3$

7. $y = -x - 7$

8. $y = -2x + 4$

On the same set of axes sketch the lines whose equations are given.

9. $y = x$ **11.** $y = x - 1$ **13.** $y = x - 3$

10. $y = x + 1$ **12.** $y = x + 3$ **14.** $y = x - 5$

15. $y = -x$ **17.** $y = -x - 2$ **19.** $y = -x - 5$

16. $y = -x + 2$ **18.** $y = -x + 5$ **20.** $y = -x - 8$

FINDING THE EQUATION OF A LINE GIVEN ITS GRAPH

We know that the line with equation $y = mx + c$ has gradient m and cuts the y-axis c units from O.

This means that, given the graph of a line, we can

a) use two points on the line to work out its gradient, m

b) read where the line cuts the y-axis to find c and hence write down the equation of the line.

EXERCISE 21k

From the given graph

a) use the points A and B to find the gradient of the line.

b) find where the line cuts the y-axis.

c) write down the equation of the line.

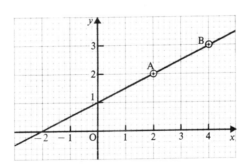

a) (From A to B we have to go 2 units right and 1 unit up.)
   Gradient $= \frac{1}{2}$

b) The line cuts the y-axis 1 unit above 0.

c) The equation is $y = \frac{1}{2}x + 1$

For each of the following graphs find

a) the gradient of the line (use points A and B if necessary)

b) where the line cuts the y-axis

c) the equation of the line.

1.
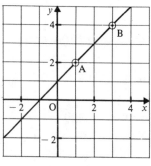

3.
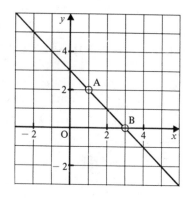

2.
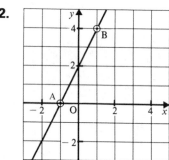

4.
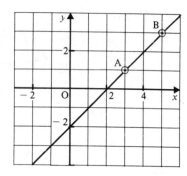

Write down the equation of each of the following lines. (If necessary, choose two points to work out the gradients.)

5.
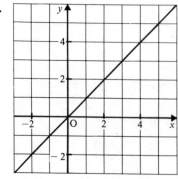

6.
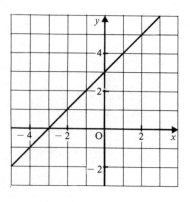

7.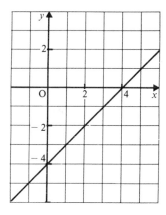

10.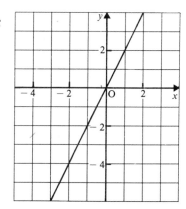

8.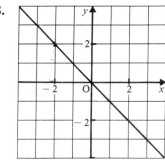

11.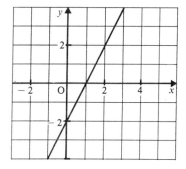

9.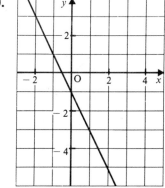

12.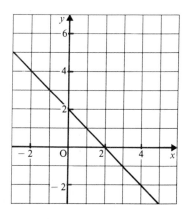

INTERSECTION OF TWO LINES

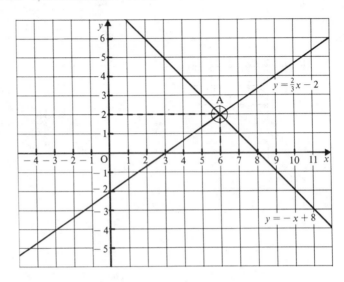

The diagram shows the lines whose equations are

$$y = \tfrac{2}{3}x - 2 \text{ and } y = -x + 8$$

The point A where they cross is called the *point of intersection* of the two lines.

This is the only point that lies on both lines. Its coordinates, from the graph, are $(6, 2)$.

We say that $x = 6$ and $y = 2$ satisfies both of the equations $y = \tfrac{2}{3}x - 2$ and $y = -x + 8$.

EXERCISE 21I

In questions 1 and 2, A is the point of intersection of the two given lines. Write down the coordinates of A.

1.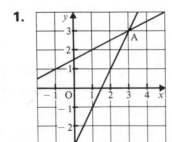

2.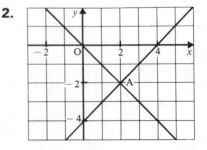

In questions 3 to 5, copy the given diagram on squared paper.

3.

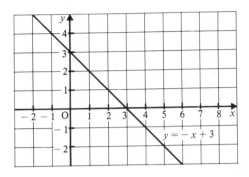

a) The equation of a second line is $y = \frac{1}{2}x$. For this line copy and complete the table

x	-2	0	6
y			

b) Using the diagram that you copied, plot these points and draw the line joining them.

c) Write down the coordinates of the point of intersection of the two lines.

4.

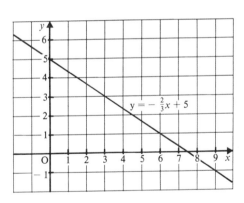

a) The equation of a second line is $y = x + 2$. For this line copy and complete the table

x	0	6	9
y			

Repeat parts (b) and (c) of question 3.

5.

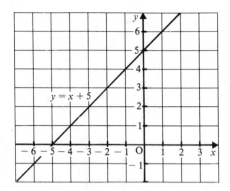

a) The equation of a second line is $y = -x + 1$. For this line, copy and complete the table

x	-5	0	2
y			

Repeat parts (b) and (c) of question 3.

THE EQUATION $y = ax^2$

EXERCISE 21m

1. Copy and complete the table for the equation $y = x^2$

x	-3	-2	-1	-0.5	0	0.5	1	2	3
y	9			0.25	0	0.25			9

Draw the y-axis down the centre of the page and the x-axis near the bottom using scales of 2 cm for 1 unit on the x-axis and 2 cm for 1 unit on the y-axis. Plot the points. Draw a smooth curve through the points.

2. Copy and complete the table for the equation $y = -3x^2$

x	-2	-1	-0.5	0	0.5	1	2
y	-12				-0.75		

Draw the y-axis down the centre and the x-axis near the top of the graph paper.
Use scales of 2 cm for 1 unit on both the x-axis and the y-axis and plot the points. Draw a smooth curve through the points.

THE PARABOLA

From the last exercise we see that the equation $y = ax^2$ gives a curve with a distinctive shape. This curve is called a *parabola*.

When a is positive
(e.g. $y = x^2$)
the curve is this way up.

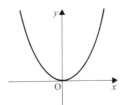

When a is negative
(e.g. $y = -3x^2$)
the curve is the other way up.

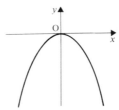

In both cases there is an axis of symmetry (the y-axis)

Knowing the shape of the graph that is expected from a particular form of equation is a great help when plotting graphs and *essential* when *sketching* graphs.

EXERCISE 21n

1. Copy and complete the table for points on the graph of $y = \frac{1}{2}x^2$.

x	-4	-3	-2	-1	0	1	2	3	4
y	8	4.5				0.5			

Draw the y-axis down the centre of the graph paper and the x-axis near the bottom of the graph paper. Use scales of 2 cm for 1 unit on both axes and draw the graph.

2. Use the graph drawn for question 1 to find
   a) the value of y when $x = 1.5$
   b) the values of x when $y = 3$.

3. Copy and complete the table of values for $y + x = 0$

x	-4	-3	1
y	4		

Use the graph drawn for question 1 and on it draw the graph of $y + x = 0$. Write down the coordinates of the points of intersection of the two graphs.

4.

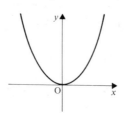

The equation of this curve could be   a) $y = 2x^2$ b) $y = 4x$ c) $y = -3x^2$. Which alternative do you think is correct ? Give a reason for your answer.

5.

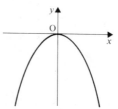

Which equation do you think is more likely to give the above graph ?
a) $y = -\frac{1}{2}x^2$ or   b) $y = 5x^2$.

6. Sketch on the same axes to graphs of $y = x^2$, $y = 2x^2$ and $y = 3x^2$. Label each curve clearly. What can you conclude about the shape of the curve as the coefficient (i.e. the number in front) of the x^2 term increases ?

THE EQUATION $y = \dfrac{a}{x}$

EXERCISE 21p

1. Copy and complete the table which gives points on the curve $y = \dfrac{1}{x}$

x	0.1	0.2	0.4	0.5	1	2	4	5
y	10		2.5	2				0.2

Draw the y-axis on the left and the x-axis at the bottom of the graph paper.
Using scales of 2 cm to 1 unit on each axis, plot the points and draw a smooth curve through them.

2. Use the graph drawn for question 1.

a) What is happening to the values of y as the values of x get bigger ?

b) What is happening to the values of y as the values of x get smaller ?

c) Use the *equation* of the curve to find the value of y when $x = \frac{1}{100}$ and when $x = \frac{1}{1000}$.

d) If you could continue the graph, would the curve ever cross the y-axis ?

3. Copy and complete this table which gives further points on the graph of $y = \frac{1}{x}$

x	-5	-4	-2	-1	-0.5	-0.4	-0.2	-0.1
y	-0.2			-1				-10

Use scales of 1 cm to 1 unit on each axis and draw the axes through the middle of the graph paper.

a) Plot the points given by this table *and* the points given by the table in question 1.

b) Draw the graph of $y = \frac{1}{x}$ for the values of x from -5 to -0.1 and from 0.1 to 5.

c) Is there a point on the curve for which $x = 0$?

THE GRAPH OF $y = \frac{a}{x}$

From the investigations in the last exercise, we see that if we consider only positive values for x the graph of $y = \frac{a}{x}$ has this shape.

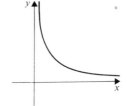

If we consider positive and negative values for x, the graph is in two parts.

Notice that each part is the reflection of the other in the line $y = -x$.

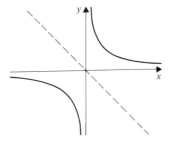

Notice also that as the value of x increases, the value of y decreases, and vice-versa.

Now the equation $y = \dfrac{a}{x}$ can be written as $xy = a$

i.e. the relationship between x and y is such that their product is constant.

We met this relationship before and said that

y is inversely proportional to x.

This means that the graph representing two inversely proportional quantities has this particular shape.

EXERCISE 21q

1. Draw a set of axes on ordinary paper. On these axes, and for positive values of x only, sketch the graphs of

   a) $y = \dfrac{1}{x}$ b) $y = \dfrac{2}{x}$ c) $y = \dfrac{1}{2x}$

2.

   a) Which equation do you think is more likely to give the above graph for positive values of x ?

   A $y = \dfrac{10}{x}$ or   **B** $y = -\dfrac{10}{x}$

   b) Sketch your chosen equation for negative values of x.

3. a) Sketch the graph of $y = -\dfrac{6}{x}$ for positive values of x.

   b) On the same axes sketch the graph of $y = \dfrac{6}{x}$

   c) Is the second sketch a mirror image of the first sketch ? If so, what is the equation of the mirror line ?

4. A school has £900 to spend on text books.

   a) How many books can be bought costing
      (i) £3 each   (ii) £5 each   (iii) £10 each ?

   b) If £C is the price of a book and N is the number of books that can be bought for £900, write down a formula relating C and N.

   c) On ordinary paper, sketch the graph illustrating the relationship between C and N.

5. A survey was carried out on a river to see if there was any relationship between the width of the river and the speed of the water flowing down the river. The results of the survey are illustrated on the graph.

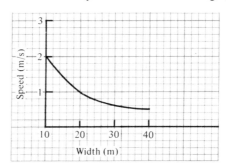

a) Use the graph to find the speed of the water when the width is 25 m.

b) Use the graph to find the speed of the water when the width is 35 m.

c) Find the product of the value of the speed and width of the river in part (a). Repeat this for part (b).

d) What relationship between width and speed is suggested by these results ?

e) Do you think that this relationship is valid everywhere on the river ?

MIXED EXERCISES

EXERCISE 21r

1. Write down the equations of the following lines.

a)

c)

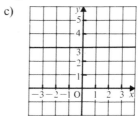

b)

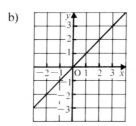

d)

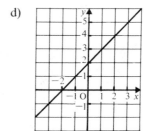

e)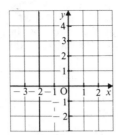

f)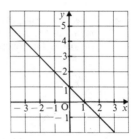

2. Use squared paper and draw axes for x and y in the ranges $-6 \leqslant x \leqslant 6$, $-6 \leqslant y \leqslant 6$, using 1 cm for 1 unit on each axis. Plot each pair of points and find the gradient of the line joining them.

a) $(1, 2)$ and $(2, 3)$

b) $(1, 4)$ and $(2, 6)$

c) $(-5, 4)$ and $(2, -1)$

d) $(-4, -4)$ and $(-5, 2)$

3. The point $(1, 2)$ lies on two of the four lines whose equations are $y = x + 1$, $y = x + 4$, $y = -x + 3$ and $y = 2x - 1$.
Write down the equations of these two lines.

4.

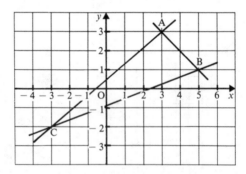

A, B and C are the points of intersection of the graphs shown. Write down the coordinates of A, B and C.

5. On squared paper draw x and y axes in the ranges $-4 \leqslant x \leqslant 10$, and $-4 \leqslant y \leqslant 6$, using 1 cm for 1 unit on each axis. On these axes draw the graphs whose equations are

a) $y = 5$ b) $y = x$ c) $x = -2$ d) $y = x - 4$

6. Using graph paper draw axes for $-3 \leqslant x \leqslant 9$ and $-2 \leqslant y \leqslant 6$. Take 1 cm for 1 unit on both axes.

a) For the line whose equation is $y = -\frac{1}{2}x + 4$, copy and complete the table

x	-2	0	6
y			

b) Plot the points and draw the line.

c) From the graph find the coordinates of the point where the line crosses the x-axis.

Questions 7 to 10 each show the graph of a line. Each line has one of the following equations.

A $y = x + 3$ **B** $y = -x + 3$ **C** $y = 2x$ **D** $y = x - 1$

For each question write down the letter that corresponds to the equation of the line shown.

7.
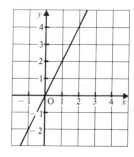

9.
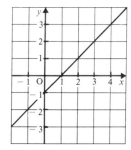

8.
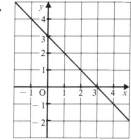

10.
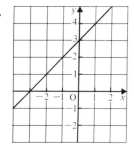

EXERCISE 21s

In this exercise each question is followed by several alternative answers.
Write down the letter that corresponds to the correct answer.

1.

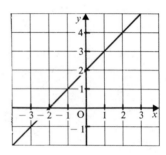

The gradient of the line shown is

A 2   **B** 1

C −1   **D** −2

2. One of the following points lies on the line whose equation is $y = x + 4$.
Which one is it ?

A $(0, 4)$ **B** $(0, 1)$

C $(1, 0)$ **D** $(4, 0)$

3.

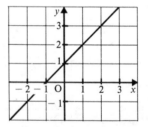

The equation of the line shown is

A $y = 1$ **B** $x = -1$

C $y = x + 1$ **D** $y = x - 1$

4. The point $(1, -2)$ lies on the line whose equation is

A $y = x + 2$ **B** $y = -x + 1$

C $y = -x - 1$ **D** $y = 2x + 1$

5.

The equation of the line shown is

A $y = x$ **B** $x = 1$

C $y = 1$ **D** $y = 0$

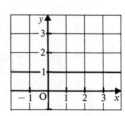

6.

The gradient of the line AB is

A 2   **B** $\frac{1}{2}$ **C** $-\frac{1}{2}$ **D** -2

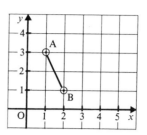

7. The equation of a line is $y = x - 3$. The graph of this line is

A

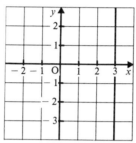

B

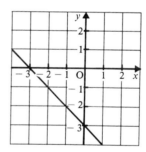

C

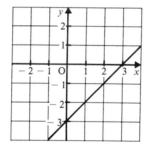

D

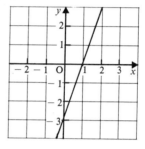

8.

The equation of the line shown is

A $y = x + 3$ **B** $y = -x + 3$

C $y = x - 3$ **D** $y = -x - 3$

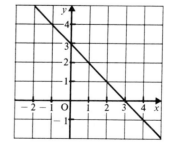

EXERCISE 21t

Each question is followed by several alternative answers. Write down the letter that corresponds to the correct answer.

1.

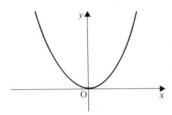

The equation of this curve could be

A $y = x$ **B** $y = x^2$ **C** $y = \dfrac{1}{x}$ **D** $y = -x$

2.

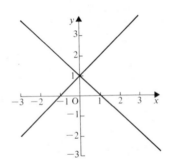

The point of intersection of the two lines is

A $(1, 0)$ **B** $(1, -1)$ **C** $(0, 1)$ **D** $(-1, 1)$

3.

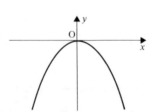

The equation of this curve could be

A $y = -x^2$ **B** $y = \dfrac{1}{x}$ **C** $y = -x$ **D** $y = x^2$

4.

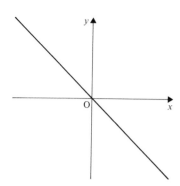

The equation of this line could be

A $y = x$ **B** $y = -x + 4$ **C** $y = -x$ **D** $y = 0$

5.

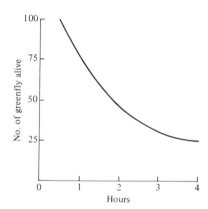

This graph illustrates the number of greenfly alive on a branch of a rose bush at various times after spraying with an insecticide.

Which of the following statements must be true ?

A All the greenfly will die eventually.

B Half the greenfly on the branch before spraying are alive two hours after spraying.

C There are 25 insects alive four hours after spraying.

D The insecticide does not kill all the insects.

6.

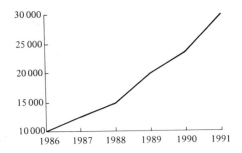

This graph shows the annual sales of 'Redmeat' dog food.

Which of the following statements must be true ?

A Sales in 1989 were double those in 1988.

B Sales rose from zero in 1986 to 30 000 in 1991.

C Sales in 1991 were double those in 1988.

D Sales in 1991 were five times those in 1986.

7. The graph of $y = 2x^2$ could be

A

C

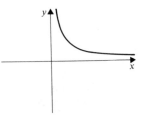

B

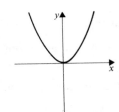

D

8. The relationship between the area, A cm^2, of a square sheet of paper and the length, l cm, of a side of the square, is $A = l^2$.
The graph illustrating this relationship could be

A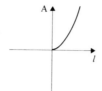

C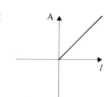

B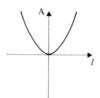

D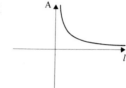

22 SIMULTANEOUS EQUATIONS

We will begin by revising the methods used in Book 3B for solving various types of pairs of simultaneous equations.

Suppose that we have two equations such as

$$3x + 2y = 5 \qquad [1]$$
$$5x - 2y = 3 \qquad [2]$$

When we add the two equations, y disappears; in this case adding gives

$$8x = 8 \quad \text{hence} \quad x = 1$$

We can find the corresponding value of y by substituting $x = 1$ in [1].

i.e. $\qquad 3 + 2y = 5 \quad$ gives $\quad y = 1$

We check our results by substituting $x = 1, y = 1$ in [2].

On the other hand, two equations such as

$$5x + 3y = 26 \qquad [1]$$
$$x + 3y = 10 \qquad [2]$$

are solved by subtracting [2] from [1]

i.e. $\qquad\qquad\qquad\qquad 4x = 16$

giving $\qquad\qquad\qquad\qquad x = 4$

The solution then continues as before.

EXERCISE 22a

Solve the following pairs of equations.

1. $4x + y = 14$
$\quad\ x + y = 5$

2. $2x + 3y = 23$
$\quad\ x + 3y = 22$

3. $2x + 3y = -8$
$\quad\ 2x + y = -4$

4. $12x + 5y = 65$
$\quad\ 9x + 5y = 50$

408

Solve the pair of equations $x - 2y = 1$

$3x + 2y = 19$

$$x - 2y = 1 \qquad [1]$$

$$3x + 2y = 19 \qquad [2]$$

[1] + [2] gives $4x = 20$

$$x = 5$$

(It is easier to use the equation with the + sign to find y.)

Substitute 5 for x in [2] $15 + 2y = 19$

Take 15 from both sides $2y = 4$

$$y = 2$$

Check in [1]   Left-hand side $= 1 = 5 - 4$

$$= 1 = \text{right-hand side}$$

Therefore the solution is $x = 5, y = 2$

Solve the following pairs of equations.

5. $x - y = 2$
      $3x + y = 10$

6. $p + 2q = 11$
      $3p - 2q = 1$

7. $3a - b = 10$
      $a + b = 2$

8. $3x - 4y = -24$
      $5x + 4y = 24$

To solve the following equations, first decide whether to add or subtract.

9. $3x + 2y = 12$
      $x + 2y = 8$

10. $x + 3y = 12$
      $x + y = 8$

11. $5p - 3q = 9$
      $4p + 3q = 9$

12. $6a - b = 20$
      $6a + 5b = 8$

Greater care is required when we have to subtract a negative term.

Solve the pair of equations $\qquad 4x - y = 10$

$$x - y = 1$$

$$4x - y = 10 \qquad\qquad [1]$$

$$x - y = 1 \qquad\qquad [2]$$

(The signs in front of the y terms are the same so we subtract:
$-y - (-y) = -y + y = 0$)

$[1] - [2]$ gives $\qquad\qquad\qquad 3x = 9$

$$x = 3$$

Substitute 3 for x in [2] $\qquad 3 - y = 1$

Add y to both sides $\qquad\qquad 3 = 1 + y$

Take 1 from both sides $\qquad\qquad 2 = y$

Check in [1] $\qquad$ Left-hand side $= 12 - 2$

$$= 10 = \text{right-hand side}$$

Therefore the solution is $x = 3, y = 2$

Solve the following pairs of equations.

13. $2x - y = 4$
$\quad\ x - y = 1$

16. $6x - y = 7$
$\quad\ 2x - y = 1$

14. $2p - 3q = -7$
$\quad\ 4p - 3q = 1$

17. $5x - 2y = -19$
$\quad\ x - 2y = -7$

15. $\ x - y = 3$
$\quad\ 3x - y = 9$

18. $2x - 3y = 14$
$\quad\ 2x - y = 10$

19. $3x - 2y = 14$
$\quad\ x + 2y = 10$

21. $3p + 5q = 17$
$\quad\ 4p + 5q = 16$

20. $3p - 5q = -3$
$\quad\ 4p - 5q = 1$

22. $3p - 5q = 7$
$\quad\ 4p + 5q = -14$

HARDER ELIMINATION

Equations are not always as simple as the ones we have had so far.

Consider

$$2x + 3y = 4 \qquad [1]$$
$$4x + y = -2 \qquad [2]$$

Whether we add or subtract neither letter will disappear, so it is necessary to do something else first. If we multiply the second equation by 3 to give $12x + 3y = -6$, we have the same number of ys in each equation. Then we can use the same method as before.

$$[2] \times 3 \qquad\qquad 12x + 3y = -6 \qquad\qquad [3]$$
$$2x + 3y = 4 \qquad\qquad [1]$$

$$[3] - [1] \text{ gives} \qquad\qquad 10x = -10$$
$$x = -1$$

Substitute -1 for x in [2] $\qquad -4 + y = -2$

Add 4 to both sides $\qquad\qquad y = 2$

Therefore the solution is $x = 1, y = 2$

EXERCISE 22b

Solve the pair of equations

$$3x - 2y = 1$$
$$4x + y = 5$$

$$3x - 2y = 1 \qquad\qquad [1]$$
$$4x + y = 5 \qquad\qquad [2]$$

$[2] \times 2$ gives $\qquad\quad 8x + 2y = 10 \qquad\qquad [3]$
$$3x - 2y = 1 \qquad\qquad [1]$$

$[1] + [3]$ gives $\qquad\qquad 11x = 11$
$$x = 1$$

Substitute 1 for x in [2] $\qquad 4 + y = 5$

Take 4 from both sides $\qquad\quad y = 1$

Check in [1] $\quad$ Left-hand side $= 3 - 2$

$$= 1 = \text{right hand side}$$

Therefore the solution is $x = 1, y = 1$

Solve the following pairs of equations.

1. $2x + y = 7$
         $3x + 2y = 11$

4. $5x + 3y = 21$
         $2x + y = 3$

2. $5x - 4y = -3$
         $3x + y = 5$

5. $6x - 4y = -4$
         $5x + 2y = 2$

3. $9x + 7y = 10$
         $3x + y = 2$

6. $4x + 3y = 25$
         $x + 5y = 19$

Solve the pair of equations $5x + 3y = 7$
                                    $10x + 4y = 16$

$$5x + 3y = 7 \qquad [1]$$
$$10x + 4y = 16 \qquad [2]$$

$[1] \times 2$ gives
$$10x + 6y = 14 \qquad [3]$$
$$10x + 4y = 16 \qquad [2]$$

$[3] - [2]$ gives
$$2y = -2$$
$$y = -1$$

Substitute -1 for y in [1] $5x - 3 = 7$
Add 3 to both sides $5x = 10$
                                      $x = 2$

Check in [2]   Left hand side $= 20 + (-4) = 16$
Therefore the solution is $x = 2, y = -1$

---

7. $5x + 3y = 11$
         $4x + 6y = 16$

10. $9x + 5y = 15$
         $3x - 2y = -6$

8. $2x - 3y = 1$
         $5x + 9y = 19$

11. $4x + 3y = 1$
         $16x - 5y = 21$

9. $2x + 5y = 1$
         $4x + 3y = 9$

12. $7p + 2q = 22$
         $3p + 4q = 11$

Sometimes we need to alter both equations before we add or subtract.

EXERCISE 22c

Solve the pair of equations $3x + 5y = 6$

$2x + 3y = 5$

$$3x + 5y = 6 \qquad [1]$$
$$2x + 3y = 5 \qquad [2]$$

$[1] \times 3$ gives $9x + 15y = 18 \qquad [3]$

$[2] \times 5$ gives $10x + 15y = 25 \qquad [4]$

$$9x + 15y = 28 \qquad [3]$$

$[4] - [3]$ gives $x = 7$

Substitute 7 for x in [2] $14 + 3y = 5$

Take 14 from both sides $3y = -9$

Divide both sides by 3 $y = -3$

Check in [1]   Left hand side $= 21 - 15$

$= 6 =$ right hand side

Therefore the solution is $x = 7, y = -3$

Solve the following pairs of equations.

1. $2x + 3y = 12$
     $5x + 4y = 23$

2. $3x - 2y = -7$
     $4x + 3y = 19$

3. $2x - 5y = 1$
     $5x + 3y = 18$

4. $6x + 5y = 9$
     $4x + 3y = 6$

5. $14x - 3y = -18$
     $6x + 2y = 12$

6. $6x - 7y = 25$
     $7x + 6y = 15$

7. $5x + 4y = 21$
     $3x + 6y = 27$

8. $9x + 8y = 17$
     $2x - 6y = -4$

9. $9x - 2y = 14$
     $7x + 3y = 20$

10. $5x + 4y = 11$
     $2x + 3y = 3$

MIXED QUESTIONS

EXERCISE 22d

Solve the following pairs of equations

1. $x + 2y = 9$
$2x - y = -2$

2. $x + y = 4$
$x + 2y = 9$

3. $2x + 3y = 0$
$3x + 2y = 5$

4. $3x - y = -10$
$4x - y = -4$

5. $5x + 2y = 16$
$2x - 3y = -5$

6. $3x + 2y = -5$
$3x - 4y = 1$

7. $x + y = 6$
$x - y = 1$

8. $3x - 5y = 13$
$2x + 5y = -8$

9. $7x + 3y = 35$
$2x - 5y = 10$

10. $9x + 2y = 8$
$7x + 3y = 12$

Sometimes the equations are arranged in an awkward fashion and need to be rearranged before solving them.

EXERCISE 22e

Solve the pair of equations $x = 4 - 3y$
$2y - x = 1$

$x = 4 - 3y$ [1]
$2y - x = 1$ [2]

(We must first arrange the letters in the same order in both equations.
By adding $3y$ to both sides, equation [1] can be written $3y + x = 4$)

$3y + x = 4$ [3]
$2y - x = 1$ [2]

[3] + [2] gives $5y = 5$
$y = 1$

Substitute 1 for y in [1] $x = 4 - 3$
$x = 1$

Check in [2] Left hand side $= 2 - 1$
$= 1 =$ right hand side

Therefore the solution is $x = 1, y = 1$

Solve the following pairs of equations.

1. $y = 6 - x$
$2x + y = 8$

4. $9 + x = y$
$x + 2y = 12$

2. $x - y = 2$
$2y = x + 1$

5. $2y = 16 - x$
$x - 2y = -8$

3. $3 = 2x + y$
$4x + 6 = 10y$

6. $3x + 4y = 7$
$2x = 5 - 3y$

As long as the x and y and number terms are in corresponding positions in the two equations, they need not be in the order we have had so far.

Solve the pair of equations $\quad y = x + 5$
$\quad\quad\quad\quad\quad\quad\quad\quad\quad\quad\quad\quad y = 7 - x$

$\quad\quad\quad\quad\quad\quad\quad\quad\quad\quad\quad y = x + 5 \quad\quad\quad\quad [1]$
$\quad\quad\quad\quad\quad\quad\quad\quad\quad\quad\quad y = 7 - x \quad\quad\quad\quad [2]$

Rewrite [1] as $\quad\quad\quad\quad\quad\quad\quad y = 5 + x \quad\quad\quad\quad [3]$

[2] + [3] gives $\quad\quad\quad\quad\quad\quad\quad 2y = 12$
$\quad\quad\quad\quad\quad\quad\quad\quad\quad\quad\quad\quad y = 6$

Substitute 6 for y in [1] $\quad\quad\quad\quad\quad 6 = x + 5$
$\quad\quad\quad\quad\quad\quad\quad\quad\quad\quad\quad\quad x = 1$

Check in [2] $\quad\quad\quad$ Left hand side $= 6$
$\quad\quad\quad\quad\quad\quad$ Right hand side $= 1 + 5 = 6$

Therefore the solution is $x = 1, y = 6$

---

7. $y = 9 + x$
$y = 11 - x$

10. $2y = 4 + x$
$y = x + 8$

8. $x = 3 + y$
$2x = 4 - y$

11. $x + 4 = y$
$y = 10 - 2x$

9. $y = 4 - x$
$y = x + 6$

12. $x + y = 12$
$y = 3 + x$

SPECIAL CASES

Some pairs of equations have no solution and some have an infinite number of solutions.

EXERCISE 22f

Try solving the following pairs of equations. Comment on why the method breaks down.

1. $x + 2y = 6$
$x + 2y = 7$

3. $y = 4 + 2x$
$y - 2x = 6$

2. $3x + 4y = 1$
$6x + 8y = 2$

4. $9x = 3 - 6y$
$3x + 2y = 1$

5. Make up other pairs of equations which either have no solution or have an infinite set of solutions.

PROBLEMS

EXERCISE 22g

I think of two numbers. If I add three times the smaller number to the bigger number I get 14. If I subtract the bigger number from twice the smaller number I get 1. Find the two numbers.

Let the smaller number be x and the bigger number be y.

$$3x + y = 14 \qquad [1]$$
$$2x - y = 1 \qquad [2]$$

[1] + [2] gives
$$5x = 15$$
$$x = 3$$

Substitute 3 for x in [1]
$$9 + y = 14$$
$$y = 5$$

Therefore, the two numbers are 3 and 5

(Check by reading the original statements to see if the numbers fit.)

Solve the following problems by forming a pair of simultaneous equations.

1. The sum of two numbers, x and y, is 20 and their difference is 4. Find the numbers.

2. The sum of two numbers, x and y, is 16 and they differ by 6. What are the numbers ?

3. I think of two numbers, x and y. If I double the first and add the second I get 18. If I double the first and subtract the second I get 14. What are the numbers ?

4. Three times a number added to a second number is 33. The first number added to three times the second number is 19. Find the two numbers.

5. Find the two numbers such that twice the first added to the second is 26 and the first added to three times the second is 28.

6. Find the two numbers such that twice the first added to the second gives 27 and twice the second added to the first gives 21.

A shop sells bread rolls. If five brown rolls and six white rolls cost 98 p while three brown rolls and four white rolls cost 62 p find the cost of each type of roll.

Let one brown roll cost x p and one white roll cost y p.

$$5x + 6y = 98 \qquad [1]$$
$$3x + 4y = 62 \qquad [2]$$

[1] × 2 gives $\qquad 10x + 12y = 196 \qquad [3]$

[2] × 3 gives $\qquad 9x + 12y = 186 \qquad [4]$

[3] − [4] gives $\qquad\qquad x = 10$

Substitute 10 for x in [1] $\qquad 50 + 6y = 98$

Take 50 from both sides $\qquad\qquad 6y = 48$

$$y = 8$$

Therefore one brown roll costs 10 p and one white roll costs 8 p.

---

7. I buy x choc ices and y orange ices and spend £2.30. I buy ten ices altogether. The choc ices cost 30 p each and the orange ices cost 20 p each. How many of each do I buy ?

8.

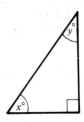

The difference between x and y is 18. Given that x is bigger than y, find x and y.

9. A cup and saucer together cost £3.15. A cup and two saucers cost £4.50. Find the cost of a cup and of a saucer.

10. The cost of two choc ices is the same as the cost of three ice lollies. One choc ice and one lolly together cost £1.75. What do they each cost ?

11. In a test, the sum of Harry's marks and Adam's marks is 42. Sam has twice as many marks as Adam, and the sum of Harry's and Sam's marks is 52. What are the marks of each of the three boys ?

12.

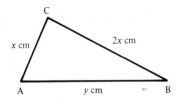

The perimeter of triangle ABC is 14cm. AB is 2cm longer than AC. Find x and y.

13.

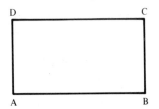

The perimeter of the rectangle is 31cm. The difference between the lengths of AB and BC is $3\frac{1}{2}$cm. Find the lengths of AB and BC.

14. The equation of a straight line is $y = mx + c$. When $x = 1, y = 6$ and when $x = 3, y = 10$. Form two equations for m and c and hence find the equation of the line.

GRAPHICAL SOLUTIONS OF SIMULTANEOUS EQUATIONS

We saw earlier that when we are given an equation we can draw a graph. Any of the equations which occur in this chapter give us a straight line. Two equations give us two straight lines which usually cross one another.

Consider the two equations $\quad x + y = 4$
$$y = 1 + x$$

Suppose we know that the x-coordinate of the point of intersection is in the range $0 \leqslant x \leqslant 5$:

$$x + y = 4$$

x	0	4	5
y	4	0	-1

$$y = 1 + x$$

x	0	2	5
y	1	3	6

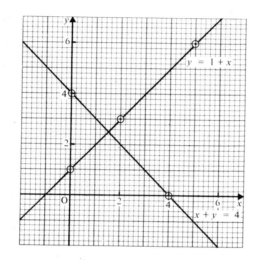

At the point where the two lines cross, the values of x and y are the same for both equations, so they are the solutions of the pair of equations.

From the graph we see that the solution is $x = 1\frac{1}{2}$, $y = 2\frac{1}{2}$.

EXERCISE 22h

Solve the following equations graphically. In each case draw axes for x and y and use values in the ranges indicated, taking 2 cm to 1 unit.

1. $x + y = 6$ $0 \leqslant x \leqslant 6$, $0 \leqslant y \leqslant 6$
    $y = 3 + x$

2. $x + y = 5$ $0 \leqslant x \leqslant 6$, $0 \leqslant y \leqslant 6$
    $y = 2x + 1$

3. $y = 4 + x$ $0 \leqslant x \leqslant 6$, $0 \leqslant y \leqslant 6$
    $y = 1 + 3x$

4. $x + y = 1$ $-3 \leqslant x \leqslant 2$, $-2 \leqslant y \leqslant 4$
    $y = x + 2$

5. $2x + y = 3$ $0 \leqslant x \leqslant 3, \ -3 \leqslant y \leqslant 3$
      $x + y = 2\frac{1}{2}$

6. $y = 5 - x$ $0 \leqslant x \leqslant 5, \ 0 \leqslant y \leqslant 7$
      $y = 2 + x$

7. $3x + 2y = 9$ $0 \leqslant x \leqslant 4, \ -2 \leqslant y \leqslant 5$
      $2x - 2y = 3$

8. $2x + 3y = 4$ $-2 \leqslant x \leqslant 2, \ 0 \leqslant y \leqslant 4$
      $y = x + 2$

9. $x + 3y = 6$ $0 \leqslant x \leqslant 5, \ 0 \leqslant y \leqslant 5$
      $3x - y = 6$

10. $x = 2y - 3$ $-2 \leqslant x \leqslant 3, \ 0 \leqslant y \leqslant 4$
      $y = 2x + 1$

SPECIAL CASES

EXERCISE 22i

Try to solve the following equations graphically. Why do you think the method breaks down ?

1. $x + y = 9$ $0 \leqslant x \leqslant 9$
   $x + y = 4$ $0 \leqslant y \leqslant 9$

2. $y = 2x + 3$ $0 \leqslant x \leqslant 4$
   $y = 2x - 1$ $-1 \leqslant y \leqslant 11$

3. $2x + y = 3$ $0 \leqslant x \leqslant 3$
   $4x + 2y = 7$ $-3 \leqslant y \leqslant 4$

4. $y = 2x - 4$ $0 \leqslant x \leqslant 4$
   $2x = y + 4$ $-4 \leqslant y \leqslant 4$

23 GENERAL REVISION EXERCISES

EXERCISE 23a

1. Find the value of $\dfrac{1.26 \times 0.89}{0.0078}$

   a) by estimation, to one significant figure

   b) using a calculator, correct to three significant figures.

2. a) Express 8.2 m in centimetres.

   b) Express $2\frac{1}{2}$ feet in inches.

   c) A road race started at 10.15 a.m. and Clyde crossed the finishing line 2 hours 50 minutes later. What time was this ?

3. A baby's weight at birth is 3.2 kg. Using $1 \text{ kg} \approx 2.2 \text{ lb}$ give the baby's weight in pounds to the nearest $\frac{1}{2}$ lb.

4. a) Simplify $4 + 2x - 3 + 5x$

   b) Factorise $3x + 9$

5.

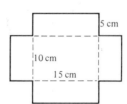

This net makes an open box. Find the volume of the box.

6. Find the mean, mode and median of each of the following sets of data.

   a) 2.2, 2.5, 2.5, 2.8

   b) 6, 5, 7, 5, 5, 6, 7, 4, 18

7. Ten of the 25 passengers on a bus had bus passes. What percentage of the passengers had a pass ?

8. A new house bought for £50 000 in 1990 depreciates by 5 % in its first year. How much is the house worth after 1 year ?

9. Write down, in terms of n, the nth term of the sequence

   a) 3, 6, 9, 12, ...

   b) $\frac{1}{3}$, $\frac{2}{4}$, $\frac{3}{5}$, $\frac{4}{6}$, $\frac{5}{7}$, ...

   c) 0, 3, 8, 15, 24, ...

10. Find the values s and t when $3s - t = 10$

and $2s + 3t = 14$

11. If $v = u - at$
   a) Find the value of v when $u = 2$, $a = -3$ and $t = 4$.
   b) Make u the subject of the formula.

12. Find the gradients of the following lines.

a) 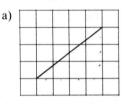   b) 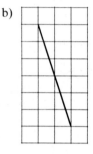   c)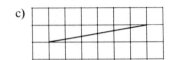

13.

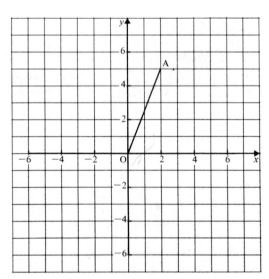

Copy the diagram.

Write down the coordinates of A′, the image of A, when the line OA is

a) reflected in the x-axis

b) rotated about O by $180°$

c) translated by $\begin{pmatrix} 2 \\ 0 \end{pmatrix}$.

14.   a) If $\tan A = 1.2735$ find $\hat{A}$.

b) Find $\cos 54°$.

c) If $\sin B = 0.1536$ find $\hat{B}$.

15.

The diagram is a rough sketch of the end wall of a garden shed.

a) Find the area of the end wall

b) If the shed is 2 m long find its volume. Give your answer in cubic metres.

260 cm

200 cm

150 cm

16.   Peter Howes is paid £4.80 an hour for a basic working week of 36 hours. For overtime he is paid £7.20 an hour. Find his pay for a week in which he works 42 hours.

EXERCISE 23b

1.   Evaluate   a) $1\frac{3}{4} - \frac{2}{3}$ b) $0.026 \div 0.7$ c) $5\frac{2}{5} \div 1\frac{4}{5}$

2.   The instructions for making up wallpaper paste state that the contents of the packet have to be mixed with 16 pints of water. The paste is to be mixed in a large bucket calibrated in gallons. To which mark should the bucket be filled?

3.   The speed limit on a motorway in France is 110 km/hr. Use 5 miles ≈ 8 km to find this speed in m.p.h.

4.   a) I think of a number then double it and add on 3. The result is 11. What number did I think of?

b) Factorise $x^2 - 7x$.

5.

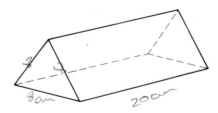

A triangular prism has a cross-section in the shape of an equilateral triangle. The sides of the triangle are 8 cm long and the prism is 20 cm long. Draw a net for making this prism.

6. Find the circumference and area of a circle whose radius is 5 cm

a) approximately, using $\pi \approx 3$

b) correct to 3 s.f. using the π button on your calculator.

7. New York is five hours behind London (i.e. when it is 5 p.m. in London it is noon in New York).

a) When it is noon in London what time is it in New York ?

b) When it is 3 p.m. in New York what time is it in London ?

c) A plane leaves London at 2 p.m. local time and arrives in New York at 5 p.m. local time. How long does the flight take ?

8.

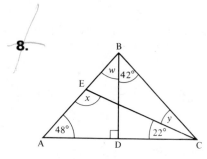

a) △ABC has a line of symmetry. Name this line.

b) Find the sizes of the marked angles.

9. Find the values of x and y for which $2x - 3y = 5$

and $3x + 2y = 27$

10. A school spent £750 on games equipment last year but has to reduce that amount by 10% for this year. How much money can be spent on games equipment this year ?

11. A hotel offers facilities and catering for parties at the following rate: £20 for hire of a room plus £12 per person for food. Make up a formula for the cost, £C, of a party for n people.

12.

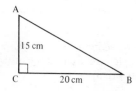

a) Find the length of AB.

b) Find $\widehat{B}$.

13. When a pilot in a glider notices a suitable landing site, his altimeter tells him he is 400 m above ground level and he measures the angle of depression of the landing site as 25°.

a) Draw a sketch to show this information.

b) Calculate his horizontal distance from the landing site.

14.

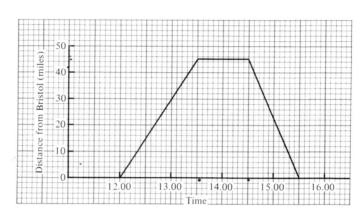

The graph represents a journey made by a coach travelling from Bristol to Cheltenham and later returning to Bristol.

a) How long did the coach take to travel to Cheltenham?

b) For how long did the coach stop in Cheltenham?

c) How far is it between Bristol and Cheltenham?

d) What was the average speed of the coach on the return journey?

15. Draw, on the same diagram, the histogram and frequency polygon for the data given in the following table, which shows the distribution of shoe sizes for the fifty-five members of a football club.

Shoe size	5	6	7	8	9	10	11	12
Frequency	3	4	5	6	7	18	8	4

a) Find the median shoe size.

b) Find the mean shoe size.

16. 'Nutz' bars of chocolate are on special offer in three shops.
In shop A, the marked price of a bar is 53 p and the offer is '10 p off marked price'.
In shop B the marked price is 55 p and the offer is '20% off marked price'.
In shop C the marked price is 60 p and the offer is '$\frac{1}{4}$ off marked price'.

a) Which shop is offering the lowest price?

b) Which shop is giving the largest percentage reduction off its marked price?

EXERCISE 23c

1. Express 0.25 as   a) a percentage   b) a fraction.

2. a) If I have £1, how many 18p stamps can I buy ?

   b) An express parcel delivery service charges £5 per kilogram or part thereof for same day delivery. Find the charge for a parcel weighing 5.2 kg.

3. Using £1 ≡ 10 French francs find

   a) the value in sterling of 450 French francs

   b) the value in French francs of £26.

4. a) Make a the subject of the formula $b = c - a$

   b) Make r the subject of the formula $\dfrac{c}{r} = 2\pi$

5.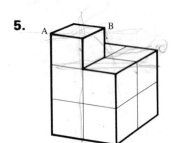

   This solid is made from cubes of edge 1 cm.

   a) How many cubes are needed ?

   b) Draw the section made by a vertical cut through A and B and mark the lengths of the sides.

6. After six completed innings a batsman has an average of 34.

   a) How many runs has he scored ?

   b) In his seventh innings he scores 55. By how much does his average rise ?

   c) After his eighth innings his average score drops to 36. How many runs did he make in his eighth innings ?

7. To make 14 oz of uncooked pastry, 8 oz of flour are needed. How many ounces of flour are needed to make 35 oz of uncooked pastry ?

8. a) Factorise $6 - 15t$

   b) Expand and simplify $x - 2(x + 1)$

   c) Find the value of x if $3 - 2x = 5$

9. If $a = 5$ and $b = -3$ find the value of

    a) $a - 4b$ b) $a^2 - b^2$ c) $\dfrac{1}{a} - \dfrac{1}{b}$

10. A square sheet of card has sides 12 cm long.

    a) Find the radius of the largest circle that can be cut from the card.

    b) Find the area of card left when the circle is cut out.
       (Use the π button on your calculator.)

11. A plane does a journey of 500 km flying at an average speed of 350 km/h.

    a) How long does the journey take ?

    b) What is the speed of the plane in metres/second ?

12.

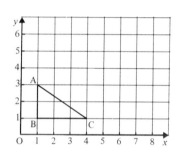

    a) Draw the enlargement, $A_1B_1C_1$, of $\triangle ABC$ with scale factor 2 and centre O. Write down the coordinates of A_1.

    b) Draw the enlargement, $A_2B_2C_2$ of $\triangle ABC$ with scale factor $\frac{1}{2}$ and centre B. Write down the coordinates of C_2.

13. Write down the gradient and y intercept for the following straight lines.

a)

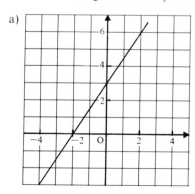

b)

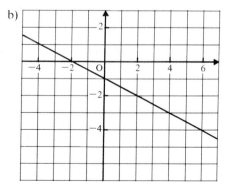

14. This table is an extract from a railway timetable. Use it to answer the questions.

Dorking → Leatherhead → London

Mondays to Fridays　　　　　　　　　　Second class only unless otherwise shown

Dorking	Boxhill	Bookham	Leatherhead	Ashtead	London Bridge	Waterloo	Victoria
dep.	dep.	dep.	dep.	dep.	arr.	arr.	arr.
		05.00	05.04	05.08	→	05.46	
		05.47	05.52	05.56	→	06.30	07.00a
06.10	06.12	→	06.18	06.22	→	07.00a	07.05
		06.17	06.22	06.26	→	07.00	07.05a
06.40	06.42	→	06.48	06.52	07.45a	07.30a	07.35
		06.47	06.52	06.56	07.45a	07.30	07.35a
06.58	07.00	→	07.06	07.10	→	→	07.48
07.10	07.12	→	07.18	07.22	08.15a	08.00a	08.06
		17.17	07.22	07.26	08.15a	08.00	
07.20	07.22	→	07.27	07.31	→	08.09	
07.27	07.29	→	07.35	07.39	→	→	08.19
		07.37	07.42	07.46	→	08.23	
07.40	07.42	→	07.47	07.51	08.45a	08.29	08.36a
		07.47	07.52	07.56	08.45	08.40a	08.38b
07.50	07.52	→	07.57	08.01	→	08.40	08.49a
† 07.59	→	→	→	→	08.49b	→	08.38
		08.03	08.08	08.12	→	08.49	
08.05	08.07	→	08.12	08.16	→	08.53	09.06a
		08.17	08.22	08.26	09.22a	09.01	09.19a
08.18	08.20	→	08.25	08.29	09.23	→	09.19a
08.31	08.33	→	08.38	08.42	→	09.19	09.34a
		08.47	08.52	08.56	10.03b	09.38a	09.34
08.50	08.52	→	08.57	09.01	→	09.38	09.48a
† 08.59	→	→	→	→	10.03b	→	09.35
09.03	09.05	→	09.10	09.14	→	09.51	
		09.15	09.20	09.24	→	10.01	10.05a
09.15	09.17	→	09.23	09.27	10.33b	10.01a	10.05
09.35	→	→	09.41	→	→	10.13	
09.40	09.42	→	09.48	09.52	→	10.30	10.35a
		09.47	09.52	09.56	10.03b	10.30a	10.35
10.10	10.12	→	10.18	10.22	11.33b	11.00b	11.05
		10.17	10.22	10.26	→	11.00	11.05a
then at the following minutes past each hour							
40	42	→	48	52	→	30	35a
		47	52	56	03b	30a	35
10	12	→	18	22	33b	00a	05
		17	18	22	→	00	05a
until							
14.10	14.12	→	14.18	14.22	15.33b	15.00a	15.05

a) Mr. Smith has to arrive at Waterloo before 9.00 a.m. What is the time of the latest train he can catch from Dorking ?

b) Ann Smith travels from Dorking to Leatherhead by train. She has to arrive in Leatherhead by 8.45 a.m. What is the time of the latest train she can catch ?

c) Peter Smith wants to travel from Dorking to Victoria, to arrive no later than 10.00. What train should he catch ?

d) What is the time of the first through train to leave Bookham for Victoria ?

e) Mrs Smith wants to travel from Boxhill to Victoria to arrive in Victoria as near to midday as she can. What time train should Mrs Smith catch ?

15.

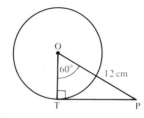

If OP = 12 cm find

a) OP̂T

b) the radius of the circle

c) the length of PT.

16. The cash price of a washing machine is £250. The credit sale terms are a deposit of £50 together with 24 monthly payments of £12. Find the difference between the credit cost and the cash price of the machine.

17. Ann's gross insurance premium for her motorcycle is £350. She qualifies for a 60% no claims bonus. How much does Ann have to pay ?

EXERCISE 23d

1. Find, without using a calculator

a) the value of $\frac{3}{4} \div 1\frac{1}{2}$

b) the value of 1.2×0.007

c) $1.2 \div 0.4$

d) an approximate value for the circumference of a wheel whose diameter is 9 inches.

2. The petrol consumption of a car averages 12 km per litre for urban driving. How far can a driver expect this car to travel in town on 20 litres of petrol ?

3. Divide £36 into two parts in the ratio 4:5

4. Write down the equations of the following lines.

a)

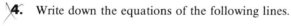

b)

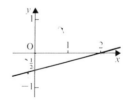

c)

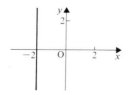

d)

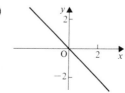

5. Use the formula $v = u + 3t$ to

   a) find v when $u = 4$ and $t = 1.5$

   b) find t when $v = 6$ and $u = 2$

   c) find v when $u = -5$ and $t = 4$

   d) make t the subject.

6.

Birmingham					
90	Bristol				
100	40	Cardiff			
300	370	400	Edinburgh		
120	120	150	400	London	
210	300	320	110	280	Newcastle

Use the mileage chart to find the distance between

   a) London and Edinburgh

   b) Bristol and London

   c) Newcastle and Birmingham

   d) Cardiff and Birmingham.

7. Simplify   a) $2p - (-p)$ b) $2s \times 3t$ c) $5(4 - 2x) - 1$

8. A salesman earns 2% commission on the value of goods sold. Find the total commission due when he sells items of value £1500, £940 and £660.

9.

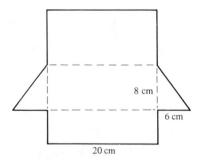

This is the net for a solid.

   a) Name the solid.

   b) Fill in the missing lengths.

   c) Find the volume of the solid.

10. I have just enough money to buy 5 pencils costing 12p each. If I decide to buy pencils costing 10p each, how many can I buy ?

11. a) Do the points $(1, 5)$ and $(-2, -5)$ lie on the line whose equation is $y = 3x + 1$?

b) Find the gradient of the line joining the points $A(5, 3)$ and $B(7, 8)$.

c) Sketch the lines whose equations are
   (i) $y = \frac{1}{2}x$ (ii) $y = -x + 4$.

12.

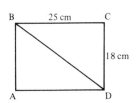

ABCD is a rectangle. Find

a) the area of the rectangle   b) the length of BD   c) $A\hat{B}D$.

13.

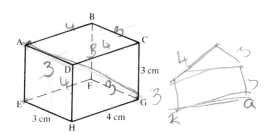

The sketch shows a cuboid.

a) Sketch   (i) the section ACGE
   (ii) the section through the middle point of AD and parallel to the face DCGH

b) Find the length of   (i) EG, (ii) AG

14. A radio mast casts a shadow 40 m long when the sun is at an elevation of 70°.

a) Draw a rough sketch showing this information.

b) Make a scale drawing of the radio mast and its shadow using a scale of 1 : 500.

c) Find the height of the radio mast.

15.

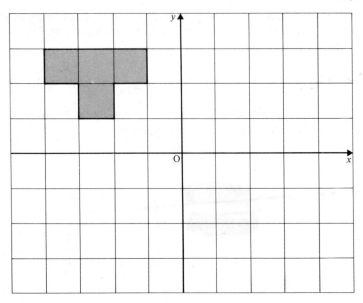

Draw the image of the shaded figure when it is

a) reflected in the y-axis

b) reflected in the x-axis

c) rotated about O by $180°$.

d) translated by the vector $\begin{pmatrix} 3 \\ -4 \end{pmatrix}$.

16. The frequency table shows the result of a survey into the times taken by 100 candidates to complete a coursework assignment.

Time, t hours	$0 \leqslant t \leqslant 2$	$2 \leqslant t \leqslant 4$	$4 \leqslant t \leqslant 6$	$6 \leqslant t \leqslant 8$	$8 \leqslant t \leqslant 10$
Frequency	40	51	5	3	1

a) Draw a frequency polygon to illustrate the table.

b) Find the mean time taken.

c) Looking at the shape of the frequency polygon, do you expect the median time to be more or less than the mean time ?

Finnish

EXERCISE 23e

1. A job is advertised at an annual salary of £12 500. If an applicant asks how much that is per week, what will the answer be ?

2. At the beginning of a quarter an electricity meter reading was 271 501 and at the end of the quarter it was 290 654. How many units of electricity were used in that quarter ?

3. The same brand of cola is either sold at 90 p per pack of 4 cans, each can containing 250 ml, or it is sold in 1.5 litre bottles costing £ 1.30 each. Which is the better buy and why ?

4. Pat was asked to buy 6 cans of cola and 10 cans of bitter lemon. If she had done so, the cost would have been £ 6.12. Pat actually bought 4 cans of cola and 6 cans of bitter lemon for a cost of £ 3.84.

    a) A can of cola costs x pence and a can of bitter lemon costs y pence. Write down two equations in x and y.

    b) Solve the equations and hence find the cost of a can of cola.

5.

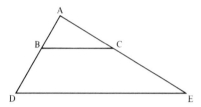

$\triangle$ ADE is an enlargement of $\triangle$ ABC.

    a) Which side in $\triangle$ ADE corresponds to AC in $\triangle$ ABC ?

    b) If BC $= 3$ cm and DE $= 9$ cm, what is the scale factor of the enlargement ?

6. A map has a scale of $1 : 200\,000$. How long is a road which on the map measures 4 cm ?

7. Tom is x rungs up from the bottom of a ladder. He then climbs a further x rungs up the ladder. If he went down one rung he would be half-way up the ladder.

    a) Find an expression for the number of rungs in the ladder.

    b) If the ladder has 22 rungs, find x.

8.

This is one pupil's attempt at a net for an open box in the shape of a cuboid with a base measuring 12 cm by 20 cm and sides that are 5 cm deep.

    a) Sketch the shape that this net would make and explain why it will not make the box described.

    b) Sketch a net that will make the box described.

9. A glass beaker is cylindrical. Its inside diameter and height are 6 cm and 20 cm respectively. How much liquid will the beaker hold ? (Use π button)

10. a) Expand and simplify $6(1-x)+2(3x+4)$

b) Find n if $2(n-4)-3=6$

11. a) Factorise $5y-y^2$

b) If $V=2n-5m$, find V when $n=4$ and $m=-2$.

12. The volume of a prism is given by $V=Al$ where A is the area of its cross-section and l is its length.

a) Find the volume of a prism when $A=24\,\mathrm{cm}^2$ and $l=10\,\mathrm{cm}$.

b) A prism has a volume given by $V=36\,\mathrm{cm}^3$. Its length is $9\,\mathrm{cm}$. Find the area of the cross-section.

c) Make A the subject of the formula $V=Al$.

13. Copy and complete the following table for the equation $y=\frac{1}{4}x^2$

x	-4	-2	-1	0	1	2	4	5	6
y									

Draw a y-axis down the middle of the page and an x-axis across the bottom. Using a scale of $1\,\mathrm{cm}$ for 1 unit on both axes, plot the points and draw a smooth curve through them.
On the same axes draw the line whose equation is $y=2$.

a) Write down the coordinates of the points of intersection of the line and the curve.

b) What values of x satisfy the equation $\frac{1}{4}x^2=2$?

14.

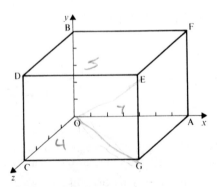

The diagram shows a cuboid where $OA=7$ units, $OB=5$ units and $OC=4$ units.

a) Write down the coordinates of (i) E (ii) G (iii) D

b) Find the length of (i) EG (ii) OG (iii) OE.

15. The nth term of a sequence is the sum of the first n whole numbers (i.e. $1 + 2 + 3 + \ldots + n$).

a) Write down the first six terms of the sequence.

b) It can be shown that the nth term of this sequence is given by the expression $\frac{n}{2}(n+1)$. Verify that this expression gives the same values for the first six terms as you found in part (a).

c) Use the expression given in part (b) to find
   (i) the 20th term   (ii) the 50th term, of the given sequence.

16.

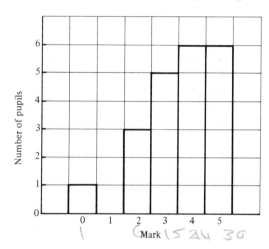

The bar chart shows the numbers of pupils obtaining marks of $0, 1, 2, 3, 4,$ or 5 in a test. State whether each of the following statements is true or false.

a) Six pupils took the test.

b) Twenty one pupils took the test.

c) One pupil was away on the day of the test.

d) The mean mark was $2\frac{1}{2}$.

e) The median mark was 4.

f) Three pupils got a mark of 5.

g) One pupil got a mark of 0.

h) More than half the pupils got more than the average (mean) mark.